I Jan Cremer

I Jan Cremer

I Jan Cremer

I Jan Cremer

I Jan Cremer

Other SIGNET Books You'll Enjoy Reading

I
JAN
CREMER

With an Introduction by
SEYMOUR KRIM

A SIGNET BOOK
Published by THE NEW AMERICAN LIBRARY

*SIGNET BOOKS are published by
The New American Library, Inc.
1301 Avenue of the Americas, New York, New York 10019*

PRINTED IN THE UNITED STATES OF AMERICA

'...*faire de la prose sans le savoir.*'
MOLIÈRE

'*Wat is een held?*
Iemand die straffeloos onvoorzichtig is geweest.'
W. F. HERMANS

'*... a levelling, rancurous, rational sort of mind that never
looked out of the eye of a saint or out of drunkards eye ...*
WILLIAM BLAKE

For Jan Cremer & Jayne Mansfield

Introduction by Seymour Krim

Jan Cremer at the age of twenty-five can rank unashamedly as the crazy sixties' brazen illegitimate son of such giants of imaginative autobiography as Louis-Ferdinand Céline, Henry Miller, Jean Genet and Maxim Gorki. What makes this book all the more mysterious in its triumph is that Cremer was primarily known as a professional narcissist, publicity-hound, tourist-hustling Action Painter—an American expression coined by the New York critic Harold Rosenberg and applied most beautifully to Jackson Pollock which Cremer imported into Holland—a trans-European cocksman and self-announced "world idol" who in his own unsweet words wrote this document to "seize power, strengthen my image and make MONEY!" He will accomplish each of these goals, thumb his elegant nose at the bourgeoisie of two continents, continue to make gold facsimile copies of his book each time it sells another 100,000 copies—he has already started this Elvis Presley-ing of literature via the Dutch edition—and with the back of his hand he will show distinguished literary men twice his age the difference between talent and authoritative originality. His book will break the heart of all but major novelists because each of its chapters contains in itself the amount of life that one confronts in a conventional novel. That a man so young, so contemptuous of "seriousness," frankly absorbed in his own ego to the point of pathology from an American middle-class psychiatric position, should break through every predictable human prejudice by the sheer authenticity of his being is a significant event that separates this book from "literature" at the same time that it inevitably creates its own place in literature which has no precise equal for it. It is unique in its not only "unprecedented" but, until you read it, more or less unimaginable blend of quietly and sharply observant narrative—almost reminiscent of the "big" nineteenth-century Russian novels—

then equally naturally comes its blunt and nasty Dutch hipster-slang lingo which admittedly borrows from an international pool of American Negro-Beat inside talk but has an undeniable effect in deflating the German-type pretentions that infuriate Cremer about Holland; yet this is still only a beginning about the writing—from here it explodes into what can only be taken to be fantasies or wish-fulfillments of murder and mutilation committed by Cremer on those countrymen of his whom he hates for the same reason that he manfully curses the country itself, its stultifying cowlikeness which squashes human growth. But the weird quality of these scenes of sadism and murder is that they seem to be inspired by crude American tough-guy private-eye work like Mickey Spillane and Henry Kane yet with a humanly real, moving, pitiful Dutch setting. The emotions it sets up in the American reader, who sees with dread the violence of his own country's fantasies acted out with stoic seriousness in a place he has always thought of as "quaint," "charming," is upsetting and almost erotic in the pleasure Cremer forces us to experience in sadism. It is impossible to describe in detail each new piece of ground Cremer's writing covers, and it should be made clear that he works all of these veins at more or less the same time —there is no switching-on and off in any manipulatory sense, you are immediately caught up in the *story* of his life and he is a most powerful and deceptively original storyteller on just that "universal" level. But his story is not just an unusually engrossing narrative even though it is loaded with hipster-masculine derring-do and probably—certainly!—heightened, invented, perhaps imagined events; the story is primarily a confession of his being, *à la* the great modern confessionists mentioned as his fathers in the first sentence although it is very doubtful if he has read them, but confession in Cremer's hands is also a weapon. He will tell you frankly for example about his fascination with every conceivable form of moving the bowels, he will speak simply about turds and their shapes and the kinds of bathrooms he likes to enjoy this basic necessity in, and you know with each sentence that he is putting you on the spot; what he says is true, not shameful at all, but the majority of us feel uneasy—at least in this country—about thinking or talking too explicitly on the subject and he makes us feel small and grateful for his freedom (not license) in not just being himself but *having a self to be*. Thus he awakens without any polemical addresses in the least the self we haven't dared use under the pressures of either conformity, insecurity or ignorance so that we can respond in a fuller way to experience than we usually do. He is by no means an uplifter nor a "nice" man, put that thought away quickly; he is aggressively (often refreshingly) conceited throughout the book, paying off old scores one might think, but doing them with a composed and slightly frightening sense of innate superiority which makes the reader sometimes feel like the lesser man. This arouses resentment because it puts down one's own ego-possibilities but it is usually soon rectified by the reader's increasing familiarity with the boldness of Cremer's actions toward everyone: running naked with a knife in his teeth in the Amsterdam streets to frighten a parasitic hanger-on who thought he, Cremer, was a professional killer, deserting from the Foreign Legion with the probability of a court-martial (he got away with it). The sex of course—and the book is drenched with sex, probably somewhat craftily to catch the modern market and certainly in keeping with Cremer's own admittedly, scornfully lowbrow American paperback tastes—again screams envy in the ordinary male reader because Cremer seems to have slept, made it, with several hundred choice girls. But once again a curious and highly testifying—to Cremer—experience occurs: exaggerated or not, and the probability is that the majority of these experiences took place except that we see them through his own usually blazing painter's eye which would be different from the way another witness would see them, they are really exciting, honestly "pornographic" in the good groiny way that adults should describe sex to other adults; but the gaminess is lifted up and will be for even embarrassed readers by the enormous self-declarative enthusiasm Cremer has for women as people of exotic beauty as well as agents for his penis. He dresses them for sex, poses them as just a happy pot-smoking (imagination-freeing) lover would do, it is all convincing, but he is richer than most lovers because he is a genuine artist in the most elementary sense of wanting to paint them and make the ecstatic moment permanent—he is not a utilitarian middle-class man, intellectual or not, who wants to satisfy the flesh, period. The very best fucks and love-bouts in Cremer's book are human, nasty sometimes, you feel the nails of the woman in his/your back but also his boredom ten minutes later and it reminds you of life, not fiction. He also irritates you because he is young and impatient and apparently spoiled by his good fortune with pussy galore, but then again he walks away from setups where those of us perhaps not quite as charismatic would hold on. Cremer as he comes to us through the pages of this unedited letter to the world accepts very little that is cheap and no matter how heroic many literary figures are they often accept cheap lays—which this at times snotty, prideful Dutchman won't do. Once again his *spirit* toward sex, women—he

ix

naïvely boasts about the number of his girl friends in a humorless and foolish U.S. college-boy way, slightly aggressively as if we won't believe him which is human enough but disappointingly immature—is what is groovy and genuinely itch-making, first-rate horny, regardless of whether Cremer is laying it on thicker than he had laid it in. But a reader would be a vicarious sucker in several ways to confine this book to sex or to think that Cremer has confined his life to it; the more one thinks about it the home-movie sex is there for pride's sake, to show the "American world" which he admires that he's as virile as Hemingway-Mike Hammer-Richard Diamond-god-knows-the-rest-of-their-names except probably an Americanophile like Jan Cremer. Also, to again acknowledge his shrewdness, the sex is present because Cremer knows it will "sell" and this boy is a garment-center operator when it comes to selling, which we'll discuss when we get to the tremendous cynical artificiality or amoral gamesmanship of his offstage career. But finally the greatest thing about Cremer's sex scenes is the unconscious honesty that also permeates his entire book and rises to the inspiration of what used to be called genius before the word became debased: like an idiot he will tell you how a chick who loved him put on her black nylons with the traditional hardon-making garter belt and the spike heels, what Jack Kerouac once called the Forty-Second Street jerkoff image, and the detailed zest with which Cremer acts out the whole scene is poignantly real because you can see him living out some mad, to him beautiful inspiration from the dingiest American girlie magazines and having his all-American fuck, so to speak, right in the heart of the Dutchland he despises—a strange and moving poetic gesture made memorable by his creative and unashamed eroticism and his lonely unspeaking love for this country which at that time he had never seen. He is a naturalist, at least the sentence-by-sentence technique is very competently realistic on the surface even when encasing the fantastic flights, but if a poet is one who in the end *sees* further than a prose writer then Cremer's uncanny ability is his vision. Vision for the details in full view that no one else sees, for example, a description of how he and the whole crew smuggled cigarettes, pot, heroin, razor blades and scores of other items into a foreign country from comically absurd secreting-places on a Dutch merchant ship including the toilet, rudder, etc., a perfect modest immediately visible funny picture. But finally vision is just that born *awareness* to see that has always cast meaning into the blanknesses of life and is an objective human virtue quite apart from the see-r's personality. Genuine seers —using the word unpretentiously just as "to see" in the preceding sentence and now extending it in the logical culmination that must have been involved in its mystical usage—must always be perceived by others who have experienced their vision; but it is futile to look for them in the world because one must deny their existence up to the moment when denial is impossible. A seer—and in however impure or immature or too-worldly a form he appears the concept fits Jan Cremer on both the elementary level and on the higher one—has only one important function which is to see more and further than the majority. Not because of any unperceivable, witch-like, fourth-rate "devil's power" but because he or she can literally see more reality than their fellows and then with varying ability compress this vision into statements that are startling to us because we haven't followed their route and are presented with only the sum. Admittedly seers can err out of common weakness, Cremer errs, perhaps the power-drive that he projects offstage away from his writing—the pop celebrity-idol aura—reveals what could become a major abuse, or prostitution, of a disturbingly rare human quality which should ideally be protected rather than self-exploited. You have to talk about the man this way because he uses the work to redeem himself; no sniveling redemption, hardly, it's a total giving apart from what he may have omitted (which is his secret alone)—a creative giving with a green fist, so to speak, not a neurotic heart-squeezing with forgiveness written over it. But it is naïve and misleading not to see that Cremer the man wants to use the success of this first large public impact to advance his notoriety and therefore cushioning against adversity in a dangerous world. One forgets how much of a hustler, con man, trickster he encouraged himself to be, trying to establish a Name as a painter-personality in an indifferent Holland, goaded by a history of lumps and kicks delivered by the world since he was an infant during the German occupation. This tremendous concern with money that one reads about in the paperstorm of Dutch publicity releases that followed the original publication and success of *Ik Jan Cremer* in March 1964—a chauffeured Rolls-Royce in London, a silver Mercedes for conspicuous home consumption, all this showy razzmatazz—can it be attributed to the early poverty alone or, as one fears, is this again protection against the majority that can't perceive the lonely uniqueness of having vision in a suspicious world where everything must be callously proved? The public wheeler-dealer Cremer, the young man *not* writing or painting, must feel confident that his superior power to see will affect and ultimately influence those people and situations with which he gets involved; but the habit of showmanship from precocious years as a Dutch dada-stuntman (*"Amsterdam's Eighteen-Year-Old Action Painter Will Perform Before Your Very Eyes!"*) reduces the potential purity of the power, puts an alloy in it, which makes all that one hears about the legend of this hipster Peer Gynt different from the person who emerges from the book. The good-looking young hotshot of real life may accomplish public wonders like the new quadruple-threat boys and girls who pace his generation (Streisand, Yevtushenko, the Beatles, Kubrick, Bobby Dylan); but because of his self-consciousness as an actor in the world of headlines, in contrast to the unselfconscious freedom his visionary eye can navigate on the page or on a canvas, these seemingly needed ego-triumphs or I-Happenings are more like a Dunninger in a nightclub making the squares pay good money for all the miserable tank-town years rather than magic for its own sake. To psychoanalyze Cremer is ultimately a bore, because the most significant part of his impressiveness comes from something as immutably a part of nature as a sixth finger or a third eye, but he evokes it by such deliberately challenging statements about his work as the often-repeated "I wrote this book for one reason: to make money!" He almost seems belligerent about getting you to believe it, but it could well be a put-on disguising a young originator's fear that he will be taken as seriously as he takes himself. If this comes to pass, what a burden as well as a final relief; he would have to labor in intense privacy when all the tempting action today is in mutual work-as-play and the solitary work of art, unless it becomes an act of discovery, is usually a dreary narcissistic grind flattered by tradition and encouraged by businesslike psychotherapists for their aimless patients. All this at the expense of that poor, abused, misunderstood, exploited but finally indifferent human miracle which the gleam of new consciousness in art always is. Cremer owns the gleam loosely—it must be unbearable to possess it in full, at least the awareness of your unceasing responsibility to articulate it, how can you live without working night and day like a measured madman knowing it will die with you and is much more important than its keeper?—perhaps because Cremer is afraid to tighten his hand on it and take it all the way. Which is certainly not the way of the world except indirectly, when the work ultimately returns like a gift to humanity after the creator—or curator—has killed himself in its care and feeding and curses his last ugly days. Why then shouldn't Jan Cremer desire to swing when he can seemingly score high, wide and handsome in several directions, "star in his own movies, establish a new concept for a daily newspaper, produce and sing on his own rock 'n' roll records," all the limitless mass-media possibilities which are now open to the new avant-garde celebrity of our time unlike his "alienated" brother of the past? When the Beats, particularly Allen Ginsberg and Gregory Corso, invaded the formal outlets of literature in the late fifties and staged the equivalent of a newsreel-covered riot at Brentano's in Paris until their underground publications were put on sale they were foolishly mocked by the university-bred "in" group. But what they unerringly showed is that a desperado generation raised amidst the mass-murder of the War, the deceits of the peace, and the disintegration of meaningful middle-class ethics has little patience in prostrating itself to some toothless trinity called Dedication, Poverty and Art. Mostly street-kids like Jan Cremer whose combined classroom and church was the movie dream-palace, they grew up wanting in some form to be Stars, that greatest image for the vindication of the personal ego that America gave to the world; and even though they had the unusual sensitivity that was to eventually make them artists they immediately smelled out the hard reality in Hollywood-style fame, money and power. Unlike an older generation of serious highbrow painters-writers-poets who were proudly superior to what they thought was the unprincipled vulgarity of pop culture, these tough and ambitious lower-middle-class "barbarians" saw no reason why you couldn't use Hollywood techniques in the invasion of the pure arts and why the rebel dramatizer of new truth couldn't become a national—or even international—celebrity like a movie star. It is right in the middle of this radical transformation of the position of the artist in our society, the opening of unprecedented doors to mass-celebrity, possible political power, an immediate influence through magnified communications greater than ever before, that Jan Cremer has appeared. The temptations are enormous to "cash in," as they say, and therefore cash out as a major revolutionary voice; it is probable that Cremer will further commercialize or theatricalize his uniqueness in this new super-lush era confronting us but he will never totally become like anyone else before or after.

EENY MEENY MINEY MO

1

I was born on the eve of World War II. There was a fog that chilly night and a bitter wind blew in the deserted streets. My mother hurried to the hospital with a hastily gathered bundle of clothing clutched tightly under one arm. It was in a sprawling, soot-drenched factory town near the German border that my mother brought me into the world. Two German nuns were in attendance when I was delivered and there was some talk of naming me Adolf (on that particular day Hitler was celebrating his birthday with a party in the Black Bunker of the Eagle). My mother wanted to call me Matto, but in the end named me Jan, after my father. He was vacationing in Turkey at the time, sleeping between pigs and Turkish peasant women. I was born at dawn under the astrological signs of Aries (the Lion in the Ascendent), the sign of Khrushchev, Landru, Lenin, Van Gogh and Jayne Mansfield. That same day my mother trudged back home, her bundle of clothing under one arm and me under the other. Our humble home was cold and damp, but the breast at which I suckled was warm.

A few days after I was born, an old, limping Jew, a soothsayer and fortune-teller, appeared at our door. After he had drunk two cups of coffee, examined the palms of my hands, sniffed at my ass, and thrust two crooked fingers experimentally in the air, he said to my mother, "The creature lying here was born to a Great Destiny. He shall bring an Important Message to the People. His sign is Fire and his nativity lies in the house of the Sun. Led in his journey by the planet Mars, his success shall be great and fame shall come to him surely." He warned my mother that growing

15

up to a Great Destiny required a proper upbringing in the path of the righteous. He composed a zodiacal chart that included the various stars, planets, and houses that would determine the course of my life. After he applied his smoldering cigar to the sole of my left foot to shield me from demons and certain questionable aspects of my horoscope, he disappeared.

Wood fire warmed my first days. Then suddenly, with no warning or declaration of war (wasn't that nasty of them!), the Enemy was in our streets. They surprised our mobile forces and the generals in command—who were undoubtedly in the sack, asleep or afuck. The whole town was flattened. Planes droned above us and their bombs split the tender flesh of our innocent nation. The Krauts stole our bikes. Food and clothing became scarce. Everything was rationed. People ate nettles, roots and potatoes in their skins . . . we burned cowflop and horseshit in our stoves and lit chunks of carbide for light . . . porcelain clattered and crumbled during bombardments . . . no one but the farmers had decent grub . . . *Lili Marlene* was sung by both sides . . . the Americans tumbled like sparrows off the roofs of Normandy . . . the Dutch fleet was sunk to the bottom of the sea . . . our phonograph records shattered . . . incendiaries transformed the bicycle-repair shop into a great flaming torch . . . huge red crosses were painted on the roofs of the hospitals . . . Germans were drowned . . . machine guns rattled day and night (not one of them was Dutch) . . . special masses were offered in the Catholic churches for liberation by the Russians . . . six million Jews were murdered (one of them was Anne Frank) and those that could, fled to America . . . one-third of our women slept with the army of occupation . . . the Queen was in England . . . Prince Bernhard tried to machine-gun enemy planes from the palace gardens . . . men and women were deported to Germany . . . the baleful whine of the interminable air-raid sirens sent people scurrying into cellars and shelters . . . courageous citizens listened to Radio Free Orange, their sets hidden under the floorboards or carpeting . . . half of the Dutch people collaborated, the other half of the Dutch people did not collaborate . . . British agents parachuted into Holland, into the waiting arms of the Krauts . . . children licked the empty soup kettles in public kitchens . . . fuck a Kraut and you get a tin of corned beef . . . our dog disappeared and a few days later we saw suspicious-looking bones at the butcher shop . . . six Jewish boys hid in our attic (after the war we found a pile of yellow stars there) . . . the Resistance Movement began to function . . . and I learned to shit in my pottie.

2

I was born in a town of factories, peasants and smoke. In the daytime a deathlike silence pervaded the streets . . . the whole town worked in the factories . . . only an occasional woman was seen hurrying through the streets, and the weather was usually rotten. My mother was always lonely, for often my father didn't return for months. He was born to bum around, so she was a deserted wife. Because she didn't speak a word of Dutch, she moved away, when she felt me coming, to have her confinement at the house of a Russian girl friend. But her friend's husband had absconded and his wife had to hotfoot it for Budapest, so my mother remained behind entirely on her own. When she wrote a postcard to my father c/o general delivery in Istanbul, he replied ordering her to return to Amsterdam, for he didn't fancy settling down in our one-horse town. Nevertheless, there I was born, but fortunately we spent only a few years there. My mother came from a very old, aristocratic Russian family that lived in Hungary, and they advised her repeatedly to return to them immediately, taking the new baby along with her. She should have let Dad and Holland drop dead right then and there, but she loved my father, and kept putting it off. When, finally, she did make up her mind, all borders were closed and she was doomed to spend a great part of her youth in this barren, cold, rotten, fog-and-frog-ridden country, whose language she could not even speak.

Occasionally, during the night, flashes of my youth shoot out of the darkness at me. Then, once again, I see Factory-town—its stolid, suspicious citizens, hard workers every one, and the sly, stinking peasants. Peeping burghers, bitchy women and their snot-nosed, snobbish children clinging to their skirts. And what a language! Whenever I hear that brittle, guttural, provincial, flat, unpronounceable dialect, I can again smell the dung, the chickens, the cow shed, the dairies and the pervasive soot-laden smoke drifting downwards from innumerable factory stacks. My mother and I lived there for several years during the war. Of my father I know nothing, save that he was a feared and dangerous adventurer, a war correspondent and explorer. His travels led him to Egypt, Saudi Arabia, Iran, India, Pakistan, the Balkans, the bleak steppes and the deserts of Asia, sometimes on foot, sometimes on a bike or in a car. He would disappear for months among the native inhabitants, writing books about them (books which were never published because after the war all frontiers were changed), and was a personal guest of sheiks, kings and other tyrants in uncharted regions of the globe. He too was an Aries, stood six-foot-two in his stocking feet, and was married four times according to the records. He carried my mother back after one of his trips to the Balkans, and she became his fifth wife. Immediately afterwards he disappeared for three months, without giving a sign of life. He had gone out to do the shopping (because my mother didn't speak the language), and ten weeks later she received a postcard from Albania, bearing his best regards and a promise that he would soon return. The only thing he left behind was a huge ironbound sailor's chest filled with pictures taken in all parts of the world. Later, when I was old enough, I was allowed to spend Sunday afternoons (if I was at home and first washed my hands) going through all the negatives and prints while my mother listened to the opera program. My father was one of the first non-Spanish bullfighters. In the chest were dozens of hand-colored photographs of matadors, all inscribed and dedicated to him. Of himself, there are two snapshots: in one, he is sitting with a bunch of naked Negroes on top of a coconut palm, waving a machete at the photographer. This snapshot is very small and, as it was taken against the sun, it isn't very clear. The second one (which for a long time I wasn't allowed to look at, and even later only very briefly, so that I finally had to steal it) is of my father standing among some buxom, naked Negro women, laughing merrily and hugging several of them. The hands of my father in that photograph are those of a giant. What a giant he was and what huge tits the women have! His motto was: "Rather a hundred guilders' worth of debts than ten minutes of foolish regrets." . . . In fact, he did die owing more than ten thousand guilders,* and furthermore, I have it on good authority that he never respected anyone, was always ready with his fist and was always a big-mouthed boaster who shouted—or knocked—down all who opposed him. Closer to home, he frequently beat my mother and once, when I was still only a baby, he wanted to throttle me. It was only my screams that brought the neighbors to my rescue. The big bastard! . . . he wanted to smother me in a blanket, according to my mother. And he used this incident as an excuse to leave us again for a few months. I was two years old when a nurse from the local hospital came to fetch my mother because my father was busy dying. He had been there a week, having been knifed during a fight with some local hoods, but he didn't want to see anyone. So my mother, when she tried to visit him, was at first turned away. She was

* A guilder is equivalent to approximately $.28.

told how he had carried on in the hospital. He kicked the doctors, knocked trays of soup out of the nurses' hands and refused to be attended by anyone other than a young German nurse. A real beauty she was . . . you have to give him that! When my mother finally followed the nurse to his bedside, he was pretty far gone and regained consciousness only for a few moments from time to time. Because of the chronic shortage of medicines, and a number of neglected tropical diseases with which he had been afflicted for years, and so on, and so on, he seemed to have kicked the bucket within an hour after my mother arrived without having spoken a word to her. She couldn't accept the fact that he had to die. When one of the nurses wanted to give my mother his clothes and the various odds and ends found on him (he was in a coma —the final one, it was suspected), he suddenly started up and began to curse the nurse and my mother like a madman. Male nurses had to be summoned to keep the dying man in bed. It was a Catholic hospital, and when the priest came to give him Extreme Unction, he bellowed obscenities at the poor bastard and told him to stick his mass up his ass. He wasn't going to die, he would show them, and, to prove it, he grabbed hold of the priest's habit and hurled the poor man right across the sickroom. They placed an armed German soldier and one member of the Gestapo outside the door. They wanted to arrest him for something or other, but the doctor attending him wouldn't allow them to see him. Nevertheless, we did have a whole army of Krauts come to our house, where they searched through his manuscripts and confiscated his cameras, which we never saw again. He died a vivid exponent of the old philosophy: no chains, no pains.

3

One night the alert sounded again. The sirens shrieked at the sleeping city. The air was alive with piercing sound and burning planes. Hastily my mother wrapped me in blankets, grabbed me to her and raced through the garden towards the shelters. We had to climb over walls and hedges to reach the cellars of the hospital. The city was already struck in many places by fierce incendiaries, which lit up the whole horizon. My mother ran like a madwoman. I was freezing. She stumbled and we fell into a thorny bush. I could see crowds of people climbing, racing and struggling in this nightmare world of fire and whining metal. It was every man for himself, each one running to save his own hide. I could see my mother fighting desperately to pull herself up out of the thorns. I was crying frantically (I must have been only three at the time)

19

and I seized the leg of a man running past—he wore black socks, I remember–who finally helped my mother to her feet. He took me in his arms and supported my mother as far as the door of the shelter. She was nearly fainting and her face and hands were bleeding. She tried to smile to reassure me, saying over and over again in her broken accent, "Is nothink, Jan darleeng, really nothink, . . ." but I knew it must be very painful for her and I couldn't stop crying.

A few days after the bombardment, her arms were horribly swollen, for she had removed the hundreds of little thorns with a sharpened crochet hook because we didn't have enough money for a doctor. I loved my mother very much.

When, that night, the unearthly noise of an air raid came again, we hurried once more to the shelter. Across the street lived some nice people (later we learned they were Nazi collaborators), whose house we often visited. They had a little girl my own age and sometimes we would take a bath together in a large tub while my mother and her parents played cards together. It was in the shelters that I first saw people fucking. I saw one chick lying down naked, trembling in her dimpled white flesh, while some guy or other climbed on top of her and got to work. On that occasion we had to stay in the shelter all day. It was jam full and every so often someone would have an attack of hysterics and begin to shriek and howl. But soon a few nurses or nuns would arrive and calm everyone down. When this chick was being fucked, all we children were turned towards the wall and people began making nasty remarks until the wardens arrived and separated them. When this had happened several times, I asked my mother what kind of game they were playing. She said it was a very dirty one. (I *did* find it dirty, but not as dirty as picking one's nose.) There were quite a few "dirty sluts" in our neighborhood; in the end they were confined to the coal cellar because they couldn't "behave decently," . . . and this was a Catholic hospital too! An excited cluster of nuns kept peeping through the hatches of the coal cellar and could be heard clucking words of disapproval, but what they said was inaudible. Many of the adults sniggered, but perhaps too heartily. . . .

4

During the war I slept in my mother's bed. It was a large double bed. When I was alone I did somersaults and pretended I was a parachutist. Next to the bed (or sometimes under the pillow) was a huge blacksmith's hammer. This was my mother's weapon, used, fortunately, only to break up large hunks of railway coke. When it was bitterly cold and there was no coal in the house, my mother and I used to stand with a baby carriage near the railway tracks. This was in the middle of the night, long after the curfew had been called. There were many large gaps in the barbed wire, for many people came to grab their coal there. I would creep through the barbed wire and hand large chunks over to my mother, who secreted them in the carriage. When it was full we went back home, a full two hours' walk. It was a very dangerous business because the Krauts had an armed patrol there with bloodhounds, and huge searchlights played continuously over the vast black mass of fuel. But I was very tiny and crept cautiously among the coal, and my mother hid as best she could on the other side. Once, on a pitch-black, ice-cold night we were stopped. Normally, when it was very cold, you didn't have to worry about the Krauts so much because in freezing weather they preferred to hug their own stoves. We were already returning home when suddenly we were plucked from the darkness by a flashlight, and my mother was interrogated. Fortunately, it was one of the good Dutch guards, and he let us go. We were really lucky because one night after this, to set an example, the Krauts picked up four men and one woman, shot them on the spot and slung them by their feet from the barbed wire. After that, we never went back.

Back at the house we lighted the stove and it continued to glow throughout the night. These large hunks were fine fuel. In the wonderful warmth that came from them we sat in the dark on the old worn coconut mat and, in the dim reddish light from the stove, ate a few hard-earned potatoes (two spuds for one large hunk of coal) which we baked in the hot cinders. They made a wondrous meal once we had removed the jackets, added a lump of lard and sprinkled them generously with salt and pepper. That's how we lived.

5

Once in a while, when there was nothing at all left to eat and nothing could be picked up in one way or another, my mother would go to work for farmers in the country, usually as a sleep-in maid. One farmer was really a filthy old bastard, stinking rich, who paid my mother starvation wages. I sensed he was a louse from the very beginning, but there was no other way of obtaining food. We were given a room and each morning my mother had to be up with the dawn to scrub and clean. This farmer was such a dirty mean old skunk that neither my mother nor the handyman really got enough to eat. The old pig radiated a stench of unwashed feet, and when he retired at night he carried the butter and the sausages with him to his bedroom for fear something would be pilfered. He shoved them under his smelly bed before he settled down for the night. Then old skinflint would proceed to wet his bed but my mother flatly refused to have anything to do with that mess.

Though it was illegal, this farmer slaughtered pigs now and then. I saw him do it. What a lot of blood! It spouted from the pig's neck into large flat pans and, mixed with rye, he made it into black blood sausage. The pig was first stunned on its screaming, grunting, fat head, and its pink neck was slashed with a sharp knife and the writhing torso slung between two posts. When it had bled to death (it seemed to take hours to die!), the old man would rip it open lengthwise, gut it, and sell the innards immediately to the local butcher. The farmer carried the best meat to his room, and what remained the handyman (a sweet old fellow) and my mother shared. The handyman—Geert was his name—had already worked for the old prick for nearly twenty years. Geert was quite old by that time, and had a head of snow-white hair. He was always very kind to me. Whenever the Krauts came—when a patrol entered the valley we could see them creeping through the rye fields an hour before they reached the farm—I was quickly hidden away in the hayloft (I still don't know why), or I was made to play behind the farmhouse while my mother was sent out to meet the patrol. Her job was to talk to the Krauts, give them coffee, and make them believe we were very very poor and would they pretty please, *bitte*, not drag the horse off with them when they departed? And then the farmer would totter out in his flannel nightgown, pretending he was desperately ill, the old bastard. And after the Krauts had left quite politely and without copping anything, the filthy old rogue would rub his stinking, greasy old hands together and guffaw at his own cleverness. Nor did he ever think of offering Geert and my mother a cup of coffee afterwards. He stored the coffeepot alongside the pisspot under his bed when the Germans took off.

After a few months we were no longer getting anything to eat. And when Geert and my mother complained to him about it, the filthy old rogue screamed like a stuck pig himself. How could they take advantage of him when they knew he was so poor? Had they no pity? One time the old crumb clouted me, enraging both Geert and my mother so much that he got scared and barricaded himself in his room. My mother almost went for him with a knife, while old

22

Geert backed her up with a pitchfork. Occasionally, the farmer would work the land, but far more often he was gone all day to the markets or into the nearby town. Profiting from his absence, my mother and Geert would pick the lock of his bedroom door and steal what food they could. Although it didn't seem to bother Geert, my mother could hardly get such food down her throat, for everything that had been stored under the bed was pervaded by the strong odor of stale piss. So in the end we usually ate dry bread that my mother baked herself, and from time to time old Geert risked wringing the neck of a chicken.

One morning Geert, the handyman, died. I sat at his bedside for a while. Uncle Geert had been so very old, Ma explained to me, and everything was finished for him really. Now, at any rate, he would never have to slave any more and he would be sure, I was told, of good meals where he had gone. The farmer refused to allow Geert's body to be picked up and buried; at the same time, he refused to do it himself because he was too lazy and mean, so Geert lay rotting on his bed day after day until, at long last, Ma dug a big hole in a field and singlehanded dragged the poor sweet old man's body to it and covered him with earth. Actually, we filled the grave over him together and each day for some time afterwards I laid a fresh bunch of wild flowers on the mound of earth. When, because the farmer became impossible, my mother decided to leave, he didn't want to pay her. She hurled at him all the Dutch obscenities she knew, and when she had exhausted her limited vocabulary, she spat in his face (as she had done several times in the past) and we split for our home in the city.

6

Our house had been ransacked and everything was destroyed . . . nothing was left of our meager household goods. This was the work of our neighbors, who, because of her German accent, thought Ma was a Nazi and hated her. They often called "Kraut" after her in the street. It was a terrible homecoming; every pane of glass had been smashed, everything of value was gone or broken, and beneath the ripped-up furnishings were the bloody bodies of rats that had attacked one another in the melee. We knew very well that our neighbor, the watchmaker, was in on it, for one of our lamps was openly flaunted in his flat and his wife and child were wearing our clothes. But there was nothing we could do about it. One day we were picked up by the security police, thrust into a cell and, after two days, sent to some kind of camp in southern Holland. I was kept busy all the time by women in uniform, who played with me while my mother was interrogated. I had to sleep on the floor next to my mother's cot in a very large cell where dozens of women slept. But everyone pampered me, and the German soldiers even provided me with plenty of blankets. They came for my mother again on the following morning, and I began to scream as they led her away. I wasn't allowed to accompany her but after about a quarter of an hour she was back, this time in the company of a gentleman who smiled at me. I was taken out of the cell. In the office of the German police we were given bread and coffee and the smiling gentleman kept on apologizing. I noticed that my mother had been crying. Later, we found out that the watchmaker—the dirty son of a bitch, the true-blue Dutch mother-fucker that he was—had gone to the security police and told them my mother was a spy. At night, he charged, she received men of various nationalities, English, Dutch and German, to whom she was supposed to have relayed radio messages. We were taken home that same day in a luxurious green Mercedes-Benz limousine. I can still remember the internment camp, a grey place, with a gaunt barbed-wire fence, four high watchtowers, and the *Blitzmädel* (German women soldiers) who kissed me goodbye.

From time to time we were scared by the noise, the droning roar of airplanes. During the day, as I watched the sky from our backyard, I often saw bombers flying low over the rooftops. One day I saw a plane skimming across the sky at a very low altitude, belching flames, while several tiny figures in parachutes fell downwards from it. The last man must have trapped his foot in the escape hatch, because he hung downwards, suspended from it, his arms flailing, as the burning wreckage crashed down on the rooftops a few seconds later. *Sieg Heil!*

7

The war neared its end and I myself was able to take part in the capitulation of the Third Reich. The Allies had already partially occupied our town. The police were jailed and, after long interrogations, the political prisoners were set free. The Dutch tricolor appeared on top of all the flagpoles. The Allies distributed chocolate bars and smokes, the women threw up their skirts and the liberators climbed into them. But in some parts of the town the Krauts were still stubbornly holding out—fanatics who would not hear of surrender, even though Hitler and Goebbels were dead, and

Goering, Streicher, Himmler and the entire staff of the Eagle's Nest were already detained in Bad-Mondorf. For *Führer, Volk und Vaterland!* From time to time they shot down a hapless nut, a drunk, a Yank with too big a load on, or some other poor bastard who wandered, unarmed, through the streets; any person who was wearing too much orange (the Dutch royal color) was a mark for such snipers. Then the Netherlands tricolor disappeared from the flagpoles again.

Early one morning, when it was still pitch-dark outside, we heard the noise of boots and voices in the alley that led from the street to our garden. The voices were German, commanding, harsh and guttural. My mother tiptoed across the bedroom and peered out the back window. The Krauts were digging in, and within a matter of hours an entire German mortar company was hidden in our garden among the bushes and weeds. The headquarters of the liberators was in the police station, a few streets away. We were sick with fright. Then, suddenly, there was a persistent knocking on our back door. It was already getting lighter. Silently we prayed, imploring God to deliver us from these wild beasts (where the hell had the Americans got to?). It seems the Krauts needed water, so they kicked down the back door and, a moment later, I heard the gush of water and the clump of heavy boots on our kitchen floor. Obviously, if they chose, they could very easily have broken down the bedroom door the same way. But they didn't. They disappeared and we listened in silent terror for their departure. It was Sunday and the streets were, as usual, pretty quiet. From time to time Ma crawled along the floor to the back window and peeped out into the garden. They were still there. We lay deadly quiet there in the bed, while I attempted to make out funny faces and figures on the flowered wallpaper.

The hours passed, but we didn't dare move from where we were, crouched miserably on the bed, waiting for the liberators. ("Don't they work on Sundays, Ma?") The room in which we were hiding had two large, curtainless windows—two massive squares of dark, glinting glass—the first overlooking the garden, the other giving on to the alley leading to the garden. Perhaps we could have escaped through the side window into the alley and across the street, but that would have been far too dangerous. The Krauts could see the alley window quite clearly through the windows at the back, so we stayed in the middle of the room. The Krauts in the garden were very silent, whatever it was they were doing, for we could hear nothing at all. Suddenly, from

God knows where, a helmeted figure was framed in the side window. The man was obviously startled by the sight of us, for he disappeared at once. Ma grabbed me and I grabbed Ma. Then we heard metal scraping along the wall and the helmet reappeared. It was an American. He was smiling, and placed one finger meaningfully on his mouth, meaning, "Be quiet! Don't be scared!" We were quiet, all right! He also indicated by his gesture that we should keep lying flat, but lower down, on the floor. Ma started crying and I had to go to the john. Together, we crept towards the back window and lay down there as close to the floor as possible.

Suddenly, there was a burst of noise from automatic weapons. The side window was shattered . . . a few strokes from the butt end of some gun or other and the blazing muzzle of a large machine gun appeared where the side window used to be. All of a sudden the whole room was filled with smoke and the deafening clatter of the gun and shouting soldiers. They were shooting directly across the room through the windows a couple of feet above our heads, directly out and into the garden where the enemy mortars were entrenched. Suddenly, the Yanks withdrew from the window again. Then we heard the Krauts shooting. Tracer bullets, the fumes of burning powder, and wild flash and flame blasted the atmosphere. The noise was almost unbearable. I hid my head in the crook of my arm. At least I wouldn't be blinded! The Americans were now shooting at the Krauts from all sides of the house. Soldiers jumped up in a continuous stream, like wooden rabbits in a stall at the county fair, framed by the window for a split second during which they pumped burning lead in a trajectory just above our heads. One second a helmeted man was there, the next second he was gone. This lasted for several minutes and then there were soldiers all around us in the room. They thrust us, not ungently, aside, and placed a mortar underneath the back window. We were liberated! The Krauts were surrounded on all sides and they began to surrender. I stared out of the window. The room behind me was thick with soldiers.

At the height of the battle, the Krauts were raked by continual cross fire from the Americans, so they began to retreat. They moved backwards toward the rear of the garden, one by one. Several of them tripped and fell into the trap holes I myself had dug just the day before. I had been at a loss for something to do and so I had dug bear traps and pits all over the garden. They were quite deep, and I had spent a considerable time covering them with branches and twigs so that, to the casual observer at least, they were quite invisible. I had done this for the physical exercise, to test my strength and, incidentally, to keep our cruddy neighbors out of our garden.

One of the Krauts had to be dragged from a hole, for he was dead. The American soldiers slapped me on the back, saying I was a big boy and had done good work. A certain amount of water had collected in the holes and so you could see at a glance which Krauts had fallen into them. They were cursing and carrying on like wild animals as they were dragged off with their arms in the air. Later on, they came to recover their dead, as well as the mortar and the various small arms strewn about the garden. The Americans boarded up our windows. To repay us for the mess they had made, they presented us with parcels of canned meat and milk.

Subsequently, I spotted one of our neighbors lurking about the garden, probably to steal some of our vegetables. I decided to allow him to fall into one of the holes. Whatever he had been doing, I was sure he was there to bug us in some way or other. Suddenly he tumbled down into one of the bear traps, screaming bloody murder. I had planted arrows, tips upward, at the bottom of the hole, sharp enough to hold any wild bear that might have fallen in.

8

It is a warm summer afternoon, just after the war ended, and I am sitting in our living room. Suddenly, outside the window, there are a dozen blue uniforms. Ma is upstairs and I am afraid. With the butts of their Sten guns, the uniformed men smash the windows. One of them steps through into the room and opens the door. I hop around the table like an alarmed rabbit. These are men of the Home Guard. They aim their Sten guns at me in mock seriousness, laughing and joking among themselves. I dart backward and forward across the room, stopped again and again by Sten-gun butts, and behind each one the laughing face of a soldier. I am not yet seven years old. A man wearing a white windbreaker asks me where my mother is and orders the rest of the men to be quiet. Ma is already on her way down, alarmed at the noise, and she is immediately seized by six of the men. In her painfully slow Dutch, she asks what is going on. "You'll find out soon, Fräulein bitch!" The men continue to snarl at her, while the man in the windbreaker reassures us that it is all merely a formality. Hastily, she gathers up some clothes and puts my shoes on. We are forced to leave with guns in our backs, and a mob of men mouthing obscenities follows us out.

When, a few days later, we are allowed to return ("It was all a small misunderstanding!"), our home has once more been ransacked. Drawers have been torn right out, cupboards broken into—the whole house is a shambles. Our clothes have been stolen, everything of value is gone. We literally have no money at all. A Jewish family gives Ma work. Twice a week she goes to clean their house. The man has eczema and my mother shakes the sheets out the window, causing a blizzard of skin flakes. On Saturdays she has to light the stove and do the cooking for the family.

9

Holland is liberated (*hooray!*) and the country is celebrating. All over the streets, orange. Bedecking the houses, orange. Bunting on the lampposts, orange. Ribbons on the bicycles, orange. Everything is orange; low down, orange; high up, orange! Parades everywhere around the streets, orange banners everywhere. For a short while the Resistance Movement, now the Home Guard, controls the country, men wearing blue overalls, equipped with British helmets and the latest Sten guns. (The Home Guard has its victims too, caused by unfamiliarity with the new weapons.) In certain respects our own Dutchmen are hard to tell from the Nazis. Juvenile hoods, pickpockets, black marketeers, cat burglars, and every other kind of homegrown pervert, pimp, cheat, con man and all-around thieving rascal, plus the downtrodden minor police officials, parasites, traitors, and so on. All this miscellaneous army of thugs is now doing the violence they used to accuse the Krauts of; all this thuggery is perpetrated under the banner of the Home Guard. The police stations are in chaos; men and women are "accidentally killed" during interrogations, or "shot while resisting arrest," another contemporary euphemism for murder.

Everyone suddenly turns out to have been a Resistance hero. Across the street from where we live, the Home Guard picks up a girl, a whore who consorted with the Krauts. A dozen swearing men kick down the door, and a short while afterwards out they come again, dragging the struggling girl. She is beaten black and blue, her hair is shaved off and she is savagely thrown into the back of an open truck. Steaming-hot tar is poured over her half-nude body and she is rolled around in chicken feathers. On her scalp a swastika is painted: she traitorously made it with the Krauts. Her father has a heart attack. Her mother faints in front

28

of the wheels of the truck, but a heavy-booted Home Guard man kicks her aside into the gutter. The truck pulls away, on the back a dozen or so bald and weeping women. Tough-looking Home Guards ride on the running boards, their carbines at the ready, and in this heroic manner they begin their victory parade across the town. The country is liberated (*hooray!*). . . .

The Home Guard organizes more parades, with brass bands and open tanks with British Tommies riding on them. The Tommies toss chocolate and cigarettes into the hysterical crowds. Dragged along behind the tanks, like so many tied-up cattle, are lines of stumbling men dressed like Krauts (or maybe they really were Krauts!), men who are kicked and beaten to their knees again and again by our heroes in blue overalls. Each time they stumble to their feet, they scream for mercy. Bread and circuses. . . . The populace is entertained, the country is liberated (*hoo-ray!*). . . .

Finally, we get some chow again. White bread from Sweden can be had with ration books through the American soldiers who are billeted in the Prince's School. I pass entire days staring through the gates at all this hustle and bustle of the Liberator. Individually, they are nice guys. All day long they let me tag along on their rounds, and in the evening they return to their barracks and present me with paper bags full of jam, butter and white bread. I am their "little Dutch mascot." The very first English words I learn are *"Tjoklat plees end sikkerets!"* The soup kitchens reopen and once again we get our meager rations of watery soup and gluey porridge. (Throughout the war we lined up at the same soup kitchen across the street, a German military headquarters, and one day a German woman-soldier came out of the kitchen carrying a huge skillet full of fried eggs. Before she reached the end of the line, she was completely mobbed. Men and women scrambled down on their hands and knees slobbering over the eggs on the cobblestones. I can still see the German staff officers crowding at the windows of the headquarters, howling with laughter.)

My mother's boyfriend Larry, a Canadian soldier, visits us here at home every day, bringing food for Ma and myself, cans of corned beef, butter and pastries. One time he even lets me examine his pistol. Underneath the plastic handgrip there is a four-leaf clover and a snapshot of Ma with me on her lap. Later on Larry disappears with his regiment. It was the pastries I missed most of all. They tasted so good!

Along with my pals on the block, I used to help the soldiers on corpse-clearance service, stuffing huge paper bags with dead people. Sometimes they carried large cardboard boxes on their wagons (they came in wagons drawn by two hefty workhorses, and I remember plucking up courage to run underneath their smoking bellies). When the soldiers weren't looking, we kids would peek into the boxes. For the most part they contained old people, all very pale with a strange green cast. The Americans kept stacking the boxes and bags on top of one another in the little morgue at the hospital, which quickly became an overflowing depot of the dead. Occasionally one of the bags would burst open, spilling filthy streams of blood, blue gook, purple intestines (or were they tape-worms?) and oozing shit. The soldiers just laughed. It looked just like the mess that came out of the pigs when that old skinflint back at the farm slaughtered them.

10

I'm the kid on the corner, the boy who's always hanging around. I came out of the town's big, crowded tenements, the soft red underbelly of the city, the darker side of long shadows and red lights, cracked windows, hurdy-gurdy music and open doors. I grew up amid flesh and perfume, flesh that was not to be hidden but to be used. I was conceived in one of those ancient iron bedsteads, beneath twisted blankets, in an explosive union hotter than those red-hot rivets driven by the workers of the North Side. Farther to the south lies The City of The Rich, a different world where we never set foot.

The men wheel and deal in booze, smokes, chicks, sports cars, jive, switch blades, cards, jazz and sudden trips to warmer lands.

The women deal in soldiers, pimps, shadows on the docks and merchant seamen: horny sailors, newly adrift from that huge slate-blue mass of eternal horizons (standing on our roof we can see, beyond the ruined church tower to the north, a small segment of grey sea), sailors browned and salty, with bulging torsos tattooed blue and green.

At the age of five I was taken to see Nosey, the tattooist. Nosey was my Aunt Sandra's lover. With his clever needles he engraved a five-pointed blue star on my left arm. I still have that star, no one can ever take it away from me. I can make it come alive. Whenever I wind up in jail and everything is taken away from me to keep me from committing suicide, I always fall back on my little blue star, gazing at it for hours on end.

The black inner ring of the city, the lower reaches of the tenements, grey with exhaust fumes from massive American cars, sooty from rush-hour trains carrying workmen, and rose-red from the glow of bare windows . . . and when the curtains were drawn, the shadows of our women moved behind them.

During the day our neighborhood is peaceful. We sleep the hours of sunshine away. From the north comes the harsh thunder of a thousand hammers, the exploding sparks and spewed lightning of welding torches. These are the docks, these are our customers.

At five in the evening, when the factory sirens scream, thousands of bodies stream out of the dockyards. Some smell of sweat and some smell of soap. The studs generally hot-foot it over to our neighborhod, drop into bars, and try to recover from the day's work. Some stay for the night, others go home first and return after dark. "Home" is cheap hotels and boardinghouses. But on Friday nights they pack all our local establishments jam full until very late at night, when the last of them have to be thrown into the streets to curse, spit and piss.

Our neighborhood comes alive at night. The nights are hot and red inside, cold and blue outside. Our women stoke lust's red furnaces for coins of gold and silver. As the spirit flags and sleep comes over us the factory whistles are already screaming. The workers arise to start their daily grind and the city wakes up. Now the decent man goes to work amid the deafening rattle of motor-bikes and the hum of dynamoes. His noise, the decent man's noise, breaks our silence for the sake of his grim duty. Daily and regular, racket and grime. . . .

11

. . . the black lower city became my hangout. I grew up there as a kid, and knew everyone. One-eyed Frankie, Tibbe the Harelip, and Nancy the Jackboot, now notorious in our neighborhood, were in my class at school.

Tibbe the Harelip has become a real dangerous cat, a most estimable stud in lower-city terms. He was a pretty tricky bastard even before he got his harelip. He got that in a fight with a Finn. You've got to be careful of those big studs, those blondhaired, Nordic bastards with their bare chests and tattoos, and watch out for the empty gin bottle they may be carrying to give you a facial. Tibbe got a knife under his nose that time, hence his harelip and his nick-name. Tibbe always fought his teachers; with dumb insolence he would kick them in the crotch, if he felt in the mood. He was finally dropped from school and disappeared from the streets for weeks. When I got around to asking his mother about him—for I was one of his pals—she hadn't a clue to where he was. Then one day our teacher came to school with a clipping from a newspaper. Tibbe had been picked up for breaking and entering. He was sure to end up in jail, the teacher predicted. But after a couple of weeks, there was Tibbe back again, not in school, but lounging outside the gates during recess. He called us over with a leer. He had some show-off bread, produced smokes, and had me green with envy. Goddammit, I had to sweat out school while he kicked around as he liked, nice and free, went where the spirit moved him, copped cabbage from his old lady (she made plenty hustling, anyway), and in general did whatever he pleased.

The teachers didn't like that. They saw Tibbe jabbering away at us at the gate and out they came and dragged us away. Tibbe was a bad boy and a bad influence. We weren't to associate with him, not to exchange a word with him. Hearing that, he laughed and screamed obscenities, called the teacher a dirty creep and a lousy little prick, and even threw stones at his retreating back. But the back continued to retreat, and didn't even turn around. For myself, I wouldn't have minded a bit being kicked out of school for keeps like Tibbe was, but it was a bit more difficult for me, because I had only been in this school a short time. Besides, I was the leader of the "Red Bulls"—on my block and in the school-yard.

Anyway, after school Tibbe was waiting for me on the corner and we went together to Auntie Sjouk's café. Auntie Sjouk was Wart's mother. We dug the jukebox, especially the records of Olga Lowina and the Andrews Sisters. Tibbe could dance, so he picked up one of the girls for a tango while I sat at the bar sipping a free Coke Auntie Sjouk gave me: after all, we were pals of Wartie's. Tibbe had already fucked one of the girls, I knew that, though I found it hard to believe. I knew they fucked only for bread or maybe if they fancied you. And how could anyone fancy Tibbe? On the other hand, Tibbe was certainly much more enterprising than I was. That was for sure. He'd feel up a chick in the street as soon as look at her, lift her skirt to "inspect her underwear," as he used to say. The broads didn't dig that, but when they turned to clout him he'd twist away and be off before they had really caught on to what was happening. Tibbe was a real pisser. I was there when he pulled this trick on Nannie, one of the girls who worked at Auntie Sjouk's. She did her hustling entirely in the nude, under a fur coat. She was talking at the bar with some stud or other when Tibbe comes along in back of her and suddenly hikes her coat over her head. So there she is, sitting on her beautiful bare ass, with only garters and black stockings for respectability. I must admit that I got alarmed when the stud who's been sitting with Nannie swirls round, grabs Tibbe by the collar and smacks him hard enough to bust his brainbox. Luckily, Auntie Sjouk and Tom came to the rescue and dragged the cat off Tibbe before he'd gone too far. Tibbe wasn't allowed to come into the café for a few weeks after that. Tom threw him out, but Tibbe didn't give a shit about that, and Wartie didn't either. Instead of going to the café, we went to Lou the Poulterer's to fight for a quarter. Lou owned a large barn where he kept chickens and turkeys. He used to make room in the middle for us to fight, and the winner got a quarter. We used to do this every day after school and it provided some handy pocket money. I was a good fighter and usually won. With One-eyed Frankie, however, this was difficult because he was such a fat bastard. Once he got on top of you, you were lost. He just had to sit on you and his sheer weight was enough to do the trick. He had a nasty habit of grinding his knees into your biceps so that later you couldn't move your arms. When Frankie had a good hold on me and tried to get me to the floor, there was only one thing to do—gouge his good eye and then he had to let go. That would make him so mad he'd try to stomp me with his feet. But as Lou used to say, "In this sport anything goes!" Lou would always stand back and cheer on the winner, invariably having a whale of a time! According to neighborhood opinion, Lou was just a "dirty old man," but we didn't give a shit as long as we got our bread. Actually, Lou later had the daylights kicked out of him by Betsy's Dad. He had to spend six weeks in the hospital that time, thanks, of course, to Tibbe. Lou had asked Tibbe if he couldn't bring along a nice young girl some time, a real young one, and so Tibbe arrived with Betsy. Betsy was a cute little chick; she'd always let you take a squint at her cunt, even feel it on occasion. But she usually went with older boys from the tough slum district, and these cats would beat us up without batting an eye.

Betsy was always telling stories of screwing old men who'd give her a florin or so, which she'd usually spend on licorice. I must say I always had a good time with Betsy. She used to sit just behind me in class, so I'd stick my hand out behind me, through the back of the bench right into her crotch. Then I'd stick it under Wartie's nose and say, "Smell cheese!" I always got more licorice from her than anyone else. Anyway, one day we took Betsy along to Lou's and he gave us each a florin to go away and leave them alone so he could fuck her in the straw. Of course we didn't talk about it, but Tibbe went to get a florin every day—a slight case of blackmail. But one day Lou wouldn't pay and kicked Tibbe out. So Tibbe went to Betsy's Dad, who'd just got home from work, and informed him that Lou the Poulterer had, on several occasions, forced Betsy to do "dirty things." Well, that did it! Betsy's Dad was a massive stud, a docker with hands like coal shovels and forearms like anvils. He barged right over and found Lou the Poulterer busy talking to a customer in his shop. Well, Betsy's Dad gave Lou such a hammering that someone called the police, Lou went to the hospital and Betsy's Dad went to jail. Betsy was yanked out of school. Tibbe and I stayed on the sidelines and kept quiet about the whole bit. But it was a rotten secret and it didn't sit well with us. Tibbe, that stupid bastard, said, "If we keep our mouths shut, they can't do a thing!"

I asked, "And what if Betsy tells her Dad it was us that took her along to Lou's in the first place?"

"Oh, man," Tibbe said. "That stud will be behind bars for weeks; besides, if the coppers *do* come they've got to have evidence, and Lou certainly won't rat on us because it'd only make things worse for him."

Nevertheless, one day during history class (that was always my favorite subject—I could just sit and daydream and listen to Mr. Bear, the best teacher in the school. He never raised his hand against a boy and, moreover, he could tell stories really well. So I'd sit there and goof off, imagining I was on Columbus' ship, or on the Crusades with Godfrey of Bouillon), a boy from the sixth grade comes into the classroom with a note for Mr. Bear, who looks at the note and then at me and says, "You, Jan Cremer, the Principal wants to see you immediately. Go straight to his office." I got up and accompanied the sixth-grader to the Principal's office. Two plainclothesmen were waiting there for me.

"Hi, kid! Why don't you just sit down over here and tell us what happened with Lou the Poulterer," one of them said with a friendly smile. But I acted like I knew nothing, and didn't answer. It was the conventional routine: one of them kisses your ass while the other cuts your throat. This first cat was obviously the "good-hearted cop." But the other one came on like gangbusters with the usual intimidating bit: "Now, you little punk, you'd better come clean and tell us what you know about this, or it'll go mighty hard on you. . . . What do you and your friend Tibbe do when you go to Lou's place, anyway? And what was the idea of taking

34

Betsy along in the first place? And just what were those dirty things that Lou did to Betsy?"

I still didn't blow my cool, but continued in a low, respectful, but emotion-laden voice, to proclaim my innocence: "I don't know anything about it, Sir, please believe me!"

Nevertheless, the heavy continued the interrogation. "If you don't tell us now what Lou did to you, we'll have to take you back to the station with us, and that means you'll end up in a prison cell with Lou. Come on, don't be a stupid patsy! Don't you realize your friend Tibbe has spilled the beans? He knew it was the clink for him if he didn't sing himself free."

Now the good-natured stooge broke in: "Don't you see, son, you're making it look bad for yourself? Your pal, now, is an honest boy as far as we're concerned. And you're acting as though you weren't. Is that true?"

All this questioning began to wear me down, particularly because of the look on the Principal's face. He was staring at me so sternly from under his knitted brows that I suddenly burst into a violent crying fit; that fortunately shut them up for a bit. Yes, the crying seemed to be paying off, but meanwhile I could see some of the kids from my class jumping up and down outside the window to get a good look. The whole damn class apparently had to go for a piss all of a sudden: they knew the fuzz was in the Principal's office with me, and just had to see what was going on.

Then the "good-hearted cop" came over beside me, put his arm round my shoulders and said, "Come on now, boy, be a good kid, let us have it straight. Tell us if Lou ever did anything nasty to you, like with his mouth, here . . ." and he pointed to my fly.

But I acted like I didn't quite understand what he meant, so he tried to make it clearer: "I mean your pee-shooter, son, did he ever suck it?"

Just at that moment I happened to glance at the window and caught sight of Wartie's rubbery nose pressed against the windowpane. When he saw I was looking at him, he contorted his face obscenely, rolled his eyes and poked his forefinger into a circle he made with his other forefinger and thumb—all this right behind the Principal's back. And when he knew I'd seen what he was up to, he let his jaw drop, stuck his tongue out and panted like a dog. When he did that, I broke up, almost crippled with laughter.

The detectives must have thought I was laughing about the question they'd just asked me, and the friendly cat continued: "So you do appreciate a joke, eh? But it's not really funny, kid. All we want is a statement from you that he blew you."

But I didn't answer. My fit of laughter had restored my equilibrium, and I kept my trap firmly shut from that minute on. That, however, made the other guy start off again. He said I was a sneaky little bastard, that if I didn't watch out I'd turn into a dirty old man like Lou, and that I was forcing them to go see my mother. And the Principal said, "All right, Jan Cremer, march yourself into the corridor and wait there until you are called. I forbid you to talk to anyone. Stand with your face to the wall."

I hope you all drop dead, I was thinking, but I kept quiet and went into the corridor and stood there facing the wall with my head bowed. It was recess now, and after a few moments the bell rang and the kids began to single-file along the corridors. But I was facing the wall and didn't really see what effect all this was having on them. Nevertheless, I was already beginning to feel like a hero, and some of the girls giggled and whispered into my ear, "Jan darling, I want to be yours," and old Wartie poked me in the ribs and whispered our password, "Red Bull!"

After the cops had gone I was called back in, and the Principal said to me, "We've decided to speak to your mother about this!" And I thought, OK then, go ahead, you old stink-pot, and you're welcome. My Ma doesn't like cops, especially when they're trying to get me into hot water. The Principal made what I suppose he considered a heart-melting speech about there being so much evil in the world and how dangerous it was if kids wouldn't confide in their teachers when old men did dirty things to them. He told me I could trust him, tell him everything, that he could keep a secret, and that anything I told him wouldn't go any further. But I wasn't born yesterday. I knew what he was up to, so I told him nothing and got sent home from school. Actually, I didn't dare go straight home because the fuzz would probably be there. So I went for a walk and, when school let out for lunch, I hid myself behind a tree to wait for Wartie.

I didn't get home until late in the afternoon. Ma was upstairs and my brother Jackson was back. He looked pretty awful: he had a big bump on his forehead and was wearing a dirty brown suit, several sizes too big for him, that made him look like a walking coat hanger. My mother, sick of the two of us by this time, was very anxious about him. "Jack, you'd better leave, otherwise they'll find you. They were here only a short while ago for Jan. And you can be quite sure they'll be back. You'd better get going, because if they catch you they'll send you straight back and you'll be punished as well. They've got ways of tracing runaway kids and they'll get you, believe me. Why don't you just make up your mind to go back and stick it out till the holidays? You know what Ruggers said. After the holidays they may let you transfer to trade school."

Jackson had been caught pinching lead and slashing the tires of a patrol car. For a year now he's been in a correction home. Every two months or so he escapes. He's only fourteen, so he has to stay in the damn home at least until his next birthday, which is during the holidays. After that, he might not have to go back. But he'd got into a hassle again with one of the supervisors, so he'd cleared out and hitchhiked home. He looks terribly thin and, with a boil on his ass, the lump on his forehead and a black eye he got from somewhere, he's really a mess. And that brown sack of a suit doesn't improve things a bit. When I got there he was sitting silent at the table, chewing a sandwich as though reluctant to eat at all. He doesn't relish the idea of going back to those mother-fuckers.

Fortunately, my own problem isn't explored too deeply. My mother simply says, "In trouble again? What is it this time? You'd better watch out they don't pick you up too! You know what Ruggers said last time. [Ruggers is the juvenile magistrate in our district. By now my brother and I are wards of the court.] He said it was high time something was done about you. You're much too insolent with everyone, you're wild and unmanageable. And you know it will mean reform school if you do anything the least bit serious. I can't help it, I've done my best, I do all I can. But you'll have to learn to behave yourself, otherwise they'll be taking you away too one fine day, and I'm sure you wouldn't like that, would you? You'll have to behave better, Jan. You must get it from your Dad. You know how he died . . . it just couldn't go on . . . he always rubbed everyone the wrong way . . . a hard-headed man if ever there was one. But you're still much too young for all this misery. So look after yourself. And just don't let me catch you having anything to do with queers, just you remember that! And don't bother to deny something's been going on, because that's what the police came about and they don't go out of their way to invent things like that!"

Not much they don't, I think. I say to her, "Mom, if I say I didn't do anything bad, and nothing dirty, can't you take my word for it? Honestly, I give you my word of honor!"

"I believe you, Jan," she cries, "but you have to think of other people. The police are your enemies, always remember that. You know me, I've no reason to love them. But you must remember you are a ward of the court and I have no say in the matter. Only Ruggers, only the court counts. And they've already warned me you're on a list of boys who will be sent to reform school if there's any more nonsense."

Jackson tells me just what a cruddy place the correction home is Queerville, he says. Never enough to eat and beatings all the time.

When they catch him again he'll be forced to sleep in manacles for a whole week. As soon as he's eaten, instead of going to the recreation rooms with the other boys, he'll be marched to the dormitory and shackled to an iron bedpost. Anyone who answers back or fights with one of the supervisors is put in a small padded cell, and if he keeps on screaming to be let out they simply pump gas into the cell to knock him out. Sweet Jesus Christ! What are my brother's keepers?

After lunch I go back out to meet Wartie and One-eyed Frankie near where Tibbe lives. It's one o'clock in the afternoon and the news broadcast blares into the busy street. We push our way through the crowds of strollers, people enjoying the sunshine during their lunch hour. At Tibbe's house, we ring the bell for the second floor, where his old lady lives.

We shout up, "Is Tibbe home?" Someone comes clumping down the stairs, a big slut wearing a half-open dressing gown, unkempt, unwashed and with last night's rouge and powder like a leprosy on her face: Tibbe's mother. At the sight of us, she begins to scream like a factory whistle at full blast. "You dirty little bastards! If you get my Tibbe mixed up in any more of those dirty games of yours, I'll scratch your eyes out! I don't want Tibbe seeing any more of you, you smelly little farts, so just stay away from him, do you hear me?" Her voice is hoarse and hysterical, growing more excited all the time. Her large, well-fingered tits burst out of her dressing gown like balloons full of Jell-O. Wartie nudges me in the ribs: "Come on, let's blow before she busts a gut." But I'm slow on the uptake and try to get things straight: "But *I* didn't do anything!" The big slut hurls herself towards the door, screeching: "You never do anything, eh? Just take my Tibbe along with you on all your dirty pranks, and teach him to do God knows what with all your queer friends! Just let one of them lay a finger on Tibbe and *you'll* see! Why, you little pervert you!" With that she clouts me with a haymaker on my ear, so viciously that my head spins and stars flash in front of my eyes. Then, without a pause, she goes on, "And now get the hell out of here, and *stay* out! Go back to that family of yours, that fine brother! I hear he's on the run again. Well, they'll catch him, and it's about time they took you away too!" I'm still dazed by the slap and altogether too flabbergasted to say anything. But Frankie speaks up: "Ya

38

know what you are? A dirty rotten old whore! A dirty rotten old bag of shit!"

The big slut now becomes absolutely hysterical and totters there on the doorstep as though about to come after us. We're already a few yards away, and ready to take off at a split second's notice. Moreover, it occurs to her that the people in the street are already beginning to take an interest in what's happening, and she thinks better of it. Instead, she shouts upstairs over her shoulder: "Jaap! Jaap! Come down here, and bring your knife!" And then, glaring, at us: "You just wait, you dirty little louses, just wait till I get my hands on you!" But we aren't that stupid. We don't know who this Jaap guy is, but he's probably the cat who was with her in the café yesterday, some peasant from the provinces, maybe a wild man. So, as soon as we hear heavy footsteps clattering downstairs, we begin to beat it fast. Wartie, however, has the last word, shouting, "Hustle your closed-up cunt back upstairs to your hairy ape, you two-bit whore!" And with that we run off, laughing like mad, for now she *is* coming after us.

12

Tibbe was soon in the reformatory, the police saw to that. Later on he spent four years in a youth prison, for throwing his dear mother downstairs. She broke her neck when she fell. She's still in the asylum.

13

When school is over that afternoon, I go straight home. I just happen to look out of the window, and I notice a large black limousine, with four men inside, drive up to the curb outside. They look up at me, and I call to my mother: "They're coming for Jackson, Ma! They're outside with a car!"

My mother bites her lip, then says, "Jackson's gone already. He went to Aunt Daa's to work on the farm there." I stare at her. "They're here for you, Jan." My heart leaps. Surely I can't be hearing right? "Ruggers was here a while ago, and he thinks the fresh air will do you good. So he wants you to go to the home for a while [a different home, naturally, from the one Jackson was at—I am only eight, after all]. He thinks I'm not bringing you up right."

I'm terribly shaken up, and plead, "I'll be a good boy from now on! I'll tell everything, to anyone! Everything! But please, don't send me away again! Please! I want to stay here, I don't want to go away again!" Then the tears come and my mother begins to cry too. She says, "I'll come and see you

39

every month, Jan, and you'll only be gone a few months, I promise!" But I don't want to go. I don't want to go to different parents all the time, all those different people telling me what to do! Eat on time again! Go to bed on time again! Among strangers again! And no friends again! Alone for Christmas again! And walk with a supervisor again. . . .

There's a sharp rap at the door. Three men, all dressed in black, enter the house. One of them is Ruggers. He speaks in a jovial voice. "Come along, young fellow! We're going on a nice vacation again! You sure are lucky! So young, and so much travelling about! Oh, you'll have a grand time . . . you won't even have time to miss your mother, it's only for a month or two!"

I want to flee . . . I want to die . . I want to go, to Africa among the blacks in the sun, somewhere far away where no one can find me! I begin to cry, and in a very small voice I ask my guardian, "Please Mr. Ruggers, can't I stay here with Ma? I'll never do anything bad again, honest! I'll be good at school, do my very best, honest I will! Please Mr. Ruggers, let me stay here!"

My mother and Ruggers exchange glances . . . is there still hope? . . no! And once again I burst into tears.

Ruggers clears his throat and says, with forced joviality, "Well, I declare! Instead of being happy to get away from all this smoke and dirt, to drive in a big car, really . . . you disappoint me! Come on now, be a big boy! You'll like it. It will really be good for you!"

My heart in my stomach, my teeth clenched hopelessly, I am sat down to drink a last cup of tea. Then my mother hands me a small suitcase. She had it all ready! Why didn't she tell me what was going to happen? At least I'd have had a chance to escape. I could have gone with Jackson to Auntie Daa's farm. Why couldn't I do that? ("Because you're still much too young and must get a good education. Otherwise you'll grow up into a good-for-nothing, a street urchin, a delinquent, and then you'll join the ranks of the unemployed, become a thief, perhaps even worse. Take it from people who wish you well, this is the best for you. Believe me, many boys and girls have got back on the right path after a short time in a nice place like you're going to. You should be glad you're going to have regular meals, a warm bed and people to look after you. If you only knew how many children don't have a crumb of bread to eat and have to sleep on the ground in the cold weather, even in the snow. And when they die, who cares? Nobody!")

And so I leave, a boy of eight, my hair neatly combed and parted (so flat with brilliantine they'll know I'm a nice boy), clutching a small cardboard suitcase containing pajamas, underwear and toilet bag with soapbox and toothbrush. My legs numb, I'm led down to the waiting car, one black-clad gentleman in front and another behind me.

My guardian jabbers on like a nitwit, all crap and a yard wide. Needless to say, he doesn't actually get into the car with us, but he'll soon be coming to see me, he says. A crowd from the neighborhood has gathered around, and I spot a few of my pals. They're astonished to see that it's *me*. Now that I'm in public, I'm ashamed of my tears, and I force a laugh and wink at Wartie and One-eyed Frankie. It's quite clear that they're awed and upset because it's me being taken away in the police car. My God, I'd only just got back to the street, why, why do I have to go again? Zombie-like, I begin to shake a few hands, but this only deepens the gloom. Not one of them is laughing. Why doesn't one of my pals play some trick or other now? It's as though they don't quite catch what's going on, and, really, I don't either.

I make an announcement: "Listen, fellas, I'm just off for about a month, I'll be back soon. You can count on that."

The car doors swing open and shut. I have to sit in the back with one of the black-suited men (he has a stale, sour smell about him, just like Ruggers has, and the few priests I've spoken to), while the other guy sits in front. I open the window. The crowd has gotten bigger. One man, a pimp, addresses the driver: "Boy, you're real heroes, you are, took three of you to catch one little boy. You'd better handcuff him in case he escapes! And I'd use a muzzle if I were you. He might bite! Fucking finks!"

I wish they'd start a fight with the pimp so I could take a powder. But they don't dare go as far as that (after all, they're only men doing their job). The car begins to move and a few of my pals run after it. One-eyed Frankie and Wartie run the farthest, but when they can't keep up any longer, I call out the window to them, "Red Bull will win in the end!" Then I'm looking out of the rear window at them, watching them disappear as we pull into traffic. A feeling of helplessness overcomes me.

On to a better future!

During the journey I become drowsy and doze off once or twice. We arrive at our destination very late at night, a little town in eastern Holland. Above the gates of my new "home" is a sign: ORPHANAGE (am I an orphan? No. Only a half-orphan). As the car comes to a halt, a nun opens the front door. My escorts push me in front of them. I glance back at them hesitatingly.

41

"I'm not a Catholic," I whisper urgently, for I don't want the nun to hear.

14

My escorts have gone now and I'm left all alone in a deserted dining hall. A nun brings me a plate of warmed-over food, but I can't eat a thing. I'm struck by a deadly silence in this place. It isn't even ten o'clock yet. (At home now, they'll be listening to the Andrews Sisters' records, it occurs to me, and One-eyed Frankie and Wartie certainly won't be in the sack yet. They usually play cards with their parents or brothers— poker.) I find myself being washed by a nun (do nuns fuck too?) and I am made to wear a long grey nightshirt (just like a dress—maybe that's the way Catholics dress), and a nun takes me upstairs to the boys' dormitory. I climb up the cold stairs in my bare feet.

"I'm Sister Imelda," she says to me, "and you'll like it here, I know you will." (I don't want to like it, I just want to go home.) Hand in hand, she leads me to a darkened dormitory and turns me over to the Night Sister. Then, soundlessly, she disappears in her waving, flowing garments. It's just like a spook house at the fair here, and she's like *Anna*. I remember I went to see that film and, boy, Silvana Mangano was hot as hell!

The Night Sister whispers to me, "Hello, I'm Sister Teresa. Come along now and I'll show you your little bed. We'll un-pack your suitcase tomorrow." And, though it's as dark as pitch in the dormitory, she moves very surely at my side. There is barely any light in the room. It's illuminated by a night-light, and, as my eyes get used to the darkness, I can make out other boys lying in their beds, all of them absolutely quiet. A few of them wink at me as we pass, but not a sound escapes them. There is only an occasional noise from out-side, the rumble of a car or a bus moving in the street. I find it all very depressing, just as though someone had died. When we come opposite an empty bed, the Night Sister says, "All right then, Jan, be a good boy and kneel down and say your prayers." I look at her in astonishment and then whisper huskily, shamefacedly, "Sister, I can't pray."

It's her turn to be astonished. *"No?* Well, don't worry, we'll teach you here. We'll start very first thing tomorrow!" They'll make a fucking priest out of me yet! Then, "Goodnight!" She gives me a goodnight kiss and then does something to my forehead (after a month I find out this is the sign of the cross). I break away from her, clamber into bed, and hide myself as deeply as possible under the blankets. I can no longer hold back the tears, which roll down my cheeks as my whole body shakes. I plunge my face into my pillow and cry half the night.

15

Our Father which art in heaven, hallowed be thy name. Thy kingdom come. Thy will be done in earth, as it is in heaven. Give us this day our daily bread. And forgive us our debts, as we forgive your debts. And lead us not into temptation, but deliver us from evil . . .

16

Nevertheless, I couldn't learn to pray. I just couldn't remember, and I was always mixing everything up. Fortunately, there were also some girls in the home, and we were allowed to play with them. There was one girl especially, the daughter of a professional bicycle racer, and every goddamn night she was fucked by another one of the older boys in a corner of the playground. And when there was no nun in the recreation room, we all played "Bicycle Race." A boy had to lie down on his back on one of the long benches and she would straddle him as though she were mounting a horse, and sit there with her twat jammed down on his crotch. Then the ride began, with her wriggling and rubbing until she was exhausted. She was the oldest girl in the school, fifteen. The nuns had a very high opinion of her, so naturally she was always left in charge when no sister was about. Then we'd really swing. . . .

Another of her favorite games was "Guessing." Someone would be blindfolded and try to guess what she wanted him to do. When, finally, he had guessed correctly—say the command was "Kiss!"—a piece of ice from the fish barrel would be held in front of his mouth, and instead of his lips meeting something soft and warm and sweet-smelling, they'd come in contact with the malodorous chunk of ice. Alternatively, he would expect to drink a glass of water and get a mouthful of piss. The commands became more and more extravagant as the game continued. (Actually, "Guessing" could only be played when the very young ones were out for a walk—a category to which I belonged because of my age. But because I was one of the tallest boys in the orphanage, and the second strongest. I was allowed to play.) One time the command was "Lick!" In this instance the girl mounted the big wooden table, lifted her skirt and lowered her panties. Her underbelly was flecked with black stubble—she shaved every

43

week to get rid of her lice. The blindfolded boy was urged forward and soon found himself licking her pussy. What a gas! She screamed and moaned, slobbered and laughed hysterically, like a bitch baboon getting sucked by her blind monkey slave.

Another game we played frequently was "Daddy and Mommy." This amounted simply to her feeling your prick and your stroking her pussy. We all had a ball until, one sad day, suitcase in hand, she was led down the garden path with a nun on either side. She had gone and got herself knocked up and was never seen again. Naturally, everything came out. Each one of us was questioned closely about whether he or she had engaged in these games, but, of course, everybody denied participation.

I became very tight with the cook, a little bent old man I was allowed to help. In exchange for my help I got a fair amount of extra chow, which I used to give to the cats in the dormitory at night.

17

Once a week the governing board came to inspect the place—a troupe of old sourpusses in tailored suits and feathered hats. During their inspection we all had to parade around the recreation room, neatly washed and combed. Then, under their benign gaze, we were encouraged to play nice games like "Don't Fret" or "Monopoly." They would then ask us if we weren't having a wonderful time and when, inevitably, we answered in the affirmative, they would shake us by the hand and distribute a few pieces of cheap candy.

Sunday was Visitors' Day. Almost every boy and girl had some relative or other to visit him. Naturally, they brought presents, and since all foodstuffs had to be shared, everyone, including me, got a taste.

My mother once gave Lex, a boyfriend of hers, ten guilders to buy fruit and candy for me. He promised either to bring them personally or to send them by post, but I never saw him or the goodies . . . he kept the cash for himself, the rotten son of a bitch.

18

Once a week the Padre made his visit. The children were encouraged to talk to him individually, but I never did, for I could never think of anything I wanted to talk to him about. Then, each morning at seven sharp, we had to go to chapel. It

44

was ice-cold there, and I was always bored stiff. But if you misbehaved in chapel, you got the business, because if the nuns found out, you did without food all day and had to kneel on your bare knees on a pile of corncobs for the whole evening—praying. They really made an example of you. Instead of going to bed, you would have to sit up straight on a bench in front of a table and remain in that position all night long. You weren't allowed to fall asleep, for there would be a nun supervising your punishment. She would either be reading some prayer book or knitting, and if you happened to doze off she would prod you awake with one of her needles.

19

The first month passed and no one came to take me home. Then another month, and another one. Winter was over and the spring wore on, and still I remained there. Every morning, as we marched in file on our way to chapel, we passed under a railroad viaduct. Every time I saw a train I would think, Ma is on it. But she never was. And every time the bell rang or a car stopped outside, I would say to myself, There she is! But she wasn't. Later on I did get cards and letters from people in my street, and from time to time Ma or Ruggers would write: "Keep your chin up, Jannikins! We'll be coming to get you as soon as possible." And I'd wait.

One night, when the Night Sister left the dormitory for a few moments, I crept up to the attic with a pal of mine. This was for a bet. He had said that nuns didn't have tits, that they got an injection to get rid of them when they became nuns. I didn't believe that, because Sister Francesca bulged very obviously where her tits would have been. We had discovered, while cleaning the attic, a crack several inches long in the shutters of Sister Lucia's window. She was a young nun. If we climbed out the attic window and along the gutter, we could peek through this crack without running much risk of discovery. Very carefully, we slipped up to the attic, out of the window, and along the gutter. A light was shining through the crack. (Earlier, we had heard Sister Lucia going upstairs.) Our fear kept us as quiet as possible while we crouched down in front of the window and peeped in. Sister Lucia was undressing. She was wearing all kinds of frocks, petticoats, and underwear. One by one, she took them off until at last she stood in long knitted bloomers and some kind of short shift. Evidently, that was as far as she undressed for bed. All we got to see was her bald head, which somehow frightened us. We stayed there, absolutely quiet, until she extinguished the light, and then, noiselessly, we crept away.

20

At the home they were very concerned to stop us from using dirty words. If, for example, you said "Damn it!" at the table, you were walloped and had to finish your meal in the kitchen. Recommended synonyms were as follows: to piss was "to make water," to shit was "big business," and so on. And woe betide the boy or girl who didn't think in terms of "little" and "big businesses": a quick thrashing followed. One day the ladies of the governing board came to call. Fingernails were scrubbed, ears were cleaned with matchsticks rolled inside handkerchiefs, hair was combed, and everyone was turned out in his best clothes. We were expected to assure all these silly old ducks, with grapes and feathers in their hats, that we were completely happy in this lovely place. In return for the required misinformation, we could expect to have our cheek pinched and to receive a lump of candy. We sat on rows of wooden benches before six of these ghastly hags who were seated before us in armchairs. So there we sat, the old birds staring and winking at us. During this "inspection" I got fed up with all the bullshit. I raised my hand and said, "Please, may I go to the toilet, Miss?"

That went down all right. I left and did "a little business." The toilet was foul. When I returned I noticed the Headmistress was preening herself . . . hadn't I been one of the roughest and most ill-mannered of all the kids when I arrived, hardly able to open my mouth without uttering some curse or other? So the Headmistress nudged one of the old cronies as if to say: Now just watch how well-mannered this boy has become! To me she said, "Well, Jan, why don't you tell us where you just went now and what you did there!" Why, the old hypocrite, I thought. She expects me to come out with the old "little business," "big business" crap! So they're all so interested in my vocabulary, are they? Well, I'll show them! So I declaimed: "I just come from the shithouse where I had to piss the crap off the toilet seat, goddammit! You should see the cruddy place!" I said this loudly, articulating the words clearly and with a polite intonation, as required.

Three of the old bitches uttered a loud wail and fainted on the spot. What a walloping I got for that! Well, I was supposed to be a Catholic now, so I figured I might as well be a martyr! I was dragged downstairs to the cellar by the red-faced Headmistress herself. She was clouting me all the way down, and when we got to the cellar, she hurled me away from her, shouting. "I haven't finished with you, snot-nose!"

46

Then she slammed the door behind her and there I was, alone once more, this time for a whole week with almost nothing to eat or drink. And the rats scuttled around me in the darkness.

21

During one summer holiday I was allowed to go home for a couple of weeks. I'd been looking forward to this furlough ever since Christmas. While I was home I repaired the alarm clock (needless to say I had a few screws left over at the end!), dug up the garden a bit, went to the movies—Fu Manchu (one episode of a thirteen-part serial) and Roy Rogers, stuck bricks on trolley tracks, knocked on windows and doors, built a hen house for a neighbor, went with another neighbor to watch pigeons mating, set fire to a forest, cleaned the coal cellar, arranged a wire so that the postman tripped and bashed a hole in his skull, kicked over garbage cans, and before the first week was out I was bored stiff.

I had some pals a couple of blocks away—Freddie Baker and Robbie Klein, the intellectual—but on my own block no kids were allowed to associate with me. The girls got a hiding if they so much as looked at me, Jan Cremer the leper! I was considered a perverted type because, among other things, I had been caught one time in the john with the milkman's daughter.

Our flat was on the third floor now, just above that of Guy and Betty. Guy had returned, only about six months before, from Korea. (When he came home there was a big cardboard sign saying "Welcome Home" above his door. There were also streamers and flowers and they held a big party. Toon, Gus, Peter, Klaus and Rob, who were all Betty's lovers while Guy was away in Korea, were at the party too. Late that night— it was Christmas—Guy and his brothers turned on them and threw them downstairs, where they lay in a pool of blood. There was even blood on our door, although I have no idea whose that was.) Guy worked in a brewery. Ma spent a considerable amount of time with Betty, and I ran errands for her because I thought her altogether charming and very beautiful. And she had already asked me once if she could see my pecker. Betty was a real great broad. She was twenty-eight, had wonderful tits, beautiful long legs and a little baby, Bartje. One day when it was very hot, she called me in and told me that if I felt like going to get some strawberries at the market, she would whip up some cream. Barefoot, I ran to the store, the cobblestones stinging hot against the soles of my feet. When I got back Betty was wearing a dress with yellow flowers on it. It was so hot, she had taken off her brassiere—I noticed it hanging over the back of a chair—and she was barefoot. I watched her tits waggling as she whipped the cream. There were large sweat patches under her armpits, which made me feel even warmer. The strawberries with whipped cream were terrific. Betty sat down on the bed and stared at me, and I felt a bit nervous, though when she made an inviting gesture, I didn't hesitate to sit down next to her. All of a sudden her hand was caressing my thigh and in a matter of seconds she had unbuttoned my fly and was fondling my tool. I was too surprised to do anything, and besides, it felt so great! Soon Betty stood up and pulled her dress over her head. She was stark naked. It was the first time I had seen a real woman entirely naked. Of course I had seen various parts of women naked, a glimpse of my mother and others, but never before all at once like this. So this was The Great Adventure . . . now I was going to Fuck! Over-excited as I was, my dick became absolutely soft, but Betty soon had it standing again. How I managed it I don't remember, but at a given moment I had fucked. Thirteen years old, and I had fucked!

Betty told me not to tell anyone or I wouldn't be able to see her again, so I was careful to keep my mouth shut. I didn't breathe a word to a soul. This was pretty difficult, because Freddie and Robbie kept telling me about the pieces they had knocked off. But they were obviously lying—they didn't know a thing about it. I could tell from what they said, that the cunt was in front, right under the navel!

At Catholic school they had told me that a lustful thought was just a mortal sin, but a lustful act was an Eternal Mortal Sin.

Every morning at seven Guy left the house for work and by eight o'clock I was between the sheets with Betty. Twice that week I fucked her, and on the other days we'd just play around. I never ran as many errands for any other chick, either before or since.

If I happened to be in the street in the afternoon when Betty came home with the baby carriage, she'd say to me, "Come in and watch Bartje piss," and I'd go in with her. She would change his diaper and sprinkle a little cold water on his ass, and he'd react immediately by pissing until his little bladder was empty.

At the orphanage, of course, I told everybody what I had been doing with Betty. When I returned home again months later, however, there were new people living in Betty's flat. Guy had been sent to a madhouse. It seems he'd never gotten over a nervous shock sustained in Korea. He picked quarrels with everyone, particularly colored people, until finally he caused a man from Surinam to drown in a huge vat at the brewery. Betty took off with the kid for Germany, where she had a boyfriend she'd met during the war.

I'M LOOKING FOR
ARTHUR RIMBAUD

22

I'd filched a calling card from the desk in the home of an acquaintance. On the calling card, in curling letters, was printed:

Arthur Rimbaud
108. Bvd. Haussmann
Paris (IX)

If I ever happen to be in Paris I shall certainly look the guy up, I thought. But the calling card began to burn my fingers. Why shouldn't I simply go? After all, I have a good excuse. I could pass on regards from Gerald Staalman. And when I get back I'll be able to give Staalman Rimbaud's regards— met him in Paris, you know. That night I can't keep my eyes off the damn card and my mind is at last made up. I'm going to Paris, for the first time! I've never been there, but I'm well acquainted with the city from stories I've read. I've heard all about the artists of Montmartre, the nude chicks at the Folies Bergère, the Eiffel Tower . . . I know all about the City of Light. If you want to become an artist, you must go to Paris. If you don't know Paris, you're not an artist. Only in Paris do you find real artists. For instance, look at Toulouse-Lautrec in that film *Moulin Rouge.*

And that other one, Modigliani. If you want to become an artist, it seems to me, all you have to do is to knock on any old door in Paris and they'll receive you with open arms. Quite a difference from a hard-nosed place like Holland, that's for sure. Here your father has to be an industrialist or something, and you have to come from a rich family. Otherwise, you don't stand a chance. The art academy isn't a poorhouse!

While my mother is sleeping, I steal into the kitchen, cop ten guilders of the household money, and make myself a big bag of sandwiches. I stuff them, along with my clothes, into my cardboard suitcase and hide it in the hallway. For the rest of the night I can't sleep. I can already see Paris before my eyes. And at six o'clock, when I hear the town stirring and see lights going on in the windows, I look in my school atlas and trace out a route to Paris. I write the names of the main towns I'll pass through on a scrap of paper. It's just as well I already know some French. I'm taking along a book I bought: *What and How to Say It in French.* That should come in handy during my first visit to the City of Artists. *Zhe vay ah Paree!*

I steal out of the house, after leaving a note for my mother. It's raining, but that won't make any difference, even though I'm going to thumb my way there. By noon I've already reached the border. Now comes the question of how to sneak across without a passport. Trick No. 1: About a mile before the boundary line, I ask a truck driver to give me a lift. I'm from Flanders, and I'm lost, and because my Dad is in the police, I'll get my ass in a sling if he has to come to fetch me at the border. I've already crossed it five times the same way—without incident, I explain. Somewhat mollified, the driver allows me to sit at his feet, next to the accelerator, the brake and the clutch. A few miles past the checkpoint, I get off, missing a great opportunity to stay in the truck right through to Paris. But, hell, I can hardly say, "I'll ride with you to Paris—my Dad happens to be in the hospital there for a few days." I spend over half my travelling money in Brussels, on beer and chips, because travelling—especially in warm weather—makes me hungry and very thirsty. And the summer sun shines hot and heavy in Belgium, you can bet your ass!

After a series of adventures—a night in a hayloft, bartering smokes for fresh milk, and a roadside banquet of a piece of bread swiped from a baker the day before—I'm finally in Paris. I told the lady who gave me the last lift that it was my first visit, and she took me along to see the Eiffel Tower. She asked me what I was going to do there and I said I was going to visit relatives. She let me off in the Place Pigalle. First, I went to have a gander at all the pictures in the showcases outside the nude shows, and then I walked to the Boulevard Haussmann, for I was getting hungry and tired. The concierge didn't know any Rimbaud, said nobody by that name lived at that number all. And he never did live there, said this woman, who had a real moustache and had been living in the building for more than twenty years. Why the hell didn't that Rimbaud have his address changed on his calling card, if it was wrong? I inquired about his whereabouts from some of the neighbors, at the nearby hotels and even at the police station on the corner, but it was the same all over. Everybody shrugged, but nobody had ever heard of my Rimbaud. The gendarme at the station on the corner consulted his little book and shook his head. Sadly, I left and went into a hotel to ask for directions to the nearest youth hostel. Fortunately, the manager happened to be a Dutchman, so I told him all my troubles—and got a scolding. He said that in Paris no one was welcome, that I wouldn't find a job anywhere, that I'd certainly starve to death, and that I'd better turn right around and go back to Holland. Or go to the police and tell them I was only fourteen and had run away from home and wanted to get back. I was really bugged. Had I done all this travelling for nothing? The guy said he would allow me to sleep in the hotel if I would help him put the chairs out on the terrace the next day, so after a meal I went straight to bed. I felt rotten and wanted to cry. Next day, as I was helping the French waiter with the chairs, I was feeling a lot better. The sun was shining, French voices were jabbering away all around me, hundreds of cars went by every minute, and I thought it was all pretty wonderful. After breakfast, the manager gave me a Dutch ten-guilder note, together with a letter, which he made me promise to deliver to the Consulate immediately. From there I'd be sent back to Holland. And he made me swear never to run away again.

Once I was on the subway, I relaxed and began to enjoy the excitement of travelling on an underground train for the first time in my life. I recognized the names of some of the better-known stations as they flashed by, and suddenly I was seized with an overwhelming desire to see more of this wonderful city. If I went to the Consulate, I'd probably be sent right home. At Saint Germain-de-Pres I jumped off the subway and found myself, when I reached ground level, in the middle of very busy traffic. At once I recognized the church tower from films I had seen, and the cafés from picture books. I found a *Bureau de Change* close by and changed the ten guilders. This would enable me to take a room for the night and have a bite to eat. But I'd soon exhaust that money. I didn't know a word of French, really—in spite of my "school" French—so I was very lonely as I walked through the fascinating streets of Paris.

Nevertheless, I was soon meeting Arabs, and other rich gentlemen with large cars, who took me to lunch and dinner. Sometimes they toured the city with me or took me home with them or to their hotels. Of course, they were all queers, but at that time I didn't know any better. And, in a way, my innocence protected me—some of these fags were put off by it.

Then I met a rich woman wearing a fur coat. Her hair was grey and she had a wonderful sports car, a red racer. I was standing next to it, entranced, examining the various gleaming accessories, when she came back to the car. She invited me to go along with her. We went to a very expensive restaurant where there were all kinds of waiters in tails, then to a movie and in and out of cafés: she took me everywhere with her. She soon became very fond of me, and I of her. She installed me in a small hotel in Rue de Champollion, a place full of Negroes and beautiful broads. She paid all my bills for food and lodging. Every afternoon this rich chick would come to fetch me, and we'd drive through the city or lounge around cafés. She took me to a tailor and had a suit made to measure within an hour. Then we visited other shops and soon I was clad from head to toe in brand new things. She also taught me to speak a little French. I climbed the Eiffel Tower with her, sat in the Deux Magots, the Café Bonaparte and the Monopole, where I saw Juliette Greco in person. I was also introduced to a lady whom I later realized was Michèle Morgan. One day they told me at the hotel that my lady friend would be unable to visit me for four days, and I began to feel lonely again . . . all that hustle and bustle and everyone speaking a foreign language! Even the movies didn't interest me any longer because they spoke so quickly I couldn't understand a word. I kept seeing posters advertising the Riviera, a part of the country I had to see. I could be there and back in a couple of days. The next morning I was on my way.

The trip turned into a nightmare, a bleak journey to hell. It took a week to get there, but I made it. I felt I just *had* to see the Mediterranean. To satisfy my ravenous appetite, I stole food. I stood for hours in the burning sun and then, finally, I got a lift from an American travelling with two whores. When we got to Boulouris, I stayed with the girls. In return for my keep and for hospitality in general, it was my job to look after the tent and to cook the stew. Meanwhile, the girls would take off and turn tricks in the nearby woods and villages. I remained with them for two months. I felt fine, gradually grew tanned and well fed, and began to speak a bit more of the language. From time to time I would go for a hike. I got to know some Germans on the camping ground and chatted a lot with them—I introduced myself as Jeannie's brother (Jeannie was one of the two whores). I even tried my hand at grape harvesting, but not very successfully; it was so hot that I soon became sick and tired of the very sight of grapes.

One day the girls, all very suddenly, came back to the tent in a tiny old white convertible. We loaded the car, got in and sped back to Paris. The holiday was over.

23

Once I was back in Paris, I couldn't very well return to the little hotel where the rich old chick had installed me, so I was forced to roam the streets, sleeping at night in hallways or simply wandering through Les Halles. I didn't sleep under the bridges, however. All those *clochards* stank so much of piss and shit that I couldn't relax. It was at this time that I ran into a rich French queer and this turned out to be a big mistake. I had been giving everyone an alias and telling them my passport was at the Consulate. But I gave *him* my real name—even my correct date of birth. In the middle of the night there was a loud knocking at my door. The manager opened up, and there stood two dicks who had come for me. Evidently, I had been on an Interpol list for three months: a missing child, to be returned home.

I spent that night in a large chicken-wire cell rubbing elbows with whores, Algerians, queers, drunken brawlers, and other low-lifes. The following day, a Dutch gentleman came to see me. He asked me if the Frenchman who had turned me in had bothered me, where I had got hold of enough money to live on, where I had been all the time, and why I had run away from home.

I said I was very sorry and appeared repentant and, that afternoon, I was put on a train with two dicks. Nice fellows—they allowed me to sit in the window seat and bought me lemonade and sandwiches at various stations. They let me look at pictures of nude girls in books which they had with them. And then, at the Belgian border, they laughingly shook my hand and turned me over to the Belgian police. Fortunately, these two turned out to be very decent. With some effort on my part I was able to understand what they said, so all in all it was a pleasant trip. To some extent, as well, it was flattering, for they seemed to regard me as a hero.

It was good to hear Dutch spoken again, of course, but that didn't alter the fact that once I had crossed the border into Holland my troubles started all over again, particularly with the Dutch police.

I was greeted by angry looks from all sides. No one was laughing. On the contrary, they threatened me, tried to scare me, and came on with the old morality lecture. How shameful for a fourteen-year-old to take off on his own like that, to steal money, to associate with whores, pimps and homosexuals, to cause my poor mother such grief and unhappiness! Well, they would show me! If I thought I could just go home as though nothing had happened, I had another think coming. They would put me in the clink, or into a reform school.

Though I wanted to tell them all to drop dead, I prudently kept my trap shut. I yessirred and nosirred from beginning to end, but it didn't do me much good. When we arrived I was met by two members of the juvenile police, who said to the other cops, "Why don't you take him along to Headquarters? That'll give him a chance to think things over. Then, when we come for him on Monday, maybe he'll come to his senses." This was a pretty hard blow, for it was Friday evening, and I had been sure I would be back home with Ma for the weekend. I was dying to see her again after such a long time and to tell her all about my adventures. But now I'd probably have to sleep for three nights in that dingy police station! What a comedown from Paris! And all those cops chewing me out, trying to scare me!

I was thrown in a dark, cold cell. Soon I started kicking up a rumpus until one of the guards came, let me keep the light on and gave me a detective magazine. Nevertheless, I didn't sleep a wink all night. Every half hour I asked the guard when I'd be allowed to go home. Finally, he put my mind at rest by telling me that the juvenile police would be coming to fetch me in the morning, and that I would then be able to go home. So they had only been trying to scare me! But what if they did stay away until Monday morning? Or torture me or cut off my ears?

Next morning, after a cup of tea and two slices of bread and butter, they let me out of the cell, returned my belt, shoelaces, I.D. bracelet and the mess from my pockets. Then they drove me to the Juvenile Police Office.

There they took everything away from me again, a bad sign. After a long harangue, during which, as was my custom, I professed sincere repentance and promised to watch my behavior in the future, they took me in a black Volkswagen and delivered me to my mother. Though she was glad to have me home and began to cry at the sight of me, she suddenly became very angry and gave me a clout or two. The cop warned her to keep an eye on me, and advised her if she had any complaints to call him.

By the time the Volkswagen had turned the corner, I was already back in the street with my pals, shooting them a real embroidered line. Naturally, I became the hero of the block. And what a kick it was to tell everything! It was Saturday afternoon. My pal, Tibbe, pulled me aside. Evidently, there was going to be a Trade Fair in Leipzig. Tibbe had heard that the Fair, scheduled to open in a week, was short of workmen. We would be able to make money like water there, so I decided to go along to make some money for my mother. Less than an hour later, carrying a large wooden chest full of tools, cans of old paint and a few hardened brushes, we set out.

That evening we were at the German border. It was pitch-dark and the idea was to slither along, keeping down as close to the ground as possible, because we didn't have any passports. The rain was coming down in buckets, so the border guards were snug inside the guardpost shack, from which a thin pink light filtered out into the night. Tibbe was moving in front of me. With the tool chest on my back, and because everything was so wet, I couldn't crouch down far enough to remain unseen. At any rate, all at once the door of the shack was thrown open and one of the border guards came lumbering toward us through the mire. It was all up with us. Inside the post I owned up to everything immediately, because I didn't have eyes for winding up in the cooler again. So I told them to call Inspector Jansen of the Juvenile Police. After some delay, the Inspector himself came on to the line. "I have a kid called Jan Cremer here at the post. He said I should get in touch with you." Then the border guard listened to what was being said at the other end of the line, all the while glancing at me curiously. He asked me where I lived and what my mother's name was, and he seemed to grow more and more incredulous. "Only this afternoon, Inspector Jansen returned you to your mother, is that so?" he demanded. And when I had replied affirmatively: "Yes that's right, it's him! What shall I do, hold him till Monday? Very good. Will do!" And so there I was in the clink anyway, for the weekend, all alone again. I had at least hoped they'd put Tibbe and me together—he's always a barrel of laughs!

24

I had a girl friend who lived just across the border in Germany, a girl with lots of connections. Because smuggling was so very profitable in those days, I used to smuggle coffee into Germany every weekend. I would pack a hundred half-pound packages into a watertight sack, then take a train and a bus to a village right near the border. Once there, all I had to do was pass from a Dutch farmyard into a German one, going directly through the cornfields and crawling under the barbed wire. The trips were very profitable. I always sold the coffee at once to café proprietors I had met through my girl friend, and then spent the rest of the day in bed with her. Then, under cover of darkness, I would crawl back the way I had come.

One Sunday I let some creep come with me. He too had a girl friend in Germany and no passport. It had rained all night, and the fields were soaking wet. We crept along, close to the ground, the other guy in front. But, prick that he was, he was afraid to dirty his best suit so he walked bending down, but much too carelessly. I kept on hissing, "Get down, you idiot!" But it was too late. We had been creeping around the edges of a cornfield, sheltered by the growing corn. And then, all at once, the jerk stands up on his feet and shouts to me, "One of the guards saw us! Come on back!" And in his panic, he jumps up and down and starts running back the way we came. We were already on German soil. Quick as lightning, I threw the pack off my back and, dragging it behind me, crept back to the corner of the field. And sure enough, there stood one of the green-uniformed guards, holding a large Alsatian on a leash. He certainly couldn't have seen me, but I suppose he guessed someone was there. He shouted, "Stand where you are!" But my accomplice, like the damn fool he was, kept running, and was almost back in Holland. The guard let the dog off the leash, and she bounded away in pursuit. I inched my way further back into the cornfield, praying that the lousy dog wouldn't smell my tracks and seek me out first.

What could I do? Crouching low, nervous as hell, I dragged the fifty pounds of coffee over the wet ground like a madman. I knew I'd never make it. That damn-fool friend of mine was still running as if possessed. He had long ago crossed into Dutch territory and never looked back. Behind me I heard the heavy breathing of the running dog. At any moment she would hurl herself at my neck. When I heard her just behind me I threw myself suddenly down on to my back and waited. The animal just stood there above me and pushed her nose tentatively towards my throat. Every time I moved an inch the sharp fangs were bared. I was desperate. The dog began to bark and wouldn't let me go, I knew, until the guard got to us. He would arrest me and confiscate all the coffee, and that wasn't the worst of it: no passport, smuggling, illegal border-crossing, the works—a whole book of charges I wasn't the least anxious to face. I'd really be in trouble. However much I liked dogs, I had to do it. I still feel sorry about it, but what could I do? These Alsatians are trained to catch people and prevent their escaping; no knife, no gun, no violence can help you shake a dog like that. Only wolves' fat * or brains will help you. Now, where is the weakest point in the tracker dog? Its nose! So the next time the dog barked and moved her snout toward my Adam's apple, I seized her pointed nose between my teeth with all my power. I bit like I had never bitten before. The animal yelped and tried to wrench her head away from my mouth. But to no avail: I had immediately seized her muzzle with both hands and held it tightly closed. I could taste the dog's blood on my tongue. My jaws became cramped and stiff and in the end I couldn't maintain the pressure of my bite. I let go and ran to where I had left the sack. The dog remained where she was, whining, yelping and howling, rubbing her ruined nose with her front paw. I was terribly sorry for the poor beast, but it was the only way. Most likely they would have to destroy her—she would probably be unable to smell after that, and so would be useless to them. Or maybe they could fix her up again.

* *Wolves' fat is the only weapon against police dogs and bloodhounds. When the dogs scent a wolf, they flee. There is thus a great demand for that exotic grease, but the only place to get it is on the black market. A fragment of the skin of a wolf can be worth hundreds of guilders. Smugglers often strew a wolf's droppings in their wake as a defense against tracker dogs. In all the official tests that have been carried out, no dog has ever dared to proceed once it caught the scent of a wolf. Here the long arm of the law is powerless. Why else is the cleaning of the wolves' den in every zoo done by police who carefully pack up all the droppings and burn them under official supervision? Smugglers will even go so far as to rub their bodies with wolves' fat or dung. Once my pal, Johnny Stiletto, was forced to stand in a lineup in the courtroom at police headquarters. The identification was to be carried out by dogs of the Tracker Service, but Johnny had taken the precaution of rubbing wolves' fat on his legs. Almost as soon as they entered the courtroom, the animals leapt back and away from him, whining and howling, their tails between their legs.*

Anyway, everything had happened in less than a minute and at any moment now the guard would come running round the corner of the field and spot me. And that could be very risky indeed, for those guys carry guns, and the Krauts are real sharpshooters. I raced towards Holland with the sack. About a dozen yards from the border I felt relief surge over me as I plunged into the Dutch cornfield. I hurled the sack of coffee into a ditch and crept through the corn to the backyard of the farmhouse. I had managed to save my skin, but during the next few hours I would have to steer clear of those border guards. In the backyard, my "pal" stood, laughing merrily, a mug of coffee in his right hand. He greeted me profusely. I said nothing, but threw myself at him and belted him so hard that the blood spurted from his astonished face. "And now fuck off, you dirty coward!" I shouted at him. I was so mad I nearly ran after him to kick his ass.

I asked the farmer if he would send someone to retrieve the sack from the ditch—for twenty-five guilders. A few kids went to look for it and returned with it later. So my business was saved. I gave the farmer another twenty-five guilders and stashed the sack in his attic. He provided me with dry clothes, and I hopped a bus back to town. The German guards would, of course, complain to their Dutch colleagues, who would certainly investigate the matter, so I had to split the scene pronto.

All that day I hid in the pad of a girl friend of mine. The following morning I went back, changed clothes again, picked up the sack, went by bus to a border post twenty miles away, and there sneaked across. A short while later, I had sold the coffee at a café.

Later on, with a few other studs, I smuggled radios, cameras, butter, pistols, munitions, cats, optical instruments, and God knows what other junk, backwards and forwards across the Dutch-German border. When, in the woods at night, we occasionally heard the cry: "Dutch Customs, surrender or we fire!" we would watch very carefully for the flashes of the warning shots, which the guards always fired into the air. Then we would reply by aiming our heavy Mausers at the light flashes, and that settled their hash for them. They got out of the way quick, those Dutchmen! As soon as the sound of our shots had died away, we would hear the sound of running footsteps and the crackle of broken bushes, and then, a moment later, the reverberation of a motorbike starting up. That was our cue to get the hell out of there—we had no intention of waiting for reinforcements.

I also did quite a bit of poaching in the same area. We would sometimes be lucky enough, after a night in the woods, to come back with twenty-four marketable wild rabbits—flashlights and crude clubs were all we needed.

25

I work in a printing shop as an apprentice. All day long I have to tend the stove, glue labels on boxes, polish the boss's car, carry coffee for the staff, and run errands. My pals say I'm grossly underpaid (I earn twenty-five guilders a week and they earn forty), but it's easy work, easy money for kicks. Of course, I do this boring work to please my mother and my guardian. Besides, people on the square are convinced that I'm a worthless spendthrift, too lazy to work at anything worthwhile. Well, I'll show them, I Jan Cremer!

The boss is an old lecher. I've seen him grab two different office girls—both hot little pieces, according to the scuttlebutt. One of the printers is a little man who wears a beret and rides a motorbike (I get a guilder for cleaning it), and this cat keeps on telling me stories about the office girls, really crude tales that tend to nauseate me. "What does this mean, then?" he asks when no one is listening. And he sticks his thumb between his index and middle fingers. "Fucking," I reply, simply to please him, and he's satisfied, for he really gets horny with his stories about cunt, shit, piss, turds, pussy and other hairy topics. And yet he seems such a decent little chap. It used to bewilder me. Polite as an Englishman when the boss or the foreman questioned him, they had only to turn their backs and off he would go, making obscene gestures, pointing to where his prick would be under his pants and sticking a slobbery tongue out between his false teeth and twitching lips. He's a married man, too, and he and his wife have three pretty little children; on Saturdays, his wife and kids come to fetch him. "Those chicks upstairs," he announces, giving me a long look, "are just asking to be fucked! They've all got the hots . . . shitty-ass-rat-fuck, all ready to be laid, no lie!"

As for myself, I don't even want to get laid. I'm only fourteen and I've fucked the neighbor's wife already, haven't I? I have a secret agreement with Betty: when I'm just a little older and have made a pile of money, I'll go and get her in Germany. And Bartje can damn well stay with the Krauts, or we'll smother him or something.

Almost every day I'm in trouble with the boss—I'm late, or I talk back to him, and it's obvious I don't want to learn anything, that I just fritter away my time and never do my work properly. What does he expect for the money he pays? When there's paper to be cut, I take care to adjust the guillotine so that the blades are promptly ruined. Then, of course, I'm in for it. Red, the foreman—now there's a real son of a bitch, the redheaded bastard! I often flick spitballs after him as he walks through the machine shop. He's the one that always complains about me to the boss. Of course, those two are hand in glove, especially since Red began courting the boss's daughter. And is she a stuck-up bitch! She attends private school and owns a new motorbike. Red is in charge of all typesetting. That's why, one day, to get my hunk, I jumbled up all the boxes of type. The next morning the shit hit the fan, but good! Of course they couldn't prove it was me . . . and it cost them a whole day's work to get everything sorted out again.

On the other hand, I do get along fine with the office girls. I hang around them quite a bit when I get the chance. One of them is Dotty, a very nice kid; she isn't very good-looking, but who cares about that? She has acne. One time Dotty made a grab at my crotch. I get all mixed up with the girls' skylarking and all the questions they ask me. And when I have to go up with their coffee I usually find I've got a hard-on. When they notice the bulge in my pants, they scream with laughter. I feel I want the ground to open and swallow me up. I run out of the office, and leave them to laugh themselves to tears. It gets worse every day. All the time they grow more and more forward. When I go in they're sitting quite normally in their chairs, but as soon as I approach they open their legs wide and hike their skirts up to their panties. I'm not interested, but the bare flesh is right there in front of me . . . I can't avoid seeing it.

Dotty is more forward than any of them. She's always telling filthy jokes in the printing shop. Once I stealthily clipped some rubbers to her coat. Actually it wasn't my idea —it was the brain-work of some of the men in the shop. They gave me the prophylactics and I just clipped them to her coat. Dotty left at five-thirty every night, and this particular evening the entire staff waited to see her go. They all screamed with laughter. Of course, the following day I found myself on the carpet again. Naturally it was the guy with the beret who informed on me to Red and, as Red was no friend of mine, that meant another interview with the boss. He told me that if there was just one more complaint I would have to go. Moreover, he wasn't going to put any more stamps on my unemployment-insurance card, and, to top it off, he had the cheek to call me a dirty little pig. All that was bad enough, but what really bugged me was the fact that my colleagues never stuck up for me, not once did they defend me or help me in any way. So there was only one thing to do—counterattack: I put salt in their coffee.

One day the ratfink who wore the beret accused me of stealing money from him. I lost my temper and went for him with one of the cutting knives. They dragged me along to the boss's office. He stood with his hands clasped behind his back and his legs apart, rising and falling on the balls of his feet. "If you admit you stole the money, and admit that you put sugar in my gas tank, you can stay. Otherwise, I'm going to fire you right here and now! And don't think for a minute you'll get a reference out of me!"

The point was that I hadn't stolen the money, though I had poured sugar into his gas tank. I decided, however, to clam up about both capers, so I again found myself unemployed. But at least the Labor Exchange Office forced my boss to give me a reference.

Later on, I worked in a luncheonette as a busboy in "Ice Cream and Cold Drinks." ("What do you want to be when you grow up, Jan?" "A soda jerk and a Negro!") A couple of pretty waitresses from the country work in the place. Sometimes I slip them a wink, sometimes an ice cream. Whenever I need more ice or clean trays, I have to walk to the kitchen. And that's where the two girls, Willy and Elly, hang out when the place isn't too busy. And once a day, while I'm in the kitchen, I drink a glass of fresh cream—very expensive stuff!

"Why do you always drink so much cream?" Elly asks. "Do you have a girl?"

"Four of them," I reply.

"Just what we thought!" exclaims Elly, while Willy giggles in the background, peeping through the service hatch to make sure the headwaiter isn't coming.

"If you let me see yours, I'll let you see mine," Elly says. Since I've been working here I've been asked this about ten times a day. And they're always so insistent—they never miss a chance! But I stick to my work, gathering up the dirty plates and preparing sundaes all day long: vanilla with fruit salad, mocha, strawberry, banana and peach melba, and all the time these chicks are coming on with me. One day I give in. Elly leads me through the kitchen and into the dressing room, and I feel myself growing excited. I play with Elly's peach for her, and two days later I have to do the same for Willy. This groping goes on for a few days until finally we go all the way, myself just for kicks because they need it. I find it a very exciting sight: one of the broads—already curvy and cute-assed in her black-and-white waitress' uniform, her large money purse slung around her belly—lifting her skirt and lying down carefully either on the floor or on the narrow wooden bench next to the wall. Naturally, we've got to get it over with quickly—between serving an ice-cream soda and clearing the dishes off table number four, for example. Meanwhile, the daily glass of cream becomes a pint, besides quite a few portions of whipped cream. God! Finally, sick and tired of all that cream, I change jobs.

26

Now I work as an apprentice to a commercial artist, for twenty-five guilders a week. I don't do much except blow putty through a blowpipe at passersby, throw little balls of it onto plates at the restaurant across the street, play jokes with the other two employees, wash out the brushes ("You have to treat those marten-hair brushes like they were people!") and sweep out the studio ("You want to become an artist? First of all you've got to learn how to keep your studio clean!"). I can't paint letters. The pigment always runs, especially when I'm doing those large display signs, perched on a wobbly ladder forty feet above the ground. One time I fall and the ladder and rigging come tumbling down. A Volkswagen bus that happens to be standing across the street saves my life. As I fall, I hear screams and shouts from passersby, then a grinding noise as bicycles are overturned by the falling ladder. Meanwhile my boss (who had kept shouting from below, "Go higher up, idiot! The ladder won't fall, shithead!") and the other assistants clear out of the way but pronto. I really thought I had had it that time. It all happened so quickly, and there I was glued to the ladder like a leech when the upper part of it came banging down onto the roof of the little bus and broke off. The jolt simply set me down on my feet, and there I was, standing on the street quite safe, but shivering. From a height like that you don't usually land as though you had jumped onto a mattress. That bus had saved my life, and, of course, I myself was commended in the evening paper for my cool behavior and presence of mind. True, I was jolted and shaken, but there were no bones broken. So here I was, an unwanted apprentice with a bad record, written up like a hero in the local tabloid!

Now, I had been hired as an apprentice painter, but it was soon evident I hadn't much talent for commercial art. I kept drawing the letters larger and larger, with crooked strokes. I painted on holidays, spoiled the brushes, and was generally the clown of the place. "Jan," they would put me on, "go fetch a tin of IT at the paint shop." And I would go home, have myself a nice hot cup of tea and a cookie, shoot the breeze a bit and return about an hour later. When I got back to the shop I bullshitted with a straight face: "They didn't have any IT at the shop, boss." Then they would all scream with laughter, especially when, with straight face and stupid look, I would recount how I had gone from shop to shop, and finally to the wholesaler, who had just sold his last can. Next I was sent for Ain (sailor's shit on a chain), an ounce of Nada, a card of buttonholes, a tin of wind, one square yard of invisible glass, fishtail brushes, and so forth. I always went along. That way I got enough time to do some work on my own. I copped brushes, paint, paper and thumbtacks from the studio, and went home to paint . . . for myself!

A real artist used to call at the shop a few times a week. He painted stuff you couldn't make head or tail of—all abstract. He had a big beard and wore stovepipe pants. One time he condescended to look at my work. "Very sensitive and quite talented," he said. That was encouraging. In the neighborhood they began to call me Blotchy Jan, because my paintings were abstract too. Very difficult, you know! But the artist told me that to gain experience, I first had to learn how to paint what I saw. He gave me books on Klee, Miró and Cézanne, picture postcards of Notre Dame and a cathedral in Barcelona, and *Ten Heads for Drawing*. I was supposed to study these carefully and then draw them. Painting with oils would come later, like writing with a pen at school.

My artist friend was a teacher at the local academy. On Wednesday evenings he taught Commercial Art. "Just drop in some evening, if you like," he had said to me. I was to get there around nine o'clock and ask for him personally. Then the porter would show me the way. The following Wednesday evening, by eight o'clock I was already pacing up and down in front of the building. I continued to do so until a quarter to nine. Then I counted up to a thousand and went in. The porter directs me upstairs. The corridors smell of paint and ink. There are good-looking girls on the stairs, real artistic broads with ponytails. Someday I'm going to marry a movie star with a ponytail. I reach the Commercial Art Department. My friend is busy and tells me to have a look around. There are heaps of drawings lying on large tables, huge photographs scattered about and posters on the wall. I glance through the door of the next classroom, but there's not a nude in sight. And I had heard the academy was a club for nude women! I wish I could study at the academy, but that's out. The academy is only for "responsible" people.

Phonies, braggarts and the like, rich men's children who are able to study at the academy thanks to their fathers' bread. "My son attends the Academy of Fine Arts, of course!" But these students really don't know a damn thing about anything—they couldn't even drive a nail into the wall. Rich shits, that's all they are! My friend is busy at a litho press, so I take a peek at a large drawing pinned to his board. It's of a town, not just any town, but a town with all kinds of harsh lights and ugly houses, like no real town ever was. Everyone in the class is very busy, bent over their boards, never allowing their gaze to wander.

Over in the corner there's a real artist. His hair is very long, just like Jesus Christ's, with a beard as well. From time to time he looks up and blinks at the glaring fluorescent light. He's getting his inspiration, you can tell right off. Meanwhile, a bell starts ringing. My friend and his pupils collect their stuff and shove it into bags. You can see the rulers sticking out. We all go downstairs, and there I am walking among the Artistic Ones, girls with green nails, ponytails and jeans. For the most part the boys have beards and wear heavy sweaters, their bare feet in sandals. There are, among them, some who are normally dressed, but they probably aren't quite yet Artists—or aren't allowed to be by their parents. If my pals from the block could see me now, walking with all these Artists!

Later on, though, I too get artistic inclinations. I have my trousers pegged, buy a loden coat, comb my hair forward, and remove the mudguard, the light and a few spokes from my bike, which I paint a bright yellow. For an artist has to be poor and miserable, hasn't he? I begin to smoke a pipe, puff-cough-puff, and allow some artistic stubble to accumulate on my chin. For an artist without a beard is like a fish without bones, isn't he? Worthless, all those middle-class types with their absurd society! Take off, bourgeois fink! Make way! Don't you see it's an artist behind the wheel? Out of my way, robots! To your washtubs! To your factories! Work the guts out of your worthless bodies! What do you say, bourgeois boob? Don't come on with me! Who's a pretender, a phony? What crust! You'll never understand my Soul! I am like Jesus Christ—I turn the other cheek. Split! Away to your slippers, your nightly cup of tea, your crossword puzzle! Out of my way!

27

They bug me in the studio, they bug me in the street, they bug me everywhere. But I endure it. For an artist must suffer.

I now paint quite regularly and my friend says I am making progress. If I keep on with my work and do my very best, it's possible I may get a grant from the academy.

The boss at the studio is connected with the Rehabilitation Service. He puts me to the test. Once a month he sends me to the bank with a hundred guilders in an open envelope. Finally I just can't resist the temptation and squander the money in a single day with a few pals and girl friends. Later, of course, I don't dare go back to work. Well, a few days later my boss comes looking for me. He will forget everything, but I must come back and work without pay for four weeks. Shamefaced, I return to work. But at the end of the month, I once again must deliver the hundred guilders, and once again I can't resist the temptation. And so it goes on, for months. Except for that one day a month, I never have much spending money. Whatever I do have, I earn by running errands and distributing advertising leaflets. One guilder a thousand. I deliver ten thousand a night: a hundred in one mailbox and thousands buried in a garden. All my new pals from the academy have plenty of pocket money. They often treat me to drinks and cigarettes, and I have to give something in return once in a while, don't I?

One day I have to take a message from my boss to a large department store: my boss will charge eight hundred guilders for a job including advertisements with texts on temporary partitions. I tell the manager of the department store that I will do the job myself for half the money. He agrees. So I return to my boss and tell him I was asked to inform him that the deal was off, that they had engaged someone else. Naturally, my boss is hopping mad, since he had thought the deal was closed. Then, I scare up all the kids on my block, buy paint on credit and, bright and early one morning, hours before they have to be at school, ten small boys are splashing paint on the temporary partitions, according to my instructions, at twenty-five cents an hour. At eight o'clock, I go to my job. At lunchtime I return to give further instructions to my staff, and at six o'clock I go back and do the finishing touches myself. The letters and everything turn out well. My boss, however, happens to drive by in his Mercedes and sees what's up. Goggle-eyed, he approaches and asks me who I'm working for. I tell him I'm working for myself. He fires me on the spot. Tough break! Was he mad! The next day I picked up my cabbage from the department store. They were entirely satisfied. It turned out to be a really good-looking partition, a terrific eye-catcher, and I made a profit of three hundred guilders on a four-hundred-guilder job. I spent part of it on clothes, paint and an easel, but also gave part of it to my mother for my room and board.

A few days later, after a night of heavy rain, I passed near the department store and noticed a stream of blue water bubbling along the gutter. The closer I came to the store, the stronger the blue color became. Then I remembered I had bought cheap powder paint and mixed it with water, because I couldn't get expensive oils on credit. The rain had washed my advertisement right off the temporary boarding, so my former boss landed the job after all. Fortunately, they couldn't do a thing to me. It had been a cash transaction, and I had signed no receipts.

28

Thanks to the intervention of my friend, the Commercial Art teacher, I am allowed to join the Saturday afternoon class at the academy. I turn out to be the most promising pupil in the class, a Real Talent, a wondrous talent with a special feeling for color. But, the trouble is, I don't seem to be able to take criticism from any of the teachers. I won't pay any attention to what they say, so it seems I'm just not cut out to be an Artist. When, in September, I send in my request for admission as a full-time student, I am shown the door. The Director refuses even to see me. I can't make head or tail of it. My mother phones to find out why I am refused admission. The Director, Abe Hardnose, declares, "Your son, Cremer, is totally unsuited, a juvenile delinquent, hostile to his teachers and impervious to all instruction." He goes on to say that he will do everything in his power to prevent my admission. I am no good and they won't admit me. Actually, I had never spoken a word to this Director in all my life. I had never even seen him. Nevertheless, he warned those girls who knew me that they were not to associate with me. According to him, I am a scoundrel, and he threatens to kick out of the school anyone who is seen even once in my company. My mother calls my friend, the teacher, and asks him why I am not being allowed to attend classes at the academy. He replies, "Please understand, Madam, personally I am very fond of your son, and I am convinced, as are some of my colleagues, that he possesses an unusual talent. But I cannot really tell you why he isn't being admitted. All I can say is that the Director seems to have a personal aversion to him. Maybe Jan himself knows why, but, much as I should like to have him in the academy, I have no power to contest the Director's decision. Off the record, I think there's been a miscarriage of justice, but I have a family, a wife and four children, and I really cannot jeopardize my own position over this matter." So his advice is that I try another academy, because it seems the Director will not admit me under any circumstances.

Even my guardian can't get any satisfaction when he makes some inquiries. In spite of the fact that I had never exchanged a word with this fine, artistic Director, and that he had never seen any of my work, he felt confident in telling my guardian, "Cremer a painter? Not if he lives to be a thousand! The place for Cremer is in prison. You'll find that there isn't an academy in the country that will consider him. He has no talent worth mentioning, and I don't want an influence like that in my school. This is no reform school! This is an Academy of Fine Arts!"

Two days later I am accepted by another academy. I had gone for my interview with a portfolio of drawings and the Director said, "It seems you're not really old enough but, considering your talent, I feel you should join the academy at once. Can you come tomorrow? We must begin right away!" These words were music to my ears.

Years later, when I had become a celebrated artist and examples of my work were in every Dutch collection—and many important foreign ones—the National Art Institute organized an exhibition at the museum in the very town where I had been so summarily excluded from Hardnose's academy. Hardnose, in his capacity as Director of the academy and President of the local art committee (he himself painted sweet-looking landscapes and rose-colored nudes), threatened to cancel the entire exhibition if my name were not removed from among the list of twenty-five participating artists. I withdrew myself. That Hardnose! How are you, Abe?

29

So I find myself enrolled in an art academy. During the first two months I had to commute. I boarded the train at seven o'clock in the morning and got home for dinner at six. It was very tiring, particularly so because I had just met a very cute girl. Later on a friend of mine managed to convince his father, who in turn had to convince my guardian, that my friend and I should be allowed to rent a room together in the town where the academy was located—it would be much better for our studies. So our request was granted. But, during the four weeks that I shared quarters with this pal of mine, the landlord had several near heart attacks, and his wife had a small nervous breakdown. One caper we got up to was to short-circuit some electric cables so that the city authorities had to dig up our street in the middle of the night. We broke four shop-windows, set fire to various places, destroyed furniture, retouched meadow-and-windmill landscapes into abstracts, chased customers out of our landlord's photographic shop and had girl friends visiting us in our room almost every night. "You want to see some genuine Mondrian and Klee plaintings?" we used to tell them. "Then fall by at four o'clock." Then, during lunch hour, we quickly painted some "Mondrians." Sometimes the chicks stayed with us overnight. As a matter of fact, on one occasion the landlady found me in the bath with one of them. Sometimes we pitched large plaster figures out of the window at drunks. Singing at the top of their voices, they lurched along the street below, their harsh songs splitting the night. Hunks of plaster would explode at their feet, sending them staggering backwards in a daze. What a gas that was! No visitors were allowed in our lodgings after eleven P.M., but hardly a night went by when we didn't smuggle a load of people upstairs.

Now it so happened that I was receiving a grant from the Institute to cover the cost of my room and board. This arrangement was a provisional one, of course: "We shall just see whether it's workable," my guardian had said. Unfortunately the experiment was somewhat unsuccessful. For the first week everything went well. I paid all my bills promptly. But after that I stopped paying them—all of them except the bill I ran up at the corner bar, which my weekly allowance just about covered. We were no longer eating; we didn't have money for food. Meanwhile, I began going with a girl I had met at the academy—the daughter of a rich industrialist—who was on the point of marrying the son of another rich industrialist from the same suburb and of the same religion. What a scandal I caused—both families were up in arms! I hadn't known a thing about the girl's marriage plans, but one day her fiancé came to me to protest. The guy was studying medicine, so I gave him a bop on his learned nut. Then the bastard decided to write a letter to the Director of the academy. One day soon after, Annabel—that was her name—was removed from the school by that stinking-rich daddy of hers. They drove off in their Chevvy. Nevertheless, a few days later Annabel was at my door again, having run away from home. I managed to hide her with some acquaintances of mine.

Her father called with a police escort, looking for his daughter. After that I was followed by fuzz wherever I went, real unobtrusive boys. They hoped I would lead them to where she was hiding out. But they didn't know Jan Cremer! I gave them a real run for their money, had them trailing me from one end of town to the other, in and out of coffee-houses and expensive hotels. What a lark! Even my friends were shadowed. But it was no good. And finally her father fell on his knees in front of me, right down on the dusty floor of the Director's office, and literally begged me to return his daughter to him! I stated my conditions: that I would accept his hospitality at his country estate, that his daughter would be free to associate with me, that he would overlook the question of my religion, and that he would revise his opinion of me. He had said, and really believed, that I was a heathen, a scoundrel, a good-for-nothing pimp. But now he was ready to do anything and everything for me: he would even make me foreman at his factory. So I said, "If I give you back your daughter and you don't keep your promises, I'll see to it that you roast in hell!" So everything was fine and dandy again!

On weekends I was a guest at their country house. Like many good Catholic families, this was a large one. Annabel had eight sisters and four brothers. They ate in shifts, attended church in shifts, did everything in shifts. Actually, I was roped into going along to church with them, to set an example for the younger members of the family. The children might not understand how I was able to go on living without attending mass; having been brought up to swallow whole the pill of Catholicism, they might find it hard to understand why I wasn't struck down on the spot by the Deadly Fire. So I went along. But after I had, on four successive Sundays, created scenes in the halls of holiness, I was finally relieved from churchgoing. I had, for example, raised hell when the Holy Father, armed with a toilet brush, sprinkled holy oil on my white suit. On another occasion I went back three times to get free holy wafers, and was finally dragged back to the pew by my prospective father-in-law. Nobody drags me into a pew!

Another time I fell asleep during the sermon. What a lot of bullshit that is: you're not even allowed to answer back when those priest guys insist that you are a sinner. You know what I mean. "Sinner that you are, you will burn on Judgment Day, for, when they asked him 'Shall you crucify me?' did not Matthew reply, 'Before the cock has crowed thrice, a flood shall plague the earth!' At which utterance Peter transformed his staff into a snake and a black plague came down upon Nazareth, so that the people prayed for rain. And lo! it rained. And it rained. So hard that there was a flood (And a Spark went into His Crotch when He

70

saw Her Pussy) that spread over all the earth. And a certain Noah, who knew the score, had built himself an ark against the watery main. And called unto him . . ." (Now this Noah is always unjustly represented as some kind of animal-lover. But the fact is that he took all those cattle along for provisions. How could he have known the rain would stop so soon and leave him perched on Ararat?)

This and many other things will such a priest bellow, finally pointing an accusing finger at you and shouting, "Stand on your feet, sinner!" But what can you do? If you stand up, your neighbor pulls you down again; and if you remain seated, you are a "dirty pharisee." So I usually had myself a nap during the sermon. Once, unfortunately, I fell forward in my seat with a loud bang. In my confusion I thought my prospective father-in-law had pushed me, and I can tell you that if I'm awakened abruptly. . . . Once, too, I wouldn't let go of the collection box—the kind with a tassel on a stick—and I remember the old beadle pulling and pulling to try to get the loot away from me! Man, do those guys dig loot!

I was definitely discharged from churchgoing when, one fine Sunday morning, having smoked a quickie outside the door, I went back inside to take my place in the pew and found my seat occupied. For that is the way of religion: everyone wants to sit in the best seat, at the head of the class—a matter of "conspicuous consumption," of being seen by master and competitor. "I'm all right Jack, and, thanking you kindly, I've got me my seat!" For an ass-space on a bare wooden bench down near the front you pay a hundred guilders a year. You can just figure what it costs for a family of fifteen. And with all that kneeling every time the bell rings, you soon ruin the crease on your pants, so all those pants have to go to the cleaners every week, and so on. When I got to my seat—I didn't pay for it, of course, but my prospective father-in-law did—it was occupied. My father-in-law pointed quietly to a pew up front—gesturing as silently as a pantomimic—and I went meekly to sit on the front bench.

All of a sudden a little man comes over and kneels down in the aisle beside me. He is obviously in a great hurry, and very upset, and he whispers loudly in my ear, "You are sitting in my seat!"

My God! so what? This is supposed to be God's house, isn't it, and open to everyone? His blessing is for every man, isn't it? Am I, sinner that I am, not to be allowed to occupy a seat? But, of course, as a reasonable human being, I also have to consider the man's point of view. Let's assume he's a good Catholic, that he's paid his contribution to the "club," that he carries his green card on him, that he doesn't use too much holy water (for only the sun rises for free) and that he has a seat right in front of the altar so that when his employees see their boss sitting up there they will realize he has good reason for refusing them a raise in wages. Live and let live! The guy probably drops buttons and prewar coins into the collection box every week, for there isn't just one collection, no sir! The old plate goes round five times in all: once for the church, once for the pastor and his vassals, once for the missionaries in China, once for the cardinal's new bicycle, and, finally, once for the poor. For the poor they make up a parcel every Christmas: a pig's foot, a sack of oatmeal, a bologna, a loaf of rye bread, an ounce of tea, two pounds of apples, a slice of bacon, soap to keep them next to Godliness, and a dishrag.

Meanwhile, this little jerk continues to pull my sleeve. He's as nervous as a cat, anxious to get out of the aisle. For—who knows?—the very next minute the roof may be struck by lightning or a small tank may bulldoze its way through the wall! I tell him for the umpteenth time that there's no room for him, there are already too many people in the pew. But he insists, "That is my seat you are sitting in! You will have to move! Sit somewhere else!"

What does he take me for? Does he think I'm going to wander around the packed church like an idiot, looking for a seat? I am quite comfortable where I am, but he just won't take no for an answer. He shoves me along the bench to make room for himself, amid mutterings from the people all around. The Faithful are becoming excited. Quiet, Flock! pay attention to your priest! Now the little man starts to act most rudely. He spreads himself as wide as possible, takes out his prayer book with a great deal of fuss and pretends to read it. I behave very calmly—I am, after all, a very calm person. I have made myself as small as possible, but finally I can't stand it any longer. The stale smell of his ridiculous Sunday suit attacks my nostrils, and I get a sudden urge to spread myself out too. I take a deep breath when the man happens to be in a most unstable position: he has one hand over his closed eyes, holds the bridge of his nose with forefinger and thumb, and rests his elbow on the rail in front of him. All of a sudden his elbow slips from the rail, his feet trip over his kneeling stool, and he tumbles down with a loud thud into the aisle. Anyway, when he crashes onto the wine-red tiles, his spectacles fly from his face like a guided missile. The way that little man leapt back into the pew, you would have thought the tiles were red-hot!

Later on, my girl friend, who had caught the entire scene (at least you can get some kicks in church, and she thought it all very funny—she personally has no use for religion, but of course she doesn't have any choice in the matter), tells me that the little guy fell out of the pew at exactly the holiest moment of the mass, during Silent Devotion. Anyway, I couldn't restrain myself any longer. Bursting with laughter, I ran out past the grim red faces of my prospective in-laws and the rest of the faithful. From that Sunday on, I no longer accompanied them to church. Instead, while the family was at church, I played badminton, popped popcorn, or inspected the wine cellar. For they wouldn't let me stay in bed: to sleep late on Sunday morning was a kind of blasphemy.

30

After four months I had to leave the academy. The Director, Dr. Baggy-Pants, exclaimed, "I warned you! I warned you many times that if you ever called me a 'Dirty bastard' or a 'Pig-fucker,' in front of the entire class, you would have to go. Where did you ever learn such language? There is nothing more to be said. I simply cannot have you here any longer!"

Actually the Director was rather a nice guy. He had tried to do right by me. He really believed in me, but there you are, I just wasn't cut out to be a polite pupil. There was, however, more to it than that. The Director had come to the academy at the same time I did. And he, together with Hank, a would-be revolutionary who taught "Techniques and Materials," regarded my paintings as "mental aberrations— very interesting from a psychiatric point of view" (just a year later, he developed some of my "aberrations" and exhibited them as his own work). The three of us had many enemies in the school. There were even whispers of a "triumvirate." That was the real reason the Director had to drop me. I became the scapegoat. I was the uncouth wrongdoer. Every day I had to take his bit about how he had picked me up out of the gutter and how he only helped me because of his friendship with my guardian. Once, when Dr. Baggy-Pants decided to lead the academy in a new direction (after all, he was a Big Success now, and this was *his* academy), he assigned to me the task of getting rid of a hundred and forty-four plaster statues. I took a hammer and pulverized them. It took me six hours to finish the job, during which I discovered that I had a most destructive side to my character when properly aroused.

My teacher in "Painting" had a nervous tic in his left eye. He found me a most difficult pupil, but nevertheless regarded my work as very interesting. But I had to learn how to paint from scratch, he insisted. "You must paint from nature," he used to say. "Look here: when you paint a plum, you should feel that you could actually pick it off the canvas!"

Naturally, this led to conflict, for my ambition was not to paint pickable plums. So I painted plums that looked like plums, but couldn't be picked. Meanwhile, all my class-mates were painting plums that could be picked—they must have *liked* plums. They were mostly farmers' sons from the sticks. At lunchtime they ate coarse brown bread with let-tuce, raw beets, onions, endives, turnips and garlic. The first time one of them offered me a sandwich, I thought, "Oh good!" but I would have been better off taking a bite of shit. These pupils, who were constantly held up to me as examples, and who were regarded as the best in the school (one had been there eight years and another six), came early in the morning, wearing blue smocks, corduroy pants and sandals on their bare feet. They had to hoof it all of six miles from their homes every morning, and they always looked pretty bad, with large pimples on their faces and pale rings under their eyes. This wasn't from fucking or any-thing, for they neither smoked, drank or fucked: that would have been against Art. I suppose that's why I didn't become an Artist.

All day long they would talk about Art, about how Cézanne painted apples, how Rembrandt captured a sun-beam on a copper pot, how Morandi managed to keep his bottles so pale, how to thin oil with turps, how to look at nudes: "Take a really good look," they used to tell me. "See how beautiful the muscles are on the calf of the leg!"

"Yes," I'd say. "Yes . . . yes!"

Boy, they were some artists! The one who had been there for six years had, during the last five, painted nothing but bottles, coffeepots, trumpets, glasses, dried flowers, and end-less portraits. He philosophized all day about Morandi, Klee, Mirò and Picasso, and was such an asshole that he spelled "cunt" with a "d." Needless to say, when they had a party I was sure not to be invited. They all gossiped about me as if I were John Dillinger's son. They tried to turn everyone against me, and ratted to the teacher that I had painted moustaches on the portraits they were working on. Yet now he claims that he was my best friend at the school. It is really touching how many friends I acquired all of a sudden, as soon as I became rich and famous. I spent a total of four months at that institute, and it seems now that I shared my rooms with three hundred and twenty-four soul mates. "A friend of yours from school asked me to look you up," people tell me. But the truth is, I didn't have a friend there, not a single one. Whenever I have an exhibition, some "best friend" of mine always manages to turn up with photos of his paintings, and tells the owner of the gallery that I sent him. "Yes, Cremer is very enthusiastic about my work and thinks you ought to give me a show." Just like the chicks who have a cup of coffee with me and then tell the papers, "Yes, I lived with him for a while but he was so mixed-up that finally I just had to leave him."

There was one drawing teacher who hated me so much that during committee meetings he would tell all sorts of stories about me. I had thrown an inkwell at his head. I had called him an impotent bastard. I had crapped in his washbasin. I had stolen money from his overcoat. I had threatened him with a penknife. I had used a sling to shoot pebbles at him. I had poisoned the school's atmosphere. Moreover, I had insulted his religious beliefs by saying that the priest was like an over-roasted chicken on a spit—quite indigestible. All this I got from Dr. Baggy-Pants, who had me on the carpet after every committee meeting. But I knew all these accusations were bullshit, so I never even batted an eye.

31

Once I had been dropped from the academy, the Director tried to screw me up in every way possible, particularly when it turned out that my guardian had no immediate plans to have me sent to another correction home. Dr. Baggy-Pants prohibited everyone from associating with me and spread it around that I was an undisciplined roughneck who wouldn't stop at rape and who, having seduced women, threw them aside quite ruthlessly. I was a communist as well, of course. The intensity of his dislike was explained to some extent by something I had said to him during a reception. It had seemed to me that he was showing too much interest in Annabel, so I said to him, "Listen, Baggy-Pants, you keep hanging around her and you're in for a kick in the balls!" Actually, I had meant it as a joke—I am an uncouth fellow, there's no doubt about that. But he took it the wrong way, maybe because I'd seen him coming out of a whorehouse —he had ducked quickly into a dark alley when he saw me coming. In a word, I had become too dangerous and he wanted to get me out of the way. So, an institution had to be found for me.

Meanwhile, everyone was putting me down because I wanted my freedom and was going to split even though Annabel was pregnant. The fact is, things were becoming too difficult. I told Annabel "I'll be back, but I don't know when." Annabel had a little money from home, so she had rented an attic in town. I left her there and fled the scene as I had so many times before.

32

It was a grim, grey, cold building. By the driveway stood an old weather-beaten sign, "Observation Home." The full name was "Observation Home for Wayward Youth," but the fact is, it was simply a youth prison. No more, no less. When I first arrived I really hated the place, but I can get used to anything. I can adapt myself to any situation, anywhere, if I have to, whether it's a coal boat to Tanganyika, an ice floe in the North Atlantic, or a concentration camp for delinquents and psychopaths in Vladivostok. I made the best of it. What I was in for, I've forgotten. I've scratched my initials next to "Kilroy was here" on the walls of jails, police stations and army camps all over the place, and I can hardly keep track of all of them. I was regarded as a bad type. I had struck one of my guardians, the Director of a Catholic grammar school, on his bald noggin. I had gone joy riding. My technical skills were nil—I couldn't even turn an ignition key. I molested girls. I couldn't learn anything. I stole bread from my employers. I couldn't get along with anyone. I had the wrong kinds of friends. I drove my mother out of her mind and my guardians to distraction. I bugged the police. And I called the juvenile magistrate a chickenprick. In short, I was a difficult person, not much better than an animal, a potential bandit, an *enfant terrible*. But somewhere inside this rough and unfortunate exterior, a rare gem was hidden. The magistrate had given orders that this gem had to be found, and this was to be done in the Observation Home.

Well, I was willing to go along. But it was soon obvious that I just wasn't cut out to be a craftsman. I held the hammer the wrong way and, cursing a blue streak, drove nails so that the wood splintered. I was nervous, schizophrenic, frustrated, sadistic, perverted, sensual, sexually abnormal, a rebel, an inspirer of riots, a committer of bestiality. I paid no attention whatsoever to the judgment of my elders or to legal authority; I respected nothing and no one. Nevertheless, bless their souls, they never stopped trying to teach me respect for authority. With rapped knuckles, bloody noses, stiff necks, and all kinds of rough treatment. I spent the first few months between the craft shops and the clinic, under observation. But, because of my wild fantasies, the psychiatrist couldn't make me out. I liked going to see the headshrinker, anyway, because he always had smokes for me, as did our spiritual caretakers. I was converted in turn to the Catholic, Protestant, and Jewish faiths—until the smokes ran out. When summer came, I applied, through my supervisor, for a transfer to another section. This supervisor, by the way, was an OK character, and always tried to help me. I wanted to transfer because there were a lot of queers among the older boys in my section, and they kept bothering me. I often complained to the Director about them, but he claimed that my suspicions were totally unfounded. It was his opinion that I probably had homosexual inclinations myself if I saw a queer in every good-looking kid in the place.

> *"Major, Major! There are queers in the camp!"*
> *"How do you know, soldier?"*
> *"Because the Captain's prick tastes of shit!"*

33

I was always a difficult child. Altogether I went to thirteen schools, and I was kicked out of every one of them. In Catholic schools I was a heathen who joked about religion; in another school I used judo to floor the singing teacher and he got a piece of his broken glasses in his eye; in another I rigged a wire across a sidewalk next to the school and the arts-and-crafts teacher had an accident on his bicycle. During school outings I always ran away. I had no interest in the Stone of Amersfoort, and so, with the teacher's wallet in my pocket, I hitchhiked into Germany. In one school the physics teacher suffered a concussion—a head wound that required fourteen stitches—after I arranged his apparatus so that it exploded in the middle of his lecture. He never finished his demonstration, but ended up with his head in the radiator. My only hobby was weapons. On Wednesday and Saturday afternoons, when there was no school, I went looking for weapons with my pals. We used to find dozens of them, pistols, rifles, carbines, bayonets and grenades. Since I never paid attention during catechism, the padre would get exasperated and throw a matchbox or his pipe at me. I always threw them back—a mortal sin. The time I threw a grenade instead of his pipe, I had no idea that a priest would know enough to fall to the floor for cover. Anyway, there was no pin in the damn thing. Once a pistol went off in my pocket while I was playing with it. The bullet went right through the floor. As punishment I had to write four thousand sentences on a Wednesday afternoon. There was one teacher, Peter Pecker, who used to cane the boys: I once threatened him with a bayonet. Brother, was he scared when I shoved the sharp, gleaming steel toward his Adam's apple. I did it because he always made me remove the books and newspapers from my pants before belting me with that lousy cane of his.

34

As a matter of fact, I never thought of myself as a difficult boy. Things were always made difficult for me—because I came from the slums, because for years I spoke with a foreign accent, because I didn't feel at home in "rich men's schools," and, of course, because I used to shit on everything: on Religion, Hope and Love. School bored the pants off me, so I purposely learned nothing. All that I know I taught myself, or learned from experience. And why not? Why should I have listened to those old pricks carrying on about long division or the past perfect tense. To hell with all that! Or those drawing teachers with their "shadow field" and "the reality of a living perspective." My own kids will never go to school. School is simply a business. Scratch for cigars for the teacher because it's his birthday; cabbage for the Queen because she's been married so long and so happily; greenbacks for starving children in China; bread for a new history book; cash for Parents' Night; money for a sick classmate; coin-of-the-realm for the poor Negro who comes to tell us stories; funds for a school film; contributions for the school outing—a trip in an excursion boat through the stinking canals, then ten minutes gazing at some bloody old hunk of rock, the Stone of Amersfoort; then half an hour staring at the façade of a house where some Rembrandt or other lived. Coins for this, and currency for that—it's just like the Catholic religion. They're all parasites. And, really, some of the things they tell the kids in those schools are unbelievable. That the Silver Fleet was robbed by an old sea dog, that the Jews walked right across the sea, that the Stone of Amersfoort is world-famous, that Holland has a herring fleet, that in Africa they go around with bare asses (just look at the stamps! I've never seen a bare ass on a stamp, except Franco!). About fucking they keep their mouths tightly shut, but they go on for hours about the grafting of trees and about the whale's being a mammal. Once, in the North Sea, I personally saw how whales make it with each other. It was like a small atomic explosion. Their bodies are torpedo-shaped, with very flat dorsal fins. The rump ends in a broad, horizontal tail fin, shaped like a loving cup. The female's teats are hidden in two shallow furrows in the belly. The skeleton is rather light and soaked with bone oil; the skull is massive, but the brain inside is pretty small. The male organ is small too, a leathery skin over a blubbery mass—in larger species it's sometimes inches thick. The skin is thin and hairless. Mating takes place above water and lasts a few seconds. Every two to five years, after a pregnancy of ten to twelve months, the young whale is born; it's about a third of the length of the mother and is able to swim at once. It matures in six years, but is sexually active after only two. That, of course, is the bearded whale. Of the toothed whale and the blue whale I have also got quite a bit of information. I once saw a dead whale at a fair. He had a real man's setup, complete with rod and nuts, but pretty small. Did you know the female whale has a very nice-looking pussy? It's a bit odd, of course, such a small cunt in such a huge mass of flesh, but it really looks cute and wholesome. You could have a whale of a time!

Why do seals get so many colds? Because they fuck on the rocks! Hahahaha.

One time, while I was going to school, I found a rubber in the park during lunch hour. I picked it up carefully and took it along to school. On the way I met some pals of mine. They didn't know what it was, but of course I did. My brother Jackson used to have boxes full of them in his room. The rest of the kids were already back in the classroom. Holding the condom up like a trophy between my thumb and my fore-finger, I walked in and stood in front of the class. The teacher turned white and demanded, "What *is* that? Where did you get it? Give me that balloon[!] at once!" I tossed the rubber onto his desk. "We found it in the gymnasium, Sir, behind one of the horses," I said, and my pals backed me up. We would show that asshole gym teacher a thing or two! All the girls had a crush on him because he was so handsome and could vault over the horses so well. I had already put one over on him once before, during rope-climbing. I was the best rope-climber in the class. The night before he was supposed to show us how to climb the ropes, I half-severed one of them with a knife. Right in the middle of the show-off's demonstration the next day, he fell from halfway up. Anyway, after the business with the rubber, he had to leave school. There was an investigation, because we stuck to our story. And it came out in the inquiry that the gym teacher had grabbed some of the girls in the dressing room and pinched their tits. Well, he should have kept his hands off our girls—it was his own damn fault!

I finally ended up in a real youth prison, in the south of the country, after one of my attempts to escape. They took some nice pictures of me there. Okay now, watch the birdie! Consorting with the convicts in that place, I became a hardened criminal. I was lucky to find Barry, a friend of mine, there. I had known him in a correction school where he used to wait on tables. One day he spilled soup all over the Minister of Justice. A few hours later, after the Minister had left in his official limousine (the plates simply had "M.O.J." on them), Barry pushed a guard into the soup kettle.

35

Several years later I'm in the clink again—Amsterdam's Central Police Station. My mug of tea and two thick slices of bread and butter are late in arriving, so I begin to get worried, wondering if they have forgotten all about me or are trying out some new tactic: "The Starvation of Suspects for the Purpose of Obtaining a Total Confession." Then the news is passed along the corridor: "Have you heard? The Minister of Justice kicked the bucket. I heard it over the radio!" Well, at least I couldn't, under any circumstances, be blamed for that. I had been in preventive detention for the past four days, "for purposes of interrogation," as they say. The Public Prosecutor wanted to talk to me. Anyway, after I got a suspended sentence, they threw me out into the street again. It was snowing outside. Every time they had taken me into the detectives' room for interrogation I could look out of the window at the thick snow-flakes as they sailed and twisted downwards, endlessly, some of them disintegrating against the barred window. I knew that many a poor bastard and God knows how many old folks would have given anything to get locked away in a nice heated cell, but I preferred my freedom. I like snow. And I don't mind the cold— I have Russian blood in me. And anyway, I hadn't *done* anything!

The heating system in that Central Police Station ought to be fixed. It's murderous. It drains all the energy out of you, makes you feel feverish and stuffy. When the tea finally came, I asked for an extra cup, half of which I tossed onto the hot pipes. It sizzled on them, and for hours the atmosphere was drenched with the smell of oriental tea. I've been in dozens of cells, and I've made a careful study. Did you know that in Holland there's always an even number of rivet heads on the massive iron doors? The chicken wire in one French jail had 12,324,000 squares. Incidentally, in one clink I noticed that fourteen rivets were missing from the door of Cell 301. Does the Minister of Justice know about this?

They were coming to get me for another interrogation. You can tell they're coming from the noise the gate makes. *Lo, who cometh, children?* First, they start looking through the peephole every five minutes so that you can't even sit down to take a shit or jerk off in peace. One piece of advice for all suspects, guilty or not, and for jailbirds who somehow get their hands on this book. Pass it on. You're in jail, you've been interrogated for hours, maybe been mistreated by the strong arm of the law but they haven't yet forced a confession out of you so you can expect further torturous grilling, you don't know when, how, or what they'll do to you next, and you're going crazy from having counted the rivets, the squares of chicken wire and the rough spots on the walls dozens of times, you keep listening to the tinkle of the trolleys outside, the footsteps of the guards in the corridors and the doors slamming, when they've told you your wife intends to leave you, that your asshole buddy finked on you, that your child has fallen ill, that they'll never let you go if you don't sign, and you know that you will sign, if not today then tomorrow or the next day, for these bloodhounds will never let you go, remember that there's only one solution: listen to everything indifferently, become indifferent to everything, and wear yourself out so that you can't make mistakes. The way to do this—a way that will, besides, give you some brief pleasure—is masturbation, self-gratification. But watch out! They'll keep you from doing it if they know what you're up to. They'll stick you in the guardroom with a bunch of tough cops who can keep an eye on you. But you have to succeed. After all, it's your own body—and they can't take it away from you. You can even do it in handcuffs. And don't be ashamed! Masturbation is even recommended in the Japanese soldier's manual. Prisoners of war often do it. And it is human. They'll never legislate against it because a cop does it too—although he does it in the dark, at home, lying next to his frigid wife who doesn't approve of his job. After a few times, your tool will begin to hurt and you'll no longer have pleasant fantasies of women and that kind of thing. Still, persevere! You'll be able to sleep then, you'll be so worn out you'll sleep like a log.

Aren't the more intelligent, the more imaginative criminals, the gangsters with IQ's above 140, all followers of Buddha,

Zen and Yoga? Knowledge is power! Never forget that, baby, and you'll get rich!

After a few minutes, which nevertheless seem like hours, the heavy door opens and the guard asks you to follow him. Don't jump him, don't bash his skull in, don't stick a knife or a finger through the peephole while he's looking in—dozens of them have lost eyes that way. After all, they aren't to blame, they're just doing a job, you know, just a job. I've heard the same thing said about the police, but with them it's a completely different story. They dig their work because they're sadists, just as most firemen are pyromaniacs. But a guard actually has a kind heart and, other things being equal, he'll even give you a third cup of tea if you ask for it. He'll feed you a few words of encouragement when you're so lonely you're no longer sure if you're black or white. And if you get excited and keep knocking on the door, he'll open the trap-window and say, "Be quiet, sir, they'll be coming for you shortly." And if you ask him if he couldn't please leave the trap-window open because it gets so stuffy with everything closed, he'll probably leave it open because he trusts you. He knows very well he may be told off by one of those filthy bastards, the detectives, who regard you as a menace to society, a psychopath. Did you ever notice that escaped prisoners, or those shot down while attempting to escape, are always referred to as "psychopaths"? And did you know that you're maintaining this police apparatus with the taxes you pay? We thank you and hope that you'll keep on paying taxes so the cops can continue to get their bullets free! In Bangkok, you know, the police have to pay ten guilders for every bullet they use, and a hundred guilders if they use it without justification. But then, Bangkok is the only city in the world where someone is shot down only once in about three years. How would you like to have that kind of police department? It seems incredible to me that, while the boys on our police force ("boys" is appropriate because they never really grow up) invariably claim they aim at the legs, the bullet always seems to hit the victim in the neck. Maybe they should follow the lead of the Paris Sûreté: they are taught to shoot by an F.B.I. G-man, who makes a special air trip from Washington for each new group of trainees. A sinister and macabre example of what I am talking about occurred when a police officer of a city—best left nameless—in the western part of Holland cut down, with a saber, a "dangerous punk" on New Year's Day a few years ago, and left the "inciter to riots" dead on the cobblestones. The cop in question was pronounced "free of all guilt" because he had "meant to hit the boy in his posterior." The weird thing is that this same policeman was a champion swordsman, and had won honors during the National Foil and Saber Tournament for Police Officers.

36

Finally you are led along endless halls into a curving corridor with an alcove containing benches. There sit the people who have been summoned for interrogations, smelling of the delicious Outside with snowflakes still on their hair or caps (caps come off in the police station, just like in church). Past them is the detectives' room. And there they are, hick coppers all, Detective Tom Rhubarb, Detective Dick Bumpkin, Detective Harry Hayseed and the rest of the yokels. Oh, I guess there are, sometimes, a few nice ones among them. And don't ever think, dear reader, that only immigrants and farmers from the sticks are attracted by a policeman's pay. But many of them *are* that way. Let us call it an unfortunate conjunction of circumstances, a kind of coincidence. Of course there are "good dicks," but there aren't many of them. And you'll soon find out that the good ones are never assigned to *your* case. It just doesn't happen. You run into the hardened ones, ex-potato-diggers and cattle herders, with as much imagination as you could stick in a stuffed nostril. They'll draw up a chair and offer you a butt with an air of "let's be friends." But don't go falling for that! More than anything else this is a place where you get nothing for nothing. Once you've confessed, the source of smokes will dry up; after that, all you can get is a pack once a week on special credit at the canteen.

The interrogation begins. Detective Bumpkin (he's taking a correspondence course, *Learn to Type with Two Fingers in One Month*) seats himself behind the typewriter, ready to peck out his report. First, for about ten minutes, he practices finger movements. (They earn their pay the hard way!) Detective Hayseed stations himself just behind me, all set to slug me in case I try to escape, or to yank my chair out from under me if my answers are in any way inadequate. Meanwhile, Detective Rhubarb ("Just call me Rube, my boy!") draws up a chair in front of me and straddles it like a horse.

"Well, I hope we'll make better headway than we did yesterday. We know everything, you know. Miss So-and-so phoned this morning." (First mistake: Miss So-and-so knows nothing and has been abroad for a week.)

Me: "Oh yes?"

Him: "Yes, so let's get this over with. Do you know this kid Red Spat? We had him here too, and since he was smart enough to sign everything, he's already gone home!" (At a sign from Rhubarb, Hayseed waves a paper in front of my nose—but it might be anything, a report or whatever.)

"Come on, now, let's go! How does this guy Appie Flute fit in? What does he do in your setup?"

"Appie Flute? I don't know who you mean."

"You don't know Appie Flute? He's been seen in your company!"

"That's what you say! I'm sorry but I've never heard of any Appie Flute."

"Listen, kid, we only do this for a living. You can take my word for it, we've got to be here anyway, so we don't care if you go home today, tomorrow or sometime in 1990. But we've got to turn in a report to the Public Prosecutor. So listen, for your own good. It's no skin off our nose, but we'd like to be able to let you go home as soon as possible." (!)

I don't buy it.

"How about it? You *do* know Appie Flute, don't you? You know who we mean. Wake up, boy, out with it!"

"Appie Flute . . . Appie Flute . . . Appie Flute? Is that the cat with the pimply face?"

"That's him!" (A sigh from the dicks.)

"Appie Flute . . . doesn't he always wear a leather coat? A black leather jacket?"

"That's right."

"And doesn't he have a large Chevrolet?"

"He sure does! You see, you *do* know who we mean."

"Does he always have a blonde chick with him? With a red leather coat?"

"Yes, yes."

"Sort of a tall guy with black hair?"

"Yes, yes, yes."

"And he usually wears a red tie?"

"Yes, yes, yes, yes."

"And he hangs out every night at the Crystal Club?"

"Yes, yes, yes, yes, yes."

"And he has a big gold tooth in the left side of his mouth?"

"Yes, exactly. That's him!"

"No, I don't know him."

They blew their tops at that, screamed for the guard and had me hustled back to my cage. Anyway, at least I've been out of it for a quarter of an hour and got some fresh air.

They're bound to come for me quite a few times more. After all, it's they who need me. I don't have to deliver any report to the Public Prosecutor.

37

After a few days of this they let me go—they have to, because the Public Prosecutor won't sign a warrant of arrest for a preliminary investigation. And, by law, they can't hold me for more than two days without preferring charges. If you sign during those forty-eight hours, if you give up, then you're screwed. Nevertheless, don't start to celebrate if they suddenly tell you, "You can go." For it's quite possible that as soon as you hit the sidewalk in front of the police station they'll tap you on the shoulder again and say, "Would you mind coming along with us?" Technically, you have then been released but rearrested for a new examination. So walk calmly to the exit, making doubly sure that all the things they took from you have been given back, especially the money in your wallet. Count it. Then, by train or bus, shuttle back and forth around the city. Double back over your tracks to confuse them. Crisscross like mad for an hour or so and you should be able to shake them off your trail. Then you can go into the nearest bar and have a drink in peace, for alcohol isn't supplied in jail. When you're arrested on suspicion and held in custody, if you insist on it your food will be brought in for you from the outside. A copper will go to a sandwich shop or a Chinese restaurant for you and get your order. That is, if you have money in your pocket. Later on, in the clink, you take potluck. Cauliflower, cabbage, sauerkraut, stew and, on Sundays and holidays, potatoes with meatballs. ("Guard, I didn't get a meatball this week!" "Well, take a good look behind the potatoes, kid!") And women? No, women aren't provided in jail either. Our authorities are very backward on this point. In almost every country prisoners are allowed to have sexual intercourse, although within very strict limits. In Russia, they even have female guards—that's really something! I saw a picture of them. It should be quite pleasant to be a jailbird in a place like that. If you're a sharp-looking stud or a tough guy like me, you're in luck. Then you're OK. Naturally, the guards get first choice. I've heard of cases where people stayed inside for forty years because they liked it so much. But, you can't pull any tricks in Russia or they'll execute you—and that isn't so pleasant. Anyway, who'd want to play tricks that are punishable by death? Didn't Jesus Christ suffer enough for us on the cross?

I once shipped to Russia on a freighter. Before we got to Leningrad, we sailed into the Neva Delta near the Gulf of Finland, where Fort Brasov is located. It's a huge fort, rising like an island in the Baltic. The entire place is a prison, erected by Stalin, a kind of prisoners' island where the convicts, mostly lifers, are allowed to maintain their own society, with their women and children. Everything's OK there! Through our binoculars we watched large rowboats going around the island. The men at the oars were all prisoners. At the prow and at the stern were the only two armed guards. Our pilot told us the men were having their daily exercise. You can be sure that everything is peaceful there. Why don't they build something like that in Holland? And let the Krauts move in too, at least if they bring along some good-looking broads. For German girls, along with the Scandinavians, are still the best, the sharpest in Europe.

When I arrived at the observation home, I realized at once that I wouldn't last long. I was bored stiff and didn't feel a bit at home, especially on weekends. Weekends are terrible when you have to spend them someplace where there's nothing to do all day but play cards, checkers, ping-pong or shuffleboard or write letters. In those days a guy like me didn't have many letters to write. I could hardly send picture postcards to everyone I knew, telling them what a good time I was having. ("Wish you were here!") After all, I wasn't on vacation. Some Sundays I'd have visitors, my foster parents, a dentist and his wife. The Board of Supervisors had sent me to live in their home for a few months. My foster mother, a nice person, used to give me ten guilders for pocket money every day, which I had no trouble spending. Finally, she ran out of housekeeping money because I needed more all the time. They were really nice people. They didn't even hate me after I stole their vacation money, a box full of gold and silver dental fittings. I took it to a silversmith who knew me—I used to sell him the odd pieces of gold that my foster mother occasionally gave me for pocket money. I got 350 guilders for the whole box. I hadn't expected so much, and I didn't know what to do with it. So I took off for France. A few months later, when they brought me back, the juvenile magistrate hauled me in for questioning. I agree it wasn't a very pretty thing to have done, but a small boy is impatient of limits, and bread is bread. Like my old man used to say, money's got to roll!

The juvenile magistrate came to visit me occasionally at the
home, and some of those people from *Pro Juventute*. I'd
always behave myself then, no wildness, no pranks, so they'd
get a good impression of me. But at night, in the dormitory,
we had a real ball. We stuffed shoes inside socks and, using
them as clubs, had battles; we played hide-and-seek and
passed girlie magazines from bed to bed with a flashlight.
We had smokes. We'd put soap and shoe polish on doorknobs
and play poker for pocket money. We'd shove four beds together, stealthily cry "cool it!" and fart when a supervisor
walked through the dorm. We'd shoot at each other with
slingshots and spitballs and tell the raunchiest jokes to get
everybody horny as hell. But it was winter, so there were no
chicks around.

During the summer everyone would try to get put in the
Outdoor Section, doing farm work, because broads from the
village would come creeping through the fields at night to
get screwed. There were also several girls' homes in the
neighborhood, and we'd drop in there whenever we got the
chance. Since we all got one another horny in the dorm,
that's when the queers showed their inclinations. But once
in a while, I'll admit, I wasn't so happy. For a few days I'd
fell low and rotten. Then, late at night, when the talking
had stopped and everyone else was asleep, I'd cry for hours,
very quietly. I don't know why or what about. I just had to
cry, to cry something out of myself, but cautiously, under the
blankets, so that no one would hear me. After all, wasn't I
one of the roughest and toughest of the lot? The kid who
made everyone laugh and was liked by all? If I said, "Tomorrow, don't touch your oatmeal; we want pudding!" every
single kid would refuse to eat that slimy crap. Every last one
of them! For my word was law. Then, after we were all
sent away from the table, some of the younger kids would
pretend to faint from hunger during work. Next day there
was pudding! I showed them, I Jan Cremer! It was pudding
we wanted, pudding with fruit. And that's what we got!

39

The Director told me there was a chance I'd be allowed to
join the merchant marine after the summer vacation. I
liked that idea! Boys who behaved well and were cooperative
during their observation period were allowed to join—the
Director took care of it. One wall in the canteen was covered

with picture postcards. From everywhere, all sent by former inmates, addressed to the Director and the staff. From Sweden, Tunisia, Perth, Genoa, Casablanca, Port Said, Aden, Boston, London, Hamburg, Copenhagen, Johannesburg—in short, from all over the world. I could look at them for hours, those beautiful, multicolored waterfalls, the sunrises, the huge suspension bridges, the plush nightclubs, the good-looking half-nude Negro women, the skyscrapers, the picturesque alleyways, and that crazy kangaroo! In my dreams I visited all these places. That was great! All right, then, so cooperate, and don't stand there dreaming! But at that time I was totally apathetic. For hours I wouldn't see or hear a thing—I was a daydreamer. Poetic, ain't it?

Spring arrived and, through my guardian, I asked to be transferred to the Outdoor Section, to do farmwork. I liked animals so much, and trees and shrubs, I told them, because I had been a member of the Nature Conservation Society. And it was true! I had been a member. The Society was a bit like the Hitler Youth, a completely Nazi-like organization, set up originally by a couple of cowardly nature lovers. Every member of this organization had a membership card with a photograph of him in uniform: a dark blue shirt with an armband, a special coat, police notebooks, and so on. I had joined because the organizer had said I'd be something like a detective, with a real badge and all, which entitled you to enter every park, meadow, forest and garden, and to give summonses to boys requiring them to appear in court. I had a real ball. Every day I handed out tickets to all my pals, and I got rich on candy, peashooters, chewing gum, peanuts and pictures of movie stars. Yes, I accepted bribes. Everything was fine until one day, when I was playing Tarzan with some of the guys, I climbed a tall tree and began to throw birds' eggs like grenades at the cannibals running round in circles below me. I had just broken off a branch to use as a club when I felt myself seized by the scruff of the neck by the park guard. They gave me a full-dress trial. I was sentenced to I don't remember what, exactly, but it was a great scandal. The trial was held in front of the assembled membership of the Society and various other bystanders, and I was forced to turn in my insignia and membership papers right there in the middle of the playground. Then I was dismissed, under the gaze of hundreds of eyes. Of course, I didn't tell my guardian anything about this. Anyway, after a few weeks, I was allowed to pack up my gear and, along with a few other boys, I joined the Outdoor Section a few miles away. There I had much more freedom and worked surrounded by all of nature's beauty—that kind of crap!

It was a kind of chain gang: policemen armed with carbines followed us into the fields. But the older boys told me that the guns were only loaded with paper balls. I really dug it on the farm! We slept in bunk beds, ate in the yard, and got great suntans. My first job was in the greenhouses, but they found I was too rough on the flowers. I destroyed all the tender buds before they opened. I didn't like doing it, but it was the only way I could get to work out in the fields where we were kept busy digging, plowing, furrowing and sowing. When the sun was shining, we used to rub margarine or oil on our skin and work in the fields stripped to the waist. I passed out tea. That tastes good, a cup of tea without sugar, when you take a break after hard, tiring work.

We worked until the siren went off. That meant lunchtime, when we'd join the farmers for grub. After a few weeks, I became tanned and strong and looked the picture of health—even my digestion was good. I decided to begin looking for a chance to escape. Any prisoner has only one aim: to escape! If I escaped, of course, I'd lose my chance to muster on a merchant steamer through the good offices of the Director. But, after all, didn't Admiral Piet Hein begin his naval career with a prison record?

We had a new doctor at the home, a nice young guy with a dog like Lassie. He drove up three times a week in his expensive car to examine the boys. I'll never know how in hell Perry, one of the inmates, managed it, but one day it was discovered that he had a venereal disease. It was just the ordinary clap, but how in God's name did he ever pick it up? Everyone at the home tried to get it out of him. Was there a good-looking broad inside the home, maybe working in the kitchen? All we ever saw were a few chunky farmers' wives who were constantly swaddled up in their peasant outfits and too old to boot. At that time women from the village weren't to be seen, not until a few weeks later, when we sent them signals. After that they could be had in the woods on Saturday nights, and we made the most of our chances. Not me so much, for I didn't really need women. What I needed was a nice, sweet girl.

So everybody went after the dozens of women who came creeping along on Saturday and Sunday nights. Everyone made his choice and disappeared into the cornfield or into the ditches at the edge of the forest. But there wasn't one of them that I liked. They all looked pretty repulsive to me, and I was counting on getting back to civilization soon, where I could pick and choose. So I just went along for the walk. I remember how wonderful the hay smelled. I'd lie down in the long grass and chew on a straw. It tasted good. But I usually kept moving, because it bugged me to hear those chicks moaning as they came. Out of loyalty, I'd sometimes agree to be the lookout. But after this I never again had anything to do with this kind of organized fucking. Not when I was in a camp where all kinds of female counselors used to visit us. And not in Boulouris either, with that whore from Paris. They used to line up in front of her tent by the dozens. But not me!

40

Sometimes the new doctor would come to have a look at us in the fields. He'd always bring his dog along. One time I was making holes to plant beans in, and I whistled to the dog. Every dog can tell at once that I'm an animal lover. This one was no exception, and he came right over to me with his tail wagging and let me pet him. Doc said, "I see you're good with animals. That's nice to see. All good people like animals." (He was right. People who hate animals are no damn good. Take the Spaniards. They're animal killers, because they're too scared to look an animal in the eye.) He asked me if I wanted to look after the dog while he was working, so I said I'd be glad to. He said OK, he'd fix it up with the management. After that, I was allowed to spend some time looking after the dog, brushing her, combing her and running around with her. I was granted special free time for this, one hour before meals. One of the guards would blow his whistle and I'd go off with the dog. I liked the idea, because the dog fitted very well into my escape plan. One Wednesday the cop whistled, and I rode back to the home on the state's bike. At the home I picked up Lassie and took her along, with me pedalling and her running after the bike. When we got to the farm, I went into the fields with her. The boys were a bit jealous, for it had begun to rain and they still had to work for another half hour. A tiresome job, planting beans—four to each hole, and there were at least two thousand holes. I threw a stick and Lassie ran off to retrieve it. She returned with it. I threw it further away. Again she went after it. I threw the stick further away still, and then I ran after the stick too. In this way I gradually edged nearer and nearer to the main road. The cop, who was busy rolling a cigarette, could see me all right, but he thought I was playing with the dog. I had planned it that way. Even as a small boy I was blessed with a good set of brains, even if I didn't always use them. I was saving them for later. The plan had to succeed. For one horrible moment, the dog threatened to screw up the works—she wanted to run with the stick in the wrong direction. So I gave her a kick in the ass which sent her scooting a hundred yards in the right direction. Another kick and she was just where I wanted her. We were now entirely out of sight of the cop and the rest of the boys. The fields, the guards and the farm with its barn were all hidden now by the high bushes I was hiding behind. I had brought a piece of rope along with me, and I used it to tie Lassie to a tree. I patted her because I really hated to tie her up that way. But I had to do it. The guard wouldn't raise the alarm, because he'd think I was on my way back to the home to return the dog. He hadn't really been watching me, of this I was sure. Everything was going smoothly. The siren at the home screamed out to announce mealtime. Only after the guards had returned the boys—it would take another fifteen minutes for them to walk back to the farm, put away their tools, wash their hands and go to the table—would they notice that I was missing. If worse came to worst, they'd phone the home, but even then they'd wait a while, thinking I was probably on my way back. Or they'd send someone to look for me, and that could mean an alarm, because they'd search and find Lassie. Then they'd know I had run away, and would immediately inform the local police. What could I do? I couldn't go home —there I was sure to find the dicks from the Juvenile Police waiting at the door, and it would be the same thing at my foster parents' place. But I had already made my getaway, and I'd just have to wait and see what happened. I could only count on fifteen minutes when I could be sure they weren't after me yet. I kept running as hard as I could, alongside the main road. I didn't dare get out onto the road itself because I would have been recognized as a boy from the home—I was wearing dark blue overalls and wooden clogs and my head was shaved bald. Even from a distance people would recognize me and know at once I was a runaway. So I ran as fast as I could under cover of the bushes and along the edges of cornfields. It began to rain. That was a lucky break—people wouldn't take so much notice of things then. They'd be keeping a lookout on the roads. By the time I had gone a few miles in the direction of town, I was sweating so much and was so exhausted that I had to take a short rest. I was soaked through and the sweat and rain had run down into my shoes. After I had rested for a few minutes I began to run again until I came near a farm. It was mealtime, so the family would be at table. I skirted the farm, and slipped across the backyard. There was a sawmill behind the farm, and the doors stood wide open. So I crept along, close to the buildings so that I wouldn't be seen from inside, and when I got to the sawmill I entered quickly.

My heart was beating so hard it seemed to be in my throat. If the farmer caught me (the farmers were scared and suspicious of any boy from the home) I wouldn't stand a chance. I was hoping to find some clothes in the sawmill, an old coat or something . . . and I was very lucky. A yellow carpenter's coat was lying across a bench and a pair of rubber boots stood on a mat beside it. I quickly rolled up the coat and grabbed a white raincoat and a hat from a peg on the wall. Then I crept out again, back along the other side of the house. Again, luck was on my side. Under a dripping shelter stood a motorbike. I hesitated, but finally grabbed it, pushed it off its stand and maneuvered it along a difficult ten-yard stretch that led to the main road. They wouldn't see me if I walked bent over, but with the bike I had to walk upright. I decided not to waste any more time and just chance it. I was glad it was raining because the countryside would be deadly quiet after lunch. Not during mealtime though—farmers make so much noise when they eat that you can't even hear the radio. Anyway, I managed to get the machine onto the road without being noticed, though it was a difficult business, what with the clothes in one hand and the bike in the other. Finally I got onto the bike and drove along as fast as I could go. After about a mile, I stopped behind some bushes, hid the bike in a ditch and changed clothes. I kicked a hole in the moss and stuffed my overalls and clogs into it. The new boots were much too big on me, but I wasn't going to be walking; I had wheels. The coat, on the other hand, fit me to a tee. Wearing the coat and hat, I waited until the coast was clear, then pushed the bike back onto the road. I tore along like a bat out of hell. At the first crossroad I turned off, hid the bike in a clump of high bushes and looked around. There wasn't a house to be seen in any direction. I decided to hide there until it got dark.

I was proud of myself. So far my escape had gone perfectly. What would the boys be thinking? What would they say if they could see me like this? I even thought about riding back there the next day—just for the hell of it! Come roaring into the place, dressed like I was now! But first, I wanted a good meal, something to drink and, if possible, a chick, for I needed that badly. And I had to have some clothes—I couldn't be seen the way I was dressed in any of these hick towns. Boy, would they be surprised at the home, especially if my escape was a complete success! I would be declared AWOL. Their eyes would sure pop when a card, postmarked Turkey, was stuck up on the big bulletin board in the canteen: "To the Management, staff and my pals. Best regards from Jan Cremer!" I'd have a picture taken of me with some good-looking nude Turkish broads. Barry had been carrying on for months, "If I want to leave, I'll leave!" but he hadn't been able to do a thing about it. I cursed the rain—by now I was as wet as a drowned duck and it had begun to thunder and lightning. Once, when I was a small boy, a bolt of lightning struck the ground right beside me, and since then I've always been terrified of it. All my optimism left me when the storm thundered right above the hill I was hiding near. Fear gripped me. Here I was with a bike beside me, the only chromium-plated iron for miles around, and didn't iron and chromium attract lightning? I could already see myself fried to a crisp by a white-hot bolt of electricity. In a few days they would find my body, all stiff and purple. In Germany, I once saw two farmers who had been struck by lightning. It had gone through the scythes they were carrying on their backs, and they were all stiff and contorted by the time they hit the ground. The heat had caused the soles to curl away from their boots, and their feet had turned black in a split second. A shudder runs through me whenever I think of it. Just when I made up my mind to run out of the bushes, my arms high in the air, begging for mercy, the rain started to come down heavier than ever. That meant that the storm clouds were moving on. The thunderclaps became less distinct, too, and I figured that the storm must be a good five miles away. Then, when twilight came, I drove on, singing rock 'n' roll at the top of my voice. I felt like a real hero, even if I didn't have a cent on me and was dying of hunger and thirst. And the whole police force was after me like I was Al Capone!

An hour later the fucking bike ran out of gas. At first I tried to pedal it, but it was so heavy and moved so slowly that, just beyond the point where I started to see the lights of town, I shoved it into the bushes. After an hour's search, I got to the home of some married friends of mine, but I could see they weren't too happy to see me. I must have looked like an escaped murderer, covered with mud and dripping water all over the place. Nevertheless, they gave me food and drink and let me take a shower. Then the husband gave me some of his clothes and I decided to make my exit. After all, I couldn't ask them to shelter a fugitive— they could have gotten into plenty of hot water. I began to get cold feet. I couldn't blame them for turning me back out into the streets, but nevertheless I was in a spot. I didn't know another soul in the place. At least they lent me ten guilders so I would be able to take a bus to the railway station and hop a train to Amsterdam. I had plenty of friends there and could get all the help I needed. Then I'd really be able to enjoy my newly acquired freedom. So I left, wishing them all the best and a very Happy New Year. I felt like I had been reborn. The clothes I was wearing were much too large for me, but at least they were clean and had the pleasant odor of mothballs.

I was in a great mood when I got on the bus. I bought my ticket and looked for a seat in the back. Then, sitting down, I found myself looking directly into the face of the staff psychologist who worked at the home I had just escaped from. As luck would have it, he just happened to be on his way home.

41

I spent that night at the local police station, alone in a cell. I had to sleep on a hard cot under blankets that stank of vomit, but I still slept better there than at the home. Heavy rain beat against the thick barred windows, making a pleasant, homey sound, just like the attic I used to sleep in.

42

Of course, there was no question now of my being allowed to remain in the Outdoor Section. And I wouldn't be allowed to walk with Lassie again, though when I told the doctor the whole story, how it was, he was sympathetic and understood. The escape attempt caused me a load of trouble, all the same. No cigarettes for four weeks, no going on weekend hikes, and KP every day for two weeks. Moreover, I had to stand dorm guard, which meant reporting every half hour, to make sure I didn't get any sleep for those few weeks. And, as the finishing touch, I wasn't given any oranges on weekends. This was, of course, the worst kind of bullshit. I Jan Cremer, the boss of the syndicate, no oranges? Forget it! I made sure I got my oranges and smokes, and my KP was done for me: as king of the roost, I arranged for the new boys to serve as my stand-ins. As for the hikes, I didn't give a damn about walking on Saturday or Sunday afternoons, anyway. I preferred to play cards, all cozy with a butt in my mouth and a teapot full of gin at my elbow. (Barry could always lay his hands on gin, because he worked in the kitchen and had access to the pantry, so everything was just fine.) I wonder how they would have reacted if they had known how little their punishment affected me!

There was one guy in the home, a sports instructor, whose guts I hated. He treated us like dogs: if you didn't run fast enough during field sports you'd get an hour of knee bends, or you had to keep running around the field by yourself. He was an arrogant, cruel bastard, forever chewing out the boys during compulsory morning gymnastics. *"Achtung!"* He would make us exercise on empty stomachs: arms sideways, head forward, deep knee bends, up on your feet and forward march! He was a real Nazi type, blonde and sturdy, with a deep scar running down one side of his hawklike face. He was the only member of the staff who made out bad reports about me—with the rest of them I got along pretty well. I used to chat from time to time with the kitchen staff. This always meant a few extra plums or pears or an extra helping of pudding. "Always be pleasant to the staff," was one of my basic rules. They liked me, I was such a clown, the funniest kid in the home. Ha! I waited for months to take my revenge on that sports instructor, but when I was finally ready to carry out my plan—my idea was to put an empty tin can full of acid above the door of his room so that it would spill all over him when he opened the door—the prick was suddenly transferred.

43

I became number 301-560 in the Special Youth Prison. The Public Prosecutor had seen to that, because I refused to act decently, and was a menace to society. Following his charges, I was sentenced to an indefinite period of preventive detention. Because they were short of space, I had to share a cell with a diamond-smuggler, blackmailer and crook by the name of Jesserun Doremus. The sour smell of sweaty, dirty bodies filled our cell.

Jesserun was allowed to work—he sealed bags of sugar—but not I. I had to stand all day, to reflect, repent and mend my ways. Once a year the cells got a fresh coat of pastel-green paint. No wonder they were always so gray! Shit piled up in the latrines because they were flushed only once a day. In the morning the sun rose up out of the cold, dark dunes, breaking through the fog. That was really a nice sight . . . all was very peaceful and quiet then. About a quarter of an hour later you could hear the noise of the city waking up—the trolleys clang, the motorbikes sputter and the trucks roar past. On the wall there was a small red spot. Blood? Lipstick? A squashed gnat? A signal? In the next cell, 304, was a cat who beheaded two police sergeants, cut their bodies up into little pieces and fed them to the gulls. Once a day we were "aired," two at a time, in a kind of chicken run fenced in with heavy wire where, over to the left, a shaft of sunlight filters through. 354 always wanted to stand in it. He was an egotist! He expected to go back to work later in the year, a seasonal job as a waiter at the seashore. We played cards with labels from bags of sugar. Doremus was a nice guy. He really knew a lot. He crushed Christmas-tree balls, imported from Israel, and sold them as diamonds. After they came to get Jesserun Doremus for his day's work, I was lonely for hours on end. I looked out of the window, or I watched the mental movies I projected onto the red splotch. "And now, viewers, you see how Mr. Hades, God of the Underworld, abducts Madame Persephone, the beautiful daughter of Demeter, in his new Cadillac." Jayne Mansfield was held over daily. More, more! When I was released after three months, everybody asked, "Were you on vacation?" "Yes," I said, "in Spain."

44

Why did I use the gas pistol? I don't know. But it was his own fault.

"I'm here for my ping-ping."

"I don't owe you any bread. We're even."

"Even? Like hell! Fork over the loot!"

"Listen, take some good advice and fuck off! I haven't got any bread and you won't get any!"

"I won't get any? Well, then, I'll just take it."

"If you make any trouble, I'll call the police!" And before I know it, I've taken the pistol out of my inner pocket. There's no safety catch on the thing, the hair trigger goes off like lightning and the gas jet hits him in the face. In one second his skin is singed and his eyebrows have disappeared. He falls on the floor. I race downstairs, my eyes streaming tears from the gas, a handkerchief held tightly over my face. I run.

Once every couple of weeks, at the religious service, the padre tells us stories. How Jesus Christ changed nine jugs of water into wine when the booze ran out at a party in Canaan. How a certain god walked on water. That we are all sinners. That His father was a carpenter, and His mother was pecked by a dove. About the miracle of the food when seven baskets of bread became seventy and two fish became two thousand. Honor they father and thy mother. Thou shalt not lust after thy neighbor's wife. The padre is a bullshit artist. But we listen, intently, through the chicken wire.

45

At about nine one morning I am released. I stand outside, holding the cardboard suitcase they gave me at the home. My shoes hurt me and my suit is too tight. A guard, who leads me through the tall gates of the fortress, wishes me lots of luck. I've already been presented with the balance of my canteen credit in the office, where neat people sit behind desks, their breath smelling sweet and fresh from toothpaste, their hair neatly combed. My number becomes a name again. These people would go crazy, I think, if they paid any real, human attention to each number. But they don't, they simply do their work. But now, I am Jan Cremer again. It is midsummer. For weeks I have been dreaming of this moment, the moment when once again I would be back outside in the open street. Now I am out, but I'm afraid. I had made up my mind that I would go and sit at a café overlooking the sea, but I don't dare. I am sure everyone would notice that I've just gotten out of jail. Everyone turns around to look at me. At ten o'clock I have to be at the Foundation office downtown. I go to the railway station, check my suitcase, and walk around. Then, at ten, I report to the office.

46

The Foundation placed me as a "guest" in a Youth Remand Home. This meant I could be away from the home all day and, because of my "good conduct," I was allowed to work in town. They got me a job in a fancy bakery, a large plant that specialized in almond, spice and custard pastries. Eight bakers prepared thousands of these every day. I was the youngest of the eight, the apprentice. I left for the bakery at 7:30 in the morning and had to be back at the home by six P.M. This was the extent of my "freedom." If I returned late, even once, I could expect to be punished. When I got back at night, my sleeves and trouser legs were stuffed with pastries, which I distributed among the boys in my dorm. I also filched flavoring extracts—almond, lemon, vanilla, rum, orange. Along with another guy, who had a job as a dishwasher in a hospital and managed to swipe a quart of pure alcohol every day, I set about making booze, which we sold or bartered with the other boys. A

7-Up bottle was our measure, and everybody got stewed to the gills on our concoctions.

At the beginning, the bakers were rather formal in their behavior towards me because I was "a delinquent from the home," but after a while I gained their confidence. My boss had to write a report about me every Saturday afternoon for the Director. After the first few weeks, he began to ask me what to put into it. In the evenings I took pastry orders at the home. Thirty-four spice, fifty custard, and twenty-four almond. On the following day I would see to it that thirty-four spice, fifty custard, and twenty-four almond pastries were burned or baked hard. It provided some nice pocket money. When all the pans were in the ovens, the bakers went, one by one, into the backyard to have a look through the binoculars. Across the street there was a broad who always undressed and stood naked in the window when she saw that the bakers were looking. On warm days they drank a lot of beer and sometimes they laid a few bottles on me, so I used to do quite well.

One day the home was almost entirely emptied. All the boys went to other institutions. Only the "guests" were allowed to stay on. The boys were driven away in big Black Marias. The Youth Remand Home was being rebuilt. Bathrooms were being added on the upper floors, chairs and bamboo tables were being installed in the canteen, the dining hall was being turned into a dormitory and the kitchen enlarged into a dining hall. All this was being done because three hundred repatriates from Indonesia were about to arrive, to await relocation. They came in busloads, boys and girls, brown and scared, wearing light summer clothes and carrying straw bags and kit bags. They ranged in age from twelve to twenty-four. In the beginning we helped them with everything. They were a nice bunch. I smoked their *Krétèk* cigarettes, learned to speak Malay, ate eggs that had been buried underground for years, used a bottle of water to rinse my ass, stood on the seat of the crapper to shit, sang in the *Krontjongband,* developed a taste for Chinese food, began to talk with an accent, visited the *Tong-Tong* performances in the park, and had an affair with the best-looking chick in the group. She was a real peach, half Javanese, half Dutch. She walked like a leopard, fucked like a Japanese, and had a body like a female Watusi. Only her name was Mary Mouse—but what's in a name? I became very friendly with the Indos, who did everything for me and taught me all kinds of things. Mary furnished me with the "horsehair" (they bore a hole in the foreskin of the penis with a red-hot needle, and a disinfected hair from a

98

horse's tail is threaded through it) and I carried a tube of disinfected horsehairs along with me, just like the other guys. Years later, when fighting broke out between white and brown Dutch kids in my neighborhood, I became the gang leader of the Indos. With bicycle chains, I belted the whites against lampposts. Meanwhile, I requested a transfer from the bakery in town to the kitchen at the home. Mary wanted me to and I wanted to be among my friends. And I had grown sick and tired of all those pastries. My request was granted.

With the group of repatriates came a new Director, temporarily assigned to replace the regular one, who was on leave for a few months. This new Director was a particularly arrogant little jerk. He was about twenty-five years old and looked like a snot-nosed kid. He'd gotten my number the very first day he was there, when I asked him, "Who's the boss here, little boy?" How was I to know this creep in a blazer was the new Director? He was a bad-tempered little prick. All the Indos hated his guts, but they couldn't do a thing about it. They were in Holland, their own dear motherland, but they were not welcome. They were constantly threatened with return to Indonesia, where they were sure to get their heads chopped off. Never in my life had I met such a hateful bastard. He was a half-caste, and ashamed of it. It was easy to see he had Indonesian blood, but he cursed all Indonesians. He had studied in Holland and pretended he was a native Dutchman, but the boys from Jakarta knew better: they recognized him as a former Indonesian country cop. After they mentioned this to him he threatened to turn over to the Dutch police anyone who dared to betray his origins. And he hated my guts, probably because I had some real Dutch blood in my veins. He used to pester me and boss me around whenever he came into the kitchen, but I showed him up in front of everybody. "I don't have to listen to you, foreigner!" I told him. That made him see red. He ordered me out of the kitchen but I simply sat down at the table, because I didn't have to take orders from him. True, he was temporary Director—but only of the Indonesian section. As a "guest," I was responsible only to the representative of the Foundation, who was quite satisfied with me. Besides, he happened to hate Ruiz, the temporary Director, as much as I did. Ruiz, with his mouselike head and his blue blazer, did everything he could to louse me up. He accused me of theft, of inciting riots and of sabotage and tried to get rid of me. The other boys in my group had long since asked for transfers, because Ruiz used to bug them so much that they were afraid of being pushed too far. And giving Ruiz the business just wouldn't be worth it from the boys' point of view: they all had indefinite sentences and it would simply have meant more trouble for them. Despite the fact that everybody at the Foundation knew what a shit Ruiz was, Mr. William Ruiz, they could do nothing because he was an "authority." So, the transfer requests of the boys were granted. But I stayed on, because of Mary.

Sometimes, when the Director was pestering me, I would turn red and see stars in front of my eyes. He used to say I was a dirty thief, a rabble-rouser, mere scum, and that Mary was a whore. What could I do? I dug my nails into the palms of my hands until the blood came. I would have liked to smash his face, but he was such a coward. If I had hit him, he would simply have called for the police, who had already been warned that there was a state of unrest in the home. Not one of the boys would have dared to speak up for me, for fear that he would take his revenge later. So in this way the Director managed to remain on top. I complained to my guardian, and there was an "investigation"—which determined that I was entirely in the wrong. After all, was it not well known that I suffered from a persecution complex, that I was paranoid?

My guardian ordered me to keep quiet about it, and this I had to do. But now that the Director knew I was onto his game, he began to bother me even more. As soon as the Foundation representative had left, and our group leaders had gone upstairs, he'd come straight to the kitchen to bait me. During the short period when this man was in charge, six cooks and four assistants quit without notice. Every other day someone else would start work. One day I myself couldn't stand it any longer. There was talk that the Director was raping the girls, and it was a fact. Every day he summoned a girl to his room and told her to take a bath—in his private bathroom. He had them in there and all the boys knew it. The Director scared the girls, threatening that if they spilled the beans he would send them to a women's prison; from there they'd be put on a boat back to Indonesia. The girls, terrorized in this way, kept their mouths shut. But women are women, and soon it became a public secret. When one of the boys, Mel, heard that his sister had been called to the Director's room the previous evening, he went after him and the rest of us had to liberate the child-raper. Like a scared rat, drooling and shitting in his pants, he fled to his room, bolted the door and phoned the police, who arrived fifteen minutes later with screaming sirens, to get Mel. The boy was as meek as a lamb and quite calm. He was sitting with us in the recreation room when the Director appeared at the door with two cops. He pointed Mel out to them and they pulled him from his chair. "Please let me stay!" he shouted to Ruiz, desperately, "I'm sorry!" But the arrogant smile had reappeared on the Director's face. After the police car had driven off with Mel in it, Ruiz called everyone to the recreation room. "This will teach you what happens to boys who cannot adapt themselves. I give you warning, all of you, and especially you, Cremer. One more incident like this, and harsher measures will be taken!" I was boiling inside. To add insult to injury, all the older boys were forced to go without dinner that night.

Now I began to annoy the Director openly. I made threatening gestures at him, spilled gravy on his suit and purposely bumped into him, but I always took care to make humble excuses afterwards. If he shouted at me or annoyed me in any way, I would stand up and walk towards him with a fierce look on my face. He knew that nobody but me would dare to give him a going-over, and he knew that I was capable of doing it. I was just waiting for an opportunity. Meanwhile, I received letters from my guardian saying that the Director had complained about me and that I would have to leave the home as soon as they could find another place for me. By now Ruiz was overdoing it. He began to bother Mary and reported that I had stolen things from the kitchen. The Foundation representative made an investigation. Ruiz was really a miserable coward. If I entered his room unannounced and without knocking, he'd kick up a stink and, when I walked menacingly towards him, he'd immediately reach for the telephone, ready at all times to call the police. They were his only weapon against me.

When I was informed that I'd be leaving the home within three days, I finally went into action. I threw stones through his windows late at night. I rigged a trip wire in front of his door and yanked out the electric wires in his room, but he had them repaired immediately. Finally, I arranged with a few friends to take care of Ruiz once and for all. They were to see to it that at approximately ten P.M. that night there would be a great deal of noise in all the dorms, especially where the children slept downstairs. Meanwhile, I would hide upstairs with a few other guys in the girls' shower room, which was next to the Director's room. Other boys would lock themselves in the downstairs shower room and make a big racket, while the girls would run all over the place—the kitchen, the dining hall and the recreation room. Naturally, the group leaders would investigate the hubbub. It was Wednesday evening, and the guards would all be playing cards in the female supervisors' room. In the time it would take them to restore order I would corner my prey. I was praying that everything would go as planned—my heart was crying out for vengeance for all the times I had had to bow and scrape before the dirty bastard. And everything came off just exactly as planned. The younger children, and most of the girls, were in bed. We—the older boys—were in the recreation room. The cook left for home on his bike and the leaders went upstairs—unnoticed, they thought. In fact, we were watching them. The bell rang and everybody began to get ready to turn in. In ten minutes it would be ten o'clock, which meant lights-out and no further talking in the dormitories.

Almost all of the older kids were in on the conspiracy. We undressed quickly in our dormitory, and then four of us crept downstairs, towels over our shoulders. In case we were seen, we could claim that our shower wasn't working and that we wanted to use the girls'. Undetected, we reached the girls' shower room and they let us in. We turned on the taps. Two girls remained in the room, singing and laughing loudly. It was still a few minutes before ten, and from the window I could see the light burning in Ruiz' room. Suddenly there was a knock at the door, and little Tanja was asking to be let in. We opened the door for her. Quickly, she told us that Ruiz had just gone upstairs, to the female supervisor's room. "Shit!" I cursed, "is everything going to go wrong?" I'd been counting so much on this plan. There were still a couple of minutes to go before the leaders would be coming down to check the dorms and turn off the lights. Suddenly I got a great idea! Ruiz had a telephone in his room with a private number. I told Tanja to go right to the kitchen, dial 543481, and leave the receiver off the hook. "Go from there to the children's dorm and when you hear the phone has stopped ringing, have the girls start a racket!" She rushed downstairs. My heart was beginning to pound. After moments that seemed like hours, the telephone began to ring. If only one of the leaders doesn't come down and pick up the phone! But that was unlikely—Ruiz had some rich blond dame who often called him late at night. A few moments later, we heard quick footsteps in the corridor and Ruiz was opening his door. I signalled the girls. It was now time for them to get back to their dorm, time to run amok!

That instant, noise broke out everywhere. There was a terrible din, children screaming, doors being slammed open and shut, dozens of girls running up and down stairs, laughing, yelling, screaming, cursing, stamping. The sight of all this cooperation brought tears to my eyes. Like a flash, I darted out of the shower room and into Ruiz' room next door.

As soon as the leaders were downstairs and out of the way, the other boys would stand guard outside the door.

Ruiz was standing behind his desk, looking amazed, the telephone at his ear. Angrily, he slammed the receiver down. "What does this mean?" he snarled at me. I bolted the door. "Nothing, you fink!" I said. "I just dropped by to kick the shit out of you!"

The noise outside continued. Heavy footsteps were clomping down the stairs—the leaders. They knocked on the door. In one jump I was at Ruiz' side, behind his desk. I had noticed he was about to shout when they knocked at the door, so I threw my towel over his face and stifled his cry. The footsteps receded. Meanwhile, I needed all my strength to keep him quiet, for he was struggling like a mad dog, with all the strength of his wiry body. I applied a stranglehold that had him fighting for breath. He must have seen plenty of gangster movies because he knew enough to attempt a counterhold. He shouldn't have done that! I smacked him with an uppercut to the temple that sent him sprawling back into his chair. "Now I'm going to settle my account with you, you dirty son of a bitch!" I said and, throwing him from his chair, I lifted it up and brought it crashing down on him. He lay there now, helpless, his hands held above him for protection, looking like a scared rat. "I'll call the police!" "Oh yeah?" I said and turned around, playing a cat-and-mouse game with him. I was hoping he would try to reach the phone. Then he would see how quickly I could react! As he stumbled to his feet, I pulled a small bamboo sheath from my shorts. On it, in oriental letters, was inscribed "ADEN." I drew from it a small gleaming kris. Ruiz blanched. Shuddering, he quickly pulled back his hand which had been reaching for the telephone. Still shaking, he whined, "Have you gone crazy? Stop this at once, Cremer! Let me alone, or I'll call the police!" Cruelly slow, I walked toward him. I clutched the gleaming kris, blade upright, in my fist. Ruiz retreated and stuck his hand into the pocket of his blazer, pretending to have a revolver there. He screamed, "Stop it or I'll shoot! Stop or I'll have to shoot! Don't come any closer! I have a revolverrrrrrr . . ." The word resounded after I jumped him. He yelled with pain when the razor-sharp blade touched his arm. He grabbed hold of my arm with his free hand. I forced him around until his back was towards me and got another stranglehold on him. Then I lifted my knee sharply into his spine, and pulled the kris across his windpipe. His blood streamed over my hand. He groaned. I kept my hold on him until his body became limp and then I let it drop. He toppled slowly. I smelled shit:

sure enough the coward had shit in his pants. I turned him over with my foot. His miserable face was contorted into a grimace. Blood was still streaming from his throat. I still found him repulsive, with his miserable little head. The eyes were still open as if they were reproaching me, as if they were threatening me: "Well now, look what you've gone and done to me! They'll get you! You'll see!" I pushed the kris into his eyes and gouged them out slowly, one after the other.

47

I was on my way home on my bike, in a great mood. It was five o'clock, just before twilight. I rode easily along the long, winding road from the sea to town. Suddenly there was a police patrol jeep beside me. Two strong-arm men in black leather uniforms got out. Take their boots, leather jackets, belts and caps away from these bastards and they're nothing: anonymous, almost faceless. "Get down!" Then, "Did you steal this bike?" "No, I didn't steal this bike. It's my own." "Who are you? What's your name? Where do you live? What are you doing here? Where are you coming from?" I answer their questions, my great mood completely gone. It's just like the Gestapo! Long live freedom in Holland! One of the cops circles round me and the bike. He suddenly stoops and yanks the wire out of the taillight. "Your taillight isn't working! And don't try to tell us you didn't know it! We'll have to give you a ticket for this!"

I am boiling mad. "Sure!" I spit out at them. "What do you expect after you ripped it out with your filthy claws?"

They look astonished. "What's that? Are you accusing us? Are you looking for trouble? Is that it? Because if you are, you're talking to the right boys!" They stand in front of me, legs apart, hands on their hips, caps tilted back on their heads, daring me. I decide to let them take me in quietly, but I tell them that I plan to file a complaint later on. That does it! One of the cops slams his fist into my neck. "You can put that in your complaint too!" I try to keep calm. Wait. There must be *some* justice in this country. Even if I have to be at the station for hours, I'll demand my rights! At the police station, they drag me out of the jeep. My bike is tossed against a wall. I register a complaint against the two of them: false accusations, destruction of property, maltreatment. I am told to sit in the waiting room. A short while afterwards I am shown in to see the officer in command, a young guy. I go over it all again. The officer suggests that I go home and drop the complaint. "You've had one too many." "I haven't had anything at all! Not even a glass of beer! Only Coke and orange juice!" He tries to persuade me. "You'd better go home, son. If I'm forced to make out a report, you'll get the short end of the stick, believe me!"

But I still insist on filing a complaint. I'm taken to another "waiting room": this one is a jail cell with a bench. A few minutes later, one of the cops sticks his head in. "Oh, are you still here?" He disappears. Every couple of minutes, cops stick their heads in for a look at me, about fifteen of them in all. Then the original two come into the cell, followed by the others. They're still wearing the blue pants from their uniforms, but they've removed their coats and hats and rolled up their sleeves. "Well," says one, "so you claim we destroyed a taillight and maltreated you, eh? Did you hear that, Hank?"

I say that they didn't destroy *a* taillight, but the taillight on *my* bike, and that they hit me in the neck.

"Did you hear that, Herbert? How brutal of us!" One of them moves forward and slams his fist into my face. I hit back at him. He takes off his belt. Then all fifteen of them jump me. I am whipped, beaten, stamped on and kicked until all the breath is out of my body. This must be their daily workout! Then they hurl me into another cell. At 7 o'clock I am thrown out into the street, with two black eyes, a split eyelid, two teeth protruding through my lower lip, an aching jaw, dried blood all over my nose, ears and chin, my neck throbbing and my legs all puffed from leather-booted kicks. A doctor examines me: contusions, internal bleeding, general bruises. A friend takes the doctor's report to the Chief of Police. Result: "Said person, very drunk, was brought into the station in the condition described in the doctor's report. No blame can be attached to the police, who only did their duty."

48

"Did you really think Jan Cremer was so easily caught?" I laughed coolly. "Stand against the wall!" They stood against the wall, their hands above their heads, scared and pale. I swung forward, hitting out at him with the rifle butt, using it like a sledge-hammer. "Spit it out, buster," I snarled. He bent his head painfully, and blood streamed from his mouth. Teeth clattered like pebbles onto the floor. Fierce hate overcame me and before I could control myself I had struck him again, smashing the butt into his lowered head. I thought his skull would split. I jumped aside and he fell forward. The other one, his hands still held high, started heaving and vomit came gushing out of his mouth. I gave him a kick in the stomach that bent him double.

"That's for your cooperation, Judas," I said, "and the next time you bother me I'll really fix you." He nodded. "And now get lost!" I snarled at him.

49

"What do you think you're doing with that knife?" I asked calmly. "You'd better throw it away or put it back in your pocket before you cause an accident. And get the hell out of here!" But he kept moving toward me and I saw that the situation was dangerous. I opened my coat and whipped out my Colt 45. I felt the sweat on my palm as I aimed the gun at his face. "Come on, scram!" I wanted to warn him. But he had already lunged at me. Now I had no choice. The steel of his knife glanced off my elbow. I pushed the barrel right into his face and pulled the trigger. A smoky roar, a sizzling sound, and his blackened face snapped back. He reeled and fell away from me. The crowd began to mutter and I raced away.

50

I felt quite at home with the foster parents I was placed with through the Foundation, except for the religious bit. The wife was Catholic, although the husband didn't care. But she wore the pants, so I couldn't swear or mention sex. They had a small daughter who studied ballet. I painted in the attic, my canvases nailed to the beams. I painted city views: red, white and black houses against green, mauve and orange skies. Still lifes: apples, pears and oranges—not fish, because fish begin to stink too soon. They had a phone call from the juvenile magistrate. Would they please keep me at home the next day? Would they get some clean clothing ready? Would they please not mention anything to me? My foster father told me anyway and drove me to the office of the harbor master near the port. I forged the signature of my guardian, the juvenile magistrate, to a paper consenting to my signing a trial agreement as an employee of the shipping line. According to the seaman's book the harbor master gave me, I was now an apprentice seaman. The seaman's book was to be kept carefully, not folded or rolled up, and in case of death was to be returned to the harbor master. I was lucky: the next day I received orders to travel, at company expense, to the north where I would actually start my service. My first destination would be Istanbul.

That day I said good-bye to friends and acquaintances. Nothing could stop me now. I was going to sea. I was going to join the tough guys, the rough men of the sea. I still had a lot to learn, but at least I had a strong body and a good head on my shoulders. Once again my guardian had decided to have me placed in a more suitable environment, even though the decision was unpleasant for him personally. For I had proved unworthy of my freedom: I had fathered a child; had consorted with women of dubious reputation and men of suspicious character; had been kicked out of two art academies; had been "caught in public in a state of undress with a female person" by a policeman and had given that Peeping-Tom policeman a bloody nose; had not reported regularly as instructed; had used obscene language in front of female employees of the Foundation; had called the Director and two teachers at the Art Institute "Gestapo goon," "hick prick" and "impotent bastard" respectively; had made an unmentionable mess of my rented room by holding bacchanals, breaking down walls, conducting immoral activities and causing gas explosions; had threatened to kill the landlord with a hatchet and to cut off his children's ears with a knife; had drunk up, in two days, the money provided by the Foundation for board and clothing, and so on. In short, I had gone down the primrose path again. My first picture postcard arrived a few days later, from Leningrad. "With best wishes from Jan Cremer."

3 HOURS ON
3 HOURS OFF

51

The day before my departure I sold my first painting on real canvas, a still life: a dark-gray bottle on a dark-gray background and an orange, with "Jaffa" printed on it, in fiery orange-red on a light-gray background. It measured about 18 by 26 inches and weighed more than a pound. The composition resembled Sisley's *Cathedral*, the only work of art of the Impressionist School that really turned me on. All that grey with that one red area . . . what talent! I sold my painting, for 100 guilders cash, to a relative of my foster parents. With the money I bought a sailor's cap with a brass anchor, a leather jacket with raised epaulets, a striped sailor's sweater, blue jeans, a compass, a map of the world, a Brownie box camera, two bed sheets, sneakers and leather boots. I stuffed all this into a duffel bag and left early in the morning by train, suffering from a terrible hangover—for I had bought a few beers too. I had to sell my foster father's bike when I didn't have enough money to pay for the beers.

52

Late at night I had to go to the doctor who was to issue my Certificate of Medical Inspection. Stewed to the gills, he examined me superficially and wrote in an unsteady hand that I was fit to serve as an "able semen." Everyone I ever sailed with had to see my Certificate. It absolutely paralyzed them!

53

My cap over one ear, a butt dangling from the left corner of my mouth, wearing my blue jeans, sailor's sweater and leather jacket, I hopped aboard the ship. My duffel bag was slung carelessly over one shoulder. Affecting a real seaman's gait, carefully copied from real sailors, I tapped the cook's shoulder. "Ahoy!" I said. "Here I am, the apprentice seaman! Can you show me the way to the Old Man?" On board, they thought I was a bit strange at first, because I looked like a real sailor. I shook hands with everybody and introduced myself, and let all the dock workers know that I was a member of the crew. I thought the place was pretty crowded for a thousand-ton coastal freighter. I hit the bosun over the head, which turned out to be a mistake. The cook, who happened to come from my neighborhood in Amsterdam, had warned me about him. He was "a tyrannical bastard," the cook had said. "You'd better give him a wallop as soon as you meet him or he'll keep pestering you throughout every trip. The last apprentice sailor left the ship the first time we pulled into port; he couldn't take it any longer."

So that evening, when he jumped aboard, I let him have it. We became friends later on, when it turned out that the cook had misinformed me. It wasn't the bosun who was the louse, but the first mate. He arrived later, just before we sailed, but I couldn't go on hitting people.

54

As it turned out, my first voyage wasn't to Turkey but to Leningrad. We had scarcely been on the open sea for an hour when I felt that I was going to die from seasickness. All of my first three days were like that. When we reached Russian soil I wanted to kiss the shore. Fortunately, after that first attack, seasickness never bothered me again—except when I was pretending, in order to get out of work. Instead of cleaning the bunks and the pantry, I would lie comfortably on my bunk reading a book. When I heard the first mate coming down the hatch, I'd hang my head out of the porthole and start heaving. Since the porthole was only just above sea level, I'd get gusts of spray in my face. Then I'd turn around, looking pale and miserable, my hand clutching my stomach.

The mate would say, "As soon as you feel better, why don't you get back to work? If you keep on working it won't bother you." I'd nod pathetically and hang my noggin out the porthole again. As soon as he was gone I'd sink back onto my bunk again, reading—Mickey Spillane, *G-Man*, *The Saint, Laugh, Sinful Love, She Was a Virgin* and so on. We had at least a hundred books on board which we exchanged among ourselves and with other Dutch ships we met in foreign ports.

With blood, sweat and tears I learned how to knot and splice, take over the helm and the watch, make soundings, brew coffee, hack off rust, paint, tar, smuggle, fight, clean up the messroom, signal, heave anchor chains, read the compass and maps, take inventory, conduct lifeboat drills, take care of the cables, batten down the hatches, and everything else.

55

The entire crew smuggled, and I immediately joined in. All over the ship we hid cartons of Camels, Lucky Strikes and Chesterfields: under the potatoes in the pantry and in sealed plastic bags on strings, which we hung down the toilet or out the portholes—everywhere.

The first time I smuggled I didn't trust the others, so I made my own stashes. Of the forty packs of cigarettes I hid, I recovered twenty-nine: months later I was still finding packs I had hung out of portholes. We handled black-market articles of every description. For Russia: nylons, women's shoes and second-hand clothing; for Spain: alcohol and rubber goods; for Scandinavia: alcohol, tobacco and cigarette paper; for the African ports: weapons—pistols, carbines and ammunition; and cigars and wine for England.

Drugs too: we sold opium, heroin, marijuana and morphine to dock workers all over Europe. That was really the cook's business—we only stashed it for him. I had discovered a really cool spot to hide goodies. Our bunks had foam-rubber mattresses that were divided into 160 hollow squares. I put my stuff into them, slipped the cover back on, and whenever customs men boarded when the ship was in port I'd lean carelessly against my bunk. The customs agents were as corrupt as they come. They'd always start out by asking, "Smokie smokie? Trinkie trinkie?"

Whenever we pulled into one port near Edinburgh, I bribed the Chief of the Harbor Police with cigars and champagne (he rubbed his hands with satisfaction every time). We had a nice little business going. Every trip we'd make at least 100 guilders. If you couldn't make that much smuggling, it hardly paid to be a sailor.

Only the Russians couldn't be bribed. They became suspicious if you offered them so much as a peppermint. If they caught you ashore at hours different from those marked on your pass, they'd push a gun under your nose. The place was lousy with soldiers and cops! When you enter Russian waters, even long before the shore comes into view, two white strips of foam appear suddenly in the water beside you. Then two submarines surface and escort you to the harbor entrance. Or a jet fighter buzzes you. You have to signal, and then it will disappear over the horizon.

In Aden I bought a fez and a hand-carved pumpkin (which broke in Rotterdam) and we watched spade kids diving for tin cans. In Barcelona, the whores were waiting for us in the men's room. In Malaga, we went to a bullfight. The mate threw a bottle at the matador, and we were all taken to the police station. In Edinburgh, I woke up under a statue of a man on horseback. The first thing I saw was an enormous prick and four legs. In Newcastle, the cook and I missed the ship and had to fly to Göteborg. In the plane we had a row about the food, sent our trays flying through the cabin and had some trouble with an Englishman whose wife caught a hot potato in her cleavage. The pilot threatened to make an emergency landing. In Göteborg we were taken off the plane by the Swedish police. We were imprisoned until our ship arrived four days later and weren't allowed ashore again.

In Leningrad, we visited The Hermitage Museum on a trip organized by the Sailors' Home. It was very beautiful—all those masterpieces. And the gold! If you could have swiped even one of those gold ornaments, you could have sold it for a few thousand guilders. But there were guards everywhere —two for every piece of gold—men and women in blue uniforms. When we left an hour later, the guide said we could take pictures for five minutes. We all snapped The Hermitage, a few cops and some trolleys, which was all we had time for.

Those Russian Sailors' Homes are the worst. All you can do is sit on your tail or play billiards or ping-pong. All the chairs are covered with sheets, just like at my grandmother's, to protect them from the dust. You can't get anything to drink except water—from beautiful decanters. In the Strait of Messina I took a picture of the sun setting beyond the Sicilian coast, but it didn't come out because the boat was rocking. The only thing I got to see in London was Piccadilly Circus, and in Edinburgh, the zoo. In Port Said I bought a fucking-ring, made of leather, with hearts and knots. I tried it on a black chick and it wasn't bad. In Malmö we had a fight with a guy who ran a hot-dog stand.

He didn't want to serve mustard with the franks, so the second mate pushed a roll into his face and I dumped a jar of pickles all over the stand. The police came and hauled us into the station. We had to pay a fine and our pay was docked. In Algiers we weren't allowed ashore because of the war. Huge silver jets flew just above our mast and fired into the city. I was sure glad to get out of there! In Mosjöen, Norway, I climbed the cliffs of a fjord on a bet. It took a day to climb it and get down again, so I lost my bet. I had said it could be done in two hours. Norway is a wonderful country. What chicks! So willing and so ripe for plucking! Just like in the ports of North and West Africa. There, before we went ashore, we'd bleach our hair using one large bucket of water and one healthy shot of bleach for the whole crew. Within minutes we were all silver blonds, and that really knocked them out—it was too good to be true. In Naples I saw Vesuvius and took a photograph of it, but that didn't come out either. In Genoa every sailor bought a canary for his mother's birdcage, but all of them turned out to be painted sparrows. In Helsinki we rented a boat and sailed over the lakes with a couple of Finnish chicks and a couple of bottles of gin. Their native booze isn't fit to drink. In the Skagerrak I misjudged my distance in the fog, fell overboard and almost drowned. In Ceylon I sat in on a poker game and lost a month's pay. I was really having a blast!

56

I had taken along a sketchbook and some pastels and once in a while I tried to make some sketches, but I only finished two—a view of Kamenka, a Russian settlement of blockhouses and telegraph poles in the Mezen Gulf, and a view of Tromsö. The whole damn crew watched over my shoulder and made wisecracks. I had to draw nude women, cowboys, cunts and pricks and pictures of the ship for them. When I tried to draw sitting over the hatch to the hold, the odor of the diesel oil would make me sick, foam from big waves would run all over my sketchbook and stain it, or my pastels would roll overboard. At sea I didn't have much time for art: we pulled three hours on and three hours off—three hours at the helm and three hours sleep. In port there was certainly no time for art: we had to go on a binge and get soused. At first I didn't run around with the crew . . . I wanted to see more of these exotic ports than neon-lighted bars and painted whores, and I wanted to do more than just fuck. So I often wandered around the ports on my own. I met plenty of nice, sweet girls but I never had the time to get anywhere with them. I was on a tramp steamer and we never knew for sure which would be our next port. We brought coal from England to Sweden, coconuts from Ceylon to Hamburg, wood from Russia to Scotland, grain from Portugal to Poland, ladies' shoes from Italy to Holland. The saying "a girl in every port" is only true for seamen in the regular mail service or those who've spent years in the coastal service.

57

At sea I finally got some rest, and I was glad when we left port for the limitless ocean. I often stood night watch alone at the wheel. With the mate in the card room, I turned off the ship's radio, quietly studied the compass, and felt a lonely but wonderful sense of peace spread through me.

Sometimes, during the day, a dot appears on the horizon, miles away. Hours later an East German, Swedish, Dutch or American tanker passes. Then you stand on the bridge and salute with the ship's horn. Very romantic. When you're near Russia you see pitch-black clouds floating in an orange sky. Gales, rain and thunder shatter the ocean's calm. You see lightning jump from the mast to the deck. I've seen lightning flashes at sea that lasted as long as fifteen minutes, looking like molten barbed wire. Several times I met nice girls: Katinka in Leningrad, Gina in Genoa, Karen in Bergen, Anuszka in Gdyina, Liselotte in Hammerfest and Eija in Helsinki, but they were only loves of a day because the sea always called me back to its wild waves. The salt water was my love. The sea took me to its bosom and I felt as at home as between the sheets with Gina. Boy, did she have a pair!

58

At Archangel I got a life-size picture of Stalin and pinned it to the wall of my bunk, replacing the nudes from my girlie magazines. I draped the Russian flag around it. I dug Russia.

I'm a Georgi Dimitrov fan. I've read all of his works, but I've stopped reading Stalin. Nikita wanted me to. Yet I did have a great admiration for Stalin. Immediately after World War II he proposed that all German leaders, marshals and officers be arrested and liquidated, thereby preventing the Krauts from starting World War III. But Churchill and Truman were dead set against it.

One time, on the way to Leningrad, the ship's screw was damaged by pack ice in the North Sea. They decided to put into Leningrad to drop off our cargo of wood and then to return to Stockholm for repairs. Two men were needed to stay over in Leningrad to guard the cargo. I volunteered immediately. So the bosun and I stayed at the Sailors' Home in Leningrad for two weeks. I knew a few women at the home and some female dock workers. On previous trips I had given them presents of cologne, nylons, lace-trimmed panties, embroidered bras and garter belts, so I was in good with them. I was anxious to do some travelling during those two weeks in Russia and the women were willing to help me. In exchange for 100 rubles and a good-looking chick, the bosun was happy to stand watch alone, as long as I made sure I got back on time. The girls at the Sailors' Home helped me get a travel permit, train tickets and enough rubles for a trip to Moscow. I arrived there at the time of the International Youth Festival. I walked around Moscow for a week but got tired of seeing no one but American, English and Dutch kids. I just couldn't seem to avoid them. So I went back. But I did have a ball in Russia. The sweetest, most gorgeous chicks in the world live there. That's where I met Katinka, *dobra malenki*. I spent every day with her until the boat returned. Good-byes are painful. To part is to die a little. I couldn't smuggle her aboard the ship because, before every sailing from a Russian port, it was inspected for hours by soldiers and customs men.

Whenever the ship was in a Russian port—I've been to Archangel, Mezen, Kola, Leningrad, Murmansk and Vladivostok—there were always two soldiers, with machine guns, on guard in front of it, watching everyone closely.

In those days a ruble, on board ship, could be exchanged for three guilders. When we went ashore, into the state-run shopping centers or restaurants, people would approach stealthily and ask if we had anything at all for sale. The Russian kids were so America-conscious that we sold old, worn-out jeans for 100 rubles. I sold my leather jacket for 300 rubles, a balalaika, a set of fourteen matching, hand-carved dolls and four bottles of vodka. A bottle of vodka or a pound of candy cost twenty-seven rubles. Sometimes these black-marketeers were dangerous; they would lure you into an alley, knock you down and steal all your clothes. Because of this kind of trouble, the Russians had very strict regulations against black-market dealings. Once I was thrown into the jug in Leningrad. The cook and I had been at a bar for hours, swilling beer and vodka. We were loaded to the gills when we started back to the ship. It was quite a walk to the docks, and the bus from the Sailors' Home had long since left. Besides, it was dangerous to ride in that bus. It was an old-fashioned open contraption which, as it rumbled over the wooden streets near the docks, caused the heavy paving planks to swing up. If you happened to be riding in the rear of the bus, you were sure to get hit. That's the God's honest truth!

We had to walk a long way through a park that night. There was still some light, for in northern Russia it never gets entirely dark during the summer. Halfway through the park, I suddenly had to piss something fierce, so when we saw a low white wall we went and pissed against it. Suddenly we heard wild whistling, and white figures appeared all around us. We ran. They were policemen and five of them ran after us, whistling and waving their nightsticks. "Let's split!" said the cook, and we ran off in different directions. They caught us both immediately and started bawling us out in Russian, but we couldn't understand a word. At the police station, a shed with wooden walls on which hung huge pictures of Stalin and Lenin, we received what was obviously another bawling out (fingers wagging menacingly and heads-off gestures—international sign language) from officers with lots of braid and stripes on their uniforms. This kept up until, finally, an interpreter arrived and asked us if we were anti-communists. "No," we said, thinking that this was a lot of fuss to make over a quick piss against a wall. Then it was explained to us that we had been walking in Lenin Park and had pissed against the base of the white marble statue of the Great Man Himself.

Russian women always smell good. They always wear a delightful scent that you recognize everywhere in the country. It's the smell of roses and blue narcissus. You smell it in the streets, in the state-run stores, in movies and theaters, walking past houses, in bars, on girls and on women. Everywhere you breathe in this lovely, piercing, entrancing perfume that makes you feel dreamy and sensual.

Russian women are beautiful, pretty, sweet, honest, erotic, romantic, clean, unspoiled and childishly eager to please. There are no whores in Russia. Prostitution doesn't exist there. If a woman likes you she goes to bed with you. Long live the Russian Woman. *Dobra devuska, karosha!*

For the children in Russia I took along matchboxes, stamps, chewing gum with pictures of movie stars, decals and cigar bands. A line of them would walk after you, shouting and singing, *"Amerikanski amerikanski karosha."* When you stopped one of them and gave him a piece of chewing gum or a matchbox, he'd run down the street to taste it or to take a closer look at it.

The Russians were so friendly. All that anti-Russian propaganda in Holland about forced labor, censorship and miserable people: Balls! Of the twenty-four countries that I have visited in my time I never saw happier, friendlier or more honest people than the Russians. Next on my list is Scotland, but there they've got pale ale and Scotch.

59

In Arabian and African ports we always ended up at the brothels, because after the bars close only the cathouses stay open. You sit in an intimate little stall with a cute Negro chick and drink until it hurts. Since it's hot as hell there, it's good to have some exercise to sweat out the booze. Those Negro broads make sure that all the bad juices and polluted body fluids gush out of you, like Niagara Falls.

To be a real salt, you work hard on board ship until you arrive in port. Then you wash, put on your good suit (the one bought ready-made for ten bucks in Singapore, which doesn't quite fit. After two wearings it starts to stretch until the seat of the trousers droops down to your knees), smear your hair with a blob of grease, comb a wave into it and go ashore. Automatically you fall by the sailors' hangouts. Pimps lure you into them and offer a nice, pretty girl if you're interested. *"Nhamselah-Nhamselah,"* it's called. Of course the "beautiful sister" turns out to be a hardened old whore, fat and blotchy, with a pockmarked ass. But you don't look too closely—you've already been at the booze for several hours. The whore gets you horny, lets you churn away between her flabby thighs, and unburdens you of a few pounds—sterling. When you get back on board you tell everybody about the terrific piece you had. You give her address to your mates, who go there the next evening, and you wait for them to come back cursing. But they too act like they've had a terrific lay and would have you believe they've screwed an angel from heaven. But you don't go back for more yourself because you still feel repelled by the whole sordid bit.

I tried doing what the other guys did—grab a taxi on the pier, drive to a dance, fool around on the way, dance with a few good-looking broads and then on to a cathouse. In some of the houses, you can pay to see a show; for a few dollars, you can command a special performance. Two women jerking each other off; a beautiful chick, dressed in black stockings and garter belt, masturbating with a purple

116

wood prick, dancing all the time; a whore sitting on a stool, her legs spread apart so you can pitch coins into her big cunt (if you score a bull's-eye, you are rewarded with the pleasure of retrieving your money); broads with wooden legs; girls wrestling each other, naked, in a huge iron tub full of slithering eels; a woman lying on a red divan, her skirt hiked over her knees and her cunt bare—through a slit in the plush curtain, you can watch her clients go to work on her. You have your choice of women from every country, every continent: Negroes, Japanese, Germans, Dutch, Surinamese, Chinese, mulattoes, black-, red-, blond-, brunette-, kinky- or curly-haired, with or without pubic hair. Gradually you become immune to them and long for a woman who'd belong just to you. For there's no better woman than your own woman.

60

I get caught in storms at sea, incredible gales of hurricane force that whip up the ocean into mountainous waves over thirty feet high. In the Gulf of Finland our ship lists heavily and we stand on the bridge in our life jackets, one leg on the wall and the other braced against the ceiling. Three hundred yards aft we see an East German freighter sinking. We hear their SOS calls on the wireless and we can actually watch their radioman sending them. We are able, only with the greatest difficulty, to save ten men out of the crew of twelve. The captain, his dog and the donkeyman drown just out of reach of our outstretched, grasping hands. An hour later the water lies as smooth as a pond.

The dog kept swimming around the spot where his master had gone down. I tried to grab the poor black mutt, but he didn't want to be saved. I stretched myself out over the side as far as I could. Every time the ship wallowed down into a portside list, my head would go underwater for a minute at a time. When the ship listed to starboard I would be suspended thirty feet above the water. Cursing like a madman and biting my lips, I grabbed for the dog, extending my body out as far as it would go. It was so frustrating! I would get to within only a few inches of the pitiful son of a bitch. It was as if he was playing with me. His frightened green eyes would briefly look at me and then down into the water again as if to plead, "First save my master!" But his master had either sunk to the bottom or drifted miles away. Crying and panting, the black dog finally went under, and they pulled me back on board.

61

I kept a diary. I lost a sounding line, an iron cable and twenty-four coffee cups. Off the coast of Finland, my crewmates threw me into the water to see whether I could swim as well as I claimed. Only the captain, the helmsman, the machinist's mate and I claimed we knew how to swim. Before I hit the water I took a deep breath and stayed under for minutes until my ears throbbed and I thought my head would burst. I was beginning to see stars when a black form plunged toward me. It was the captain. He thought I had lied about knowing how to swim and was drowning. He had on his uniform, I my jeans.

62

At every port of call a company agent would bring us money and mail. With each delivery I got postcards and letters from at least five girls. The letters were all filled with love and kisses, sometimes even dried four-leaf clovers and flowers. Whenever I felt lonely I sent postcards to my ex-girl friends at home and asked them to write to me. There would also be a letter from my guardian, the juvenile magistrate. He hoped that my career as a sailor would last longer than my twelve last jobs had, and wished me lots of success, smooth sailing and a safe return. From every African port I sent him the dirtiest picture postcards I could find, usually of nude spade chicks with tits like watermelons.

The first mate was my worst enemy on board the coastal freighter. He was a real stupid hick. I called him a "puber" and we had a terrible fight. He hit my shoulder with a hammer and I landed one above his eye with a paint scraper. We fought for weeks. Later on he asked the helmsman what a puber was. The first mate was a sneaky shit, an unreliable creep. He bugged our asses and continually bossed us around, but always brownnosed the officers. Whenever gulls were following the ship he threw out pieces of meat stuck on hooks that were attached to fishing lines. When the gulls picked up and swallowed the meat, which was just about as soon as it hit the water, he would suddenly yank back viciously on the lines, causing the barbed hooks to rip out of the stomachs of the screaming birds. One day in the Bay of Biscay I couldn't stand it any more. In the mess

I hit him over the head with the earthenware coffeepot, chased him out of the room and tried to throw him overboard. If the crew hadn't come to his rescue, I would have killed him. From that moment on he left me in peace, but he was waiting for a chance to take his revenge. Fortunately it never came. In Singapore I bought a U.S. Army Browning automatic, with bullets, for a few Singapore dollars. It was a beautiful weapon and I let him take a real good look at it and at the bullets as well. After that he was very quiet and finally left the ship at Antwerp. When he split, we all moved up one place. The bosun became first mate, I was promoted to bosun and we took on a new apprentice sailor. At last I was one of the boys and could really join in the fun.

64

We had a swinging time on board. At night we went to the captain's cabin and had us a drink! We'd just come through the Kiel Canal so our supply of drinks had been replenished with cases of Tuborg beer and lemonade. Accompanied by a guitar, we sang to the rhythm of the throbbing engines and the waves beating against the prow:

"Even if we plow right into a mine
My last words will gurgle through Heinekens and wine.
When no beer's left to drink like this,
We'll all drink horny horses' piss,
Then piss, ourselves, into the brine—
Voilà! A cup of Neptune's wine!"

When this beautiful song had come to an end and we'd brushed the tears from our eyes, we'd have another drink— port or fruit wine or a boilermaker. Then the guitarist would strum the notes of another lilting ballad.

"Oh wonderful dream of a buccaneer,
A roomful of girls and Tuborg beer!"

In our minds we'd see all those beautifully shaped bottles with their colorful labels. That was the life! Being a sailor is always a Great Adventure, with drinking bouts and the seductive charms of Turkish harem girls, specially imported, smoking our hookahs with us. Below in the hold, when there was no cargo to carry, we'd put up a bar and cozy, homey parchment lampshades with pictures of sailing ships, just like at my mother's house. Nothing to do but play cards and sip our drinks, soothed by the music of the ship's orchestra, for days on end until we reached port. And there we'd take new women aboard for the next trip. What a life! What an adventure! The only way to see the world!

In each port we had to fasten flat metal disks around our cables to guard against rats. In Tunis we forgot, however, and a few days later we noticed rats. We put out rat poison and traps, but with no success. We had to catch the rats at any price. We said nothing to the customs inspector because a ship with rats is not allowed into any European port: rats spread the plague and other diseases. An inspector would say that the ship had to be gone over by rat exterminators, official-looking little men with boots and gloves and masks over their own ratty heads. I've seen quite a few rat exterminators in my time and they all had faces like rats, just as a man comes to resemble his dog after many years. They come with all kinds of poisonous tidbits, traps and flamethrowers and start hunting. Like hounds they smell out the spots where the rats are—they have a feeling for it. They speak a language all their own: "You take the blue-well, Bill, and I'll go underneath with the weak-iron and scrape them from the splinter-beacon!" A visit from such a team would cost thousands of guilders and there'd still be plenty of fuss before the health inspector would issue a certificate stating that the ship was free of rats and other vermin.

We had tried in every conceivable way to get rid of the rats. I started getting nightmares about them. When I came off watch at night I'd see rats as large as cats run right past me along the deck. They were even in the pantry. They'd gnawed at flour sacks and cheese, and even chewed their way into the cabins. It got to be too much. After a month we thought they must all be lying dead in the hold—we had put out terribly strong poison. Dying rats will either eat one another or scurry off to croak in an inaccessible spot. But then we started seeing them again, by the dozens. We had to put an end to it. We couldn't sleep any more because of the gnawing, we were infested with lice, and we even saw rats when we looked at each other. The old man threatened to mete out stiff punishment if the ship was not clean when we arrived at the next port, which was in Russia, where they have particularly stiff restrictions.

We hit upon a plan. One day after lunch we went on a rat hunt, boots on our feet and our clothing carefully tied around us. Carrying knives on sticks, clubs and long wires we went looking for the rodents. The battle cry was "Kill without mercy!" We did kill some, but not many. After hours of chasing we were able to kill only six of them. Rats are dangerous animals. I find them revolting. I once killed one that was as large as a young cat. As soon as it had drawn its last breath, a black wave streamed through its yellow teeth—millions of lice, fleas and vermin leaving the body. When you corner a rat he sits on his hind legs, with his front legs crossed as though he was praying. A very touching sight! But if you hesitate for only an instant before killing it, he'll jump at your throat. I've seen a big guy laugh one minute, pointing at the praying rat, and scream with pain the next minute, trying to pull the rat off his Adam's apple, where they invariably fasten themselves.

I thought of a system: I brought a can of gasoline from the engine room and constructed a dragnet. Hours later—for rats are very smart—we finally caught one of them in the dragnet, poured gas over it and set it ablaze. We had closed all the doors and hatches, so the animal ran around the deck burning like a torch. It screamed like a stuck pig. We paled and sickened at the appalling sound. Did you ever hear a rat scream? It's like the scream of a baby being skinned alive! Scurrying like a fireball all over the deck, it ran into corners and bulkheads until it finally fell, still glowing, but dead. Four days after that I could still hear the poor thing's screams in my ears. Everyone got nauseous. They stood with their fingers in their ears to shut out the sound. But after a minute we saw results: from every corner, crack and porthole, from the most unexpected places, the rat's brothers and sisters came leaping out, every last one of them came diving overboard as if the devil himself was at their heels. The rats had left the sinking ship . . . it was free at last.

(Later on I worked for one of the big lines that sailed to America and Australia. I was a steward in the Emigrant Section. When the weather was rough and we were on breakfast duty we had to "jerk" our way around the dining room. With large trays of fat, smelly herrings, we weaved among the tables, shoving the stinking fish under everyone's nose. "Would you like another herring, Madam?" After a few minutes of this most of the emigrants were running from the dining room, bent double and looking green, to hang over the rails. This meant less work for us, so we could get ready for the second shift.)

A few days after I signed off the freighter, I went to Rotterdam to pick up my money from the company. I met an old buddy in a bar on the way. He had just signed on a Panamanian ship that was still short a cook's helper. After ten beers and ten brandies I went along to the office to sign on. I had told my chick that I'd be back that evening with the bread. I sent it to her by postal money order. My buddy had talked about the ship like it was a first-class luxury liner. When we got to the pier I saw, through my stupor, that it was a cruddy old barge, all rotten and rusty and without a spot of paint—only yellow and brown oil splotches and corrosion. One good push with your thumb would have made a hole in the hull. But I went along because I had no choice; not only had I signed on, but I had also mailed off all my money. I didn't even have enough left to take the train home. It turned out to be a Greek ship, sailing under the Panamanian flag, with a Turkish captain, a Chinese cook, German and Spanish sailors and a Dutch radioman. He, my buddy and I were the only Dutchmen aboard. The cabins were filthy, the head was full of dried shit and flies, the pantry smelled of cod-liver oil, the old man was constantly drunk and the grub was enough to give you scurvy. Before we reached the open sea, some of the sailors took out their rifles for target practice. They shot a few gulls and an albatross. The albatross fell into a pool of diesel oil on the deck, dead. Now the devil was sailing with us. The crew were the scum of the earth, blade-toting bastards to a man. Knifings were common. The Chinese cook was short four fingers. In stormy weather, iron plates all over the hull shook and rattled. You could have pulled out rivets bare-handed. And there was a black cat aboard, to boot. The work was heavy, but the pay was good. The engines turned in fits and spurts and the ship listed to starboard when it was loaded. The lifeboats hung on loose planks from the rusted davits. After three months, while we were in a lock in the Kiel Canal, I took off with a bag full of cigarettes for my girl friend. I made the trip in one day, with the taste of grease and diesel oil in my mouth all the way.

66

When the train finally stopped I was the first one off. I rushed with my duffle bag along the platform and through the exit. Although it would have taken only five minutes to walk to my girl friend's pad, I was in such a hurry to get there that I grabbed a taxi outside the station. After it stopped and I had paid the driver, I jumped out, threw my bag down in front of the door and rang three times. My heart was pounding, I was terribly nervous. A minute passed and the door hadn't been opened, so I rang again. I heard someone clomping down the stairs and the door was opened by the landlady. I said, "Hello, here I am again. Is Annabel home?" The old lady was struck speechless with surprise, but she finally managed to stammer, "What in Heaven's name are you doing here? I thought you were in Russia, dear oh dear oh dear, what a surprise this will be for Annabel, we were just talking about you yesterday and she said she wouldn't be surprised if you suddenly turned up because we hadn't heard from you for such a long time, and here you are, come in, come in." So I went upstairs. I asked if I could reach Annabel anywhere, but she was working in a café and wouldn't be home until late at night. The landlady kept on talking a mile a minute and I tried to get away by saying I needed rest and that I wanted my homecoming to be a complete surprise for Annabel. "But you can't get into her room, she always locks the door when she goes out, would you like a cup of coffee?" asked the old lady. But I didn't feel like listening any longer to her prattling and I finally pried myself loose by saying that I had a key.

With my heavy duffel bag, I climbed the three flights of stairs just as I had dreamed of doing the three months I was at sea: I would ring the bell, looking tanned and packing a fat wad of cabbage in my pocket. Then I'd surely be loved up by a bevy of groovy chicks (friends of Annabel's who just happened to be at her pad), followed by the triumphant climax that would see me sweep her off her pins and up into my arms and carry her upstairs to the attic. But now that I was actually there, I loathed the neatly scrubbed flights of stairs, the musty odor of the hallway, the gleaming white walls with their stupid highland landscapes and Gauguin prints and the smell of wax. But I was glad that at least the bare attic stairway hadn't been touched. Using a handkerchief, I picked the lock and then I was back in familiar surroundings: the large bed with Mexican blankets, the radio and phonograph, records, paintings by myself and Annabel on the walls, and a pile of clutter on the bare black-painted floor. I felt high as a kite, positively euphoric, a feeling I always get when I'm just back from a long trip. I put on a record and stretched out on the sack, feeling absolutely no pain. It was 11 A.M. Bright sunshine filtered through the skylight. The wail of Billie Holiday mingled with muffled street noises from below. I found the letters that had come for me while I was away. I lay down again and started to read. The next thing I knew I was being awakened by someone shaking me. It was Annabel. Was I glad to see her! We clung to each other for half an hour before I got around to trotting out my tales of High Adventure on the High Seas. By then it was 2 P.M. Someone from the art academy had spotted me at the station and right away hipped Annabel. As soon as she heard I was back, she took the afternoon off and scooted back to her pad, where she knew I'd be waiting. I unpacked my duffel bag, hauled out all the souvenirs to be duly admired and hung up my clothes. When we had finished talking and sleeping and fucking it was 9 P.M. We got up and dressed. I, of course, sported my newest rags, which were way out for this hick town. Annabel squirmed into her best outfit, straightened her nylons, and clicked smartly out in her high heels. She looked great! We had a chicken dinner in one of the big restaurants in town.

Of course, dozens of old friends from the academy came to sit at our table and say hello. There I was, surrounded by beards and culture-snobs, but I really didn't give a shit because these bums made the perfect audience for my travelogues: they swallowed every word.

After I went to sea, Annabel's father had wanted her to return home, but she absolutely refused. When he held back the bread for school and board, she insisted on supporting herself by working as a waitress in a third-rate café. She kept up with night classes, but money was a problem. She was still quite a chick: not too tall, not too heavy, not too thin, with a pretty face and a great body. And she was still crazy about me. When we got back home, she was slightly tipsy and I was roaring drunk. She told me she had decided to have the baby after all and that she wanted to marry me. I was pretty far gone, but I was expecting the subject to crop up sooner or later. It irritated me, for I had almost managed to forget it all the time I was at sea, although she had never failed to remind me of it in every one of her letters. When I got her letters I used to lie down on my bunk to read them, always touched. But I just didn't feel like getting married, either to her or anyone else, let alone raise a family. I knew that sooner or later I'd have to tell her so. But I was afraid she'd go to pieces over it, even though she was very independent and had a strong character. I felt a bit uneasy and was glad that I could bring myself to tell her, "Of course I'll marry you! Don't I want to be with you forever? And it will be swell to have a baby," because I knew that I could claim later that I'd been drunk. But it wasn't easy and I was glad that it was dark. It left a bad taste in my mouth and I felt like shit because I really did love her—but not enough to marry her. . . .

The day after my return Annabel told me that my guardian, the juvenile magistrate, had often stopped by to ask if she knew when I was coming back. He had asked her to call him at court as soon as I showed up, so I had to keep out of the way. I hadn't been able to make much bread from smuggling, but I still had a heavy gold watch that had been given to me by a Swedish queer. I took it to a hock shop and, after many complications, managed to get 200 guilders for it. The whole town is just three streets, so after several days of knocking around I had seen just about everybody and everything. Slightly bored, I felt like doing some painting. I had seen so much that had turned me on in my travels and I wanted to paint all of it. I bought a supply of paints and canvas and went to work during the daytime when Annabel was at the café. I had to cop some bread, but I couldn't quite make up my mind how. So I decided to stay with her until I had enough bread to make other plans. But I didn't stick it out for long. I had become hung on the good life: I liked my daily mugs of beer and living it up at night. I soon began to hang out in a bar where, living it up, I lushed up all my cabbage in just one week. But what really got me down was a note that came one day from my guardian: "I shall be in your neighborhood with a youth group on Saturday and shall expect to find you at home. There are several matters we must discuss at that time." One of the town busybodies must have tipped him off that I was back in circulation.

That Saturday morning, I happened to be at home when our landlady shouted upstairs that there was someone on the telephone who wanted to speak to Annabel. I went downstairs, lifted the receiver and asked, "Who's calling?" "Hello, to whom am I speaking," I heard Annabel's father ask in deep, pompous tones. "With me," I said. "Oh, are you back, then?" His question was utterly stupid, but people always ask such things when they're at a loss to say something intelligent. He wanted to know where his daughter was and I told him Annabel was at work. He asked me to tell her to take the 5 o'clock train home. I asked if I was invited too and he started shovelling the bullshit: "Oh, what a shame! If we had only known you were in town! It's too bad all the children are at home this weekend." "Cut the crap," I snapped, "Annabel's not coming without me, so if you change your tune, fall by and pick us up this afternoon. You know the address. See you!" I hated her father's guts. He was a hard-nosed square, manager of a large factory. He was always sounding off about the virtues of hard work and rolling up your sleeves. And to prove it—what a con man!—he would take a worker's place on the production line for a well-dramatized one-minute stint. At home he was the perfect little bourgeois dictator: after finding fault with everybody and issuing orders like a paranoid general, he'd retire to his den to get plastered. He made sure he attended High Mass on Sundays, then always brought the same people back home for a drink and a chat. Annabel used to come on with me about "getting to know him," but how could I ever get to know a cat who took an instant dislike to my long hair and my lower-class background?

The date with my guardian had completely slipped my mind. The bell rang and the old bitch downstairs opened the door before I could stop her. There stood His Honor! With his friendliest manner he came toward me and we shook hands like old friends. He sat down, looked at my latest painting, asked about my travels and fidgeted in his chair, looking very uncomfortable. I could see that he didn't know how to broach what was apparently a touchy subject. He stopped smiling, slowly cleaned his glasses and then asked, "What are you planning to do about Annabel's unfortunate condition?" With a grave face I told him that I didn't know, but that I'd do whatever he and the authorities thought best. Those were serious words and I could see they impressed him. I knew Annabel's father had contacted him and that there had been conferences between them. I had the impression that my guardian had been glad I'd gone away to sea. They had expected me to return sometime, of course, but not so soon.

The fat old guy really wasn't such a bad egg, even if he did have a lot of corny ideas about the rehabilitation of delinquent youths. Whenever he was called at court about my latest sexual escapade, he was sure to drop by a few days later to try and talk me into giving up my free-wheeling sex life. I always promised, with a straight face, to mend my ways and he always accepted my promises in good faith. So now we went through the same routine. When he got to the subject of "going to bed," he lowered his voice to a confidential whisper and looked furtively over his shoulder.

"Well," I said, "if all of you insist on my getting married [his jaw dropped] I don't mind going through with it just to make everybody happy. But of course you'll have to pay for everything. After all, I'm just a poor orphan!"

He promised to talk to Annabel's parents about the tying-the-knot bit (it would have to be soon) and to discuss the question of money with his superiors. He also wanted to talk to me about my plans for the future. I had been kicked out of the academy, so art was out, and my career as a sailor was apparently finished. "You got yourself into difficulties by living with a girl. Irresponsible sexual unions between minors invariably produce dire results. Consider the fact that marriage might have certain definite advantages for you. For one thing, as a married man, you'd automatically be granted the status and rights of an adult, rather than remaining a ward of the court. But it's up to you, it's your life. We shall try to help you find a solution, but in any case you can't avoid certain responsibilities." I decided it would be cooler not to tell him to his face that I didn't have eyes for the wife-and-family bit. I decided just to wait and see. I touched him for some bread. He claimed he didn't have any, but promised to give the matter some thought. So I sang him the hard-luck blues about the degrading, poverty-ridden conditions in which I—a serious, hard-working young artist —was trapped. And with an expectant wife to boot! Finally, he bought one of my paintings for thirty guilders and left with the promise that I'd be hearing from him soon.

When the front door slammed behind him, I jumped up, tossed the three ten-guilder bills over my head and did a victory dance. I decided to wait until my guardian had time to turn the corner before making for the bar. So I changed my clothes. After all, I was meeting my prospective bride in an hour.

I lifted a few in the bar, shot a game of craps and then sauntered into town. The streets were crowded with shoppers all decked out in their finest and smelling of Lux soap. They shouldered their way in and out of shops and department stores, loaded down with bulging shopping bags and packages. The kids all had balloons-free-with-the-purchase-of-a-pair-of-shoes to keep them quiet. Workers walked contentedly beside their wives and baby-filled carriages. Annabel had asked me not to meet her inside the café because the other waitresses would tease her. So I waited for her outside, feeling lonely and blue.

67

The carnival had blown into town. It opened on the day after Easter. A few days earlier I had dropped by the grounds to look around. I needed work, for I had been short of cash for quite a while and nobody had come to my rescue. The broad I was living with worked in a nightclub. When she came home in the middle of the night I had to whip her before mounting her, which was a drag. I would usually be asleep when she wanted me to make like De Sade. I'd wake up so mean and salty that I'd wallop the shit out of her, so the loot she earned mostly went to the doctor and for first aid: bandages, salves and stitches for bruises and shiners. But after a while she wanted to throw me out because she got tired of me. I had already been to the Unemployment Office, but all they had there was monotonous Post Office work and other such jobs, which didn't

127

turn me on worth a shit. I might just as well have joined the police force.

I had met her in the street and we fell for each other right off the bat. For several days we had heavy action in the sack, with wild writhing and great gobs of come, but I cooled off when her masochistic needs began to bore me. I smacked her around as we got down to the nitty-gritty, but she learned to like it so much that she had to have it that way every day. At the ripe old age of seventeen, I found it quite interesting at first but after a short while I had had enough. I would have split sooner if it hadn't been for her apartment and the Chinese delicacies she brought home from the night-club where she was barmaid: lo mein, war shew op, egg foo young, winter-melon soup or any other tidbit that grooved me. The walls of her oriental apartment were hung with countless instruments of torture—whips from the Congo, Turkey and Hungary, cat-o'-nine-tails from Mexico and Peru, clubs from Rotterdam and nude pictures of herself. She was very proud of her body, with good reason. She was a second Anita Ekberg, with breasts like Vesuvius. She made such scenes and bugged me so every night that whether I wanted to or not, I belted her around. With every lash, which would leave a bloody mark, I'd think, "That's for the war shew op" (there were no almonds in it) or, "That's for bringing burnt chicken." I was growing tired of the food to boot, but I couldn't think of a way out. I was a lone wolf, a sailor on the beach, a talented artist who had never been given a chance. I was also "a complete bastard, a rapist, a molester, a thief, a bandit" and God knows what else! If I was someday going to be the star guest in the death chamber, at least I might as well have some fun until things came to a head. So when the blond bitch threatened to throw me out I held my ground by saying that I'd go to the club and smash everything to pieces, including herself. That did the trick!

At the fairgrounds there was tremendous activity. Everybody was busy setting up. I tried the Wall of Death, but it was no soap—the stunt trio didn't need another rider. It would have been a gas to work for them, because the chick in their act was a luscious Japanese. What gorgeous quail! I dreamt of being engaged to her, of humping her against the Wall of Death and of fucking wonderful nights away in the van. I even offered to join the act as a mechanic or handyman, but they had no bread for me. I could have started working at once but wouldn't start getting paid until after the fair opened. And I wouldn't be able to go on tour with them, so I lost interest.

No use trying the Cave of Horrors: half the out-of-work cats in town were looking for jobs there. I talked to a few of the carnival people, but they had no suggestions. All they knew was that the magician was looking for someone for his vanishing trick, preferably an attractive chick, and the circus tent needed a man for the flying trapeze (I'm scared of heights and don't trust anybody. They'd probably let me fall to my death if I ever complain that I'm being underpaid). Bill Haley was being played all over the fairgrounds. He was the latest craze—rock 'n' roll was already old news in America by the time it arrived in Holland. *Rock around the Clock, See You Later Alligator, Razzle Dazzle* and all that sound. It echoed good and loud and I felt great.

Then I saw Tony. Tony was a ragpicker who lived on our block, but during the fair he boxed in the sports arena. I asked him if he knew of any jobs. He took me along to the sports arena, where they needed a few strong-arm men. After half an hour I was hired as Jack Jolly, champion bantamweight boxer from Chicago, holder of the orders of the Silver Snake, the Golden Caterpillar and the Giant Tusk.

I told the manager that I didn't speak English. "Don't worry," he said through his cigar, "just keep your trap shut." Every time I climbed into the ring, the manager, who was also the master of ceremonies, introduced me with a sob story: about my father, a big torpedo from Chicago who was blinded by a rival mobster, and about my brothers, all well-known boxers in America. "And here," he'd go on, seizing my arm and pinching it black-and-blue, "stands the youngest and most dangerous member of the Jolly family—little Jackie! Let's hear it for him! When his father was brought home blind, little Jackie went into shock. Fortunately, he recovered, but he's been deaf and dumb ever since. Let's hear it for Jackie! Who wants to fight him? Let me warn you, my friends, that Jackie swore—the day his father was blinded—to keep the art of boxing high!" Then I'd look into the crowd menacingly, make a few jabs in the direction of some cats up front, grumble a bit, do some warming-up exercises, rap the punching bag and finally throw my glove into the crowd. Not many studs had the guts to try their luck with me and when they did, nothing came of it. The tent was always jammed, because all the young girls wanted to see me box. It was a shame that I couldn't talk. During everyone else's matches I couldn't do anything but lean against the ropes looking bored, while all my cronies could at least cheer when one of our boys won and boo when someone from the audience won (I'd climb into the ring as if to take him on, but the referee would fortunately limit me to shaking my fist at him). But of course our boys rarely lost; the brass knucks in our left gloves saw to that. The first week was quite interesting and I had lots of free time because I only had two bouts a day, one in the afternoon and one in the evening.

The sports arena was always a hive of activity, with boxing, judo, jujitsu and the like. All the performers had wild, dangerous-sounding names, like Nero the Wild and Attila the Short. Nero was a heavy. Once, behind his van, when he thought nobody was around, I saw him kick a dog in the head. He was plenty strong, but he won his bouts mainly because he looked so tough. He had a typical boxer's face, with huge, floppy cauliflower ears, a flattened nose and a bull neck. And on top of it all he was bald. Big, wide furrows ran from his head to his neck. He wrenched out his opponents' limbs, "accidentally" broke their wrists, screamed like a kamikaze and was most unsportsmanlike, all by order of the management. He was, by far, the biggest box-office draw. If Nero hadn't gouged his opponent's eye or stomped on his face—or even if he himself had been forced to throw in the towel—the referee (who ran a vegetable market before the sports arena came to town) would cry out, "This thrilling, manly test of strength is declared a draw!" The opponent, lying on the floor as in the throes of death, would be helped to his feet and told to shake hands. But Nero would refuse the outstretched hand or even spit into it, then look around and thumb his nose at the crowd. The crowd, furious at such a show of poor sportsmanship, would demand a return bout. Then, of course, the referee had no choice but to "admit" that Nero the Wild had, with his huge feet, kicked around the rules most villainously and turned the noble sport into a circus of catch-as-catch-can. He would then grant the injured party a grudge match. This usually satisfied the crowd but, of course, they had to go outside again, for the return bout would be the next performance—and they'd have to pay all over again to get in to see it. The crowd outside, who had followed the entire bit on the loudspeaker, were quick to buy tickets and the tent would be jammed. The management was very happy and so was Nero, for he owned part of the company. So it went for days.

At first I was a bit scared when I had to fight a stranger, but I was assured that nothing could happen to me. If things went wrong, the manager would signal to his helpers to jump into the ring and separate us. So all I had to do was keep the other guy away from me and keep a sharp eye on the referee and the helpers. When the referee slung a towel across his shoulder, I was allowed to use my brass knucks. One uppercut was enough to dump my opponent like a sack of potatoes.

Surprised by the hardness of my punch, a victim would sometimes ask for an explanation. But the referee brushed them all off with, "What's the matter, can't you take it? You were warned to watch out for fast-as-lightning Jack Jolly and his Iron Fists!"

And, of course, I was supposed to be totally deaf, so I couldn't hear the protests from the crowd. But one of the boys would touch my shoulder and point into the crowd. Then I'd look apologetic and offer my hand to my opponent. That always got a good round of applause.

I earned twenty-five guilders plus board and lodging (a cot in a damp trailer shared by several Surinamese), but if I lost a match because of my own stupidity, I had to pay out of my own pocket the prize of ten guilders given the opponent who had beaten me.

When the air force arrived, I had a few lean days. I kept on losing because the fliers were so fast that I went down before I had a chance to use my secret weapon. Otherwise, it was all very pleasant: drinking beers in the canteen, playing cards and chasing chicks. I had discovered some good-looking quail in the Darkest Africa tent, the girls who let snakes wriggle around them.

I had broken off for good with the blond flagellant from the nightclub and had moved, with my few belongings, into the caravan. I travelled with the carnival for two months. At fourteen different fairs I tried to make Mei-Fu, the Japanese chick from the Wall of Death. But I failed every time —she was married to one of the riders.

Our season was ended by a mob of peasants from Drente, who all but demolished the tent. They didn't like being suckered in. So they raised hell, beat up all the boxers— including Nero—and proceeded to pull down the ring and the tent. When it was all over they demanded their ten guilders apiece for flooring our fighters and the company nearly went broke paying them.

With a new suit, a wallet full of saved-up bread and an expensive ring on my finger (finally wangled from Mei-Fu as an eternal remembrance—for as much as she liked me and wanted to cut out with me, it just wouldn't be right . . .), I hopped a train back home with Tony and a few boys from the Cave of Horrors. On the way, we drank like maniacs. Roaring drunk, I arrived at the home of a former girl friend who took me in with open arms. Now, at last, I would be able to develop my real talent.

MONDO CANE (1940-   )

68

The alarm clock went off with a jarring clang. I woke up with a start. It was 6 A.M., the beginning of a new day. Helen was lying next to me, snoring and wheezing. I decided not to wake her. My hung-over head was filled with the throbbing roar of fire engines, police cars and screaming sirens and my mouth felt like the inside of a rusty boiler. I eased myself out of bed and staggered toward the washbasin, a huge cast-iron monstrosity. I splashed my face with the water and cursed. It was winter and the water was ice-cold. I glanced at the still-sleeping form. How disgustingly unattractive she looked now. The mascara had run in streaks across her creased face and her raven tresses, now damp ropes, lay tangled and heavy on the pillow. The room and the whole house stank of garlic (it leaves such a bitter aftertaste, like fucking does at times), stale piss, tobacco smoke, semen, sweat and sleep. The entire morning stank until I was dressed. I put on clean socks, clean underwear and a sparkling white American shirt, for today I was to report—for the millionth time, it seemed—to a new job, this time as a working student. Students must always look neat, of course, because they invariably come from loaded families.

I ate a piece of bread with apple butter on it. Suddenly, Helen's snoring stopped and she opened her eyes.

"Morning, sweetie-pie," she said. "Is darling hubbykins going to workie for little honeykins?"

I thought, "Drop dead!" but I replied sweetly, "Yes, pussy-cat!"

132

"Would hubbykins darling please bring honeykins a glassie of water?"

I brought her a glass, which she drank in gulps and threw right up. "Doesn't honeykins get a little kissie?" I gave her a long-distance peck, grabbed my coat and hurried out the door. I might have been just another guy on his way to work. Only the thermos of tea and the orange sandwich box full of peanut-butter-and-jelly sandwiches were missing, but that was because I was a working student.

Women: they smell of stale semen and have sweaty armpits, feet and crotches. They snore, barf and gurgle—like the dirty old men in sailor hats on sight-seeing boats who bring up and spit out gobs of yellow phlegm, their faces split in tooth-less grins. Women: they have pimples, wet vaginas and matted pubic hair. They gossip about nothing, bug you and hate you. Women are always right, especially over spilt milk. Butter-milk. I like cream puffs and I can bake—cakes for Mother's Day. Show me the most beautiful woman. In bed she becomes a tigress, a lamb, a bloodsucker or a gnat. With her legs apart, she looks like a crocodile. But in an hour at the beauty parlor, she undergoes a metamorphosis, emerging The Eternal Woman, the fair but weak sex. Marilyn. Brigitte. Rita. Sophia. Yvette. Cleopatra. Gina. Booooooh!

69

Helen was a millionaire's daughter. (Rich chicks always dig me. I fascinate them. I'm something else!) She ran away from home because of me. Because of me, she gave up the red M.G. (which she shared with her two sisters), the tennis court, the private swimming pool, the frilly boudoir with French maid, the hi-fi system and the cozy rendezvous pavilion in the garden that revolved on wheels. Now she was living with an angry young man—that's what I called myself in those days. Of course we didn't really want for anything. Her father knew what poverty meant. He had started out as a simple florist and had only become a millionaire bank director with the aid of the State Lottery, from which he had twice won 100,000 guilders. He gave Helen a fat checking account with the understanding that she wouldn't give me a penny. "If this boy really loves you, he will not want to ac-cept your money," Daddy had told her. "Otherwise, it is not you that he is interested in, but your money. And your money is my money." There were plenty of hassles over money, especially after her father hired private detectives to check whether I paid my own way. It was a lousy situation. If I needed some money I had to plead for hours, and then was given a check for exactly the amount I needed: "Pay to bearer nine guilders and seventy-five cents." I stayed with her because she was a good fuck and found me interesting. Life with her wasn't too bad, and at least her pad was a warm spot for the winter.

Helen shopped; I did the cooking. Helen bought canvas and paint for me; I painted her portrait. Helen found a nice second-hand sports car; I drove it for her. Helen studied flamenco dancing; I took her to dancing school and brought her back. Helen wanted to visit nightclubs; I was her escort. I watched her like a hawk, knowing that if I lost her I'd also lose my meal ticket and the roof over my head. She was a real piece and she knew it. She had a great walk, wriggling and swinging her ass like Marilyn Monroe. Men stared hungrily after her when she went down the street and laborers made dirty cracks as she passed. She ate it all up.

Eventually our love nest exploded. I got sick and tired of waiting on her and fed up with her nagging cracks, always preceded by "Daddy says." I decided it was time to show her what I was really like, so I told her I didn't need her rich hands on my body or her florist-father's money. "Prove it, then!" she screamed hysterically. "All day long you put down my family, just because you have no money. You're jealous of anybody who has money, even if they come by it honestly. You're full of communist cant and hypocrisy. You think everyone with money is a dirty capitalist crook. According to you, everyone with a car is an oil tycoon and every attractive woman is only a whore. I'm a slut because I buy Dior gowns! Then why do you stay with me? For my money? If I were a man, I'd never accept money from a whore!"

I kept calm. "Listen, honey, you don't know what life's all about. You've always been protected, kept under wraps. You can't help it, but you don't know what poverty is. You have twenty-four pairs of shoes but you never wear twenty-three of them. You have enough dresses and coats to clothe an orphanage for ten years, but you never wear most of them because they don't suit you. If you don't get your three squares a day you scream about hunger. And, of all the conceits, you want to become a flamenco dancer! But I can work, so I don't need your money. Only your body. I don't even want your mind, for the minds in your family for generations to come won't rise any higher than tulip bulbs."

Later that evening we made up, but a short time later she said, "Oh, darling, if you'd only just show me that you were willing to work!" How could I make her understand that I did work, twenty-four hours a day, with my mind? It would have been easier to explain to her how the valves of an M.G.

134

operate. So I let it go at that and the next day, thanks to a lucky tip-off, I registered for employment as a working student. I was given a registration card and orders to report to a large meat-packing plant at 7 A.M. the following day.

70

It was still dark outside when I got on the company bus that left the station for the factory every morning at 6:30. I took a seat in the rear of the rocking bus, which was crammed with gray-faced workmen who smelled of soap and cheap tobacco. They discussed the football pools and a chick they'd seen on TV the previous evening. A few of them, glancing at me indifferently, had said, "Probably a student." "How much do they pay you guys an hour?" the man sitting next to me asked. "One guilder and twenty-five cents," I replied. "Well," said my neighbor, "I wouldn't kill myself for that kind of money if I were you." We bounced through the countryside, stopping now and then to pick up more workers. All of them carried satchels, wore caps and puffed away at soggy butts. Ignoring the sign at the front of the bus, they all spit on the floor and then rubbed the spittle into a blubbery mess with their heavy work boots. The countryside still looked grey under a low fog. It was drizzling, which was a good sign, for it meant that the below-zero temperature would rise. I thought how nice it would feel to be lying under warm blankets. But Work is Freedom, so I would persevere. We passed the last village and soon, out of the grey mist, loomed a huge fenced-in complex of buildings with tall chimneys. Thousands of dark figures streamed through the gates and the sirens screamed like whistling buoys at sea. The driver brought the bus to a halt, turned off the ignition and shouted, "Last stop, Auschwitz! Everybody out! See you at 5 o'clock."

At the gate I was given a time card and a locker number for the dressing room. From the supply department I received my uniform: a pair of light-blue overalls, rubber boots and a cap. I draped my own clothes over a large hook attached to a chain, which was then hoisted to the ceiling, taking my identity with it. Along with all the other ego-stripped workers, I became just a number again. Down with the individual! We were herded along like a bunch of cattle by supervisors in white smocks. Each of our uniforms bore the company's trademark. I was almost surprised not to see any medals or men with pistols, but MPs apparently hadn't been introduced yet. I was swept along with the work-bent mass, and suddenly found myself in front of a small office where a few sleepy girls yawned behind typewriters while their bosses sorted papers. "I'm a working student," I said, "and I'm supposed to report to the Fresh Vegetable Department." "They don't need any staff at the moment. Join that group over there. You'll be put to work in the Fresh Meat Department." I hesitated, because I didn't feel a bit like working in a slaughterhouse. At the Employment Office they had assured me that I'd only have to perform simple duties in the Fresh Vegetable or Transport division. But Fresh Meat, no! "Just go along with that group," the man in the white smock insisted, "it's 10 past 7 already and you haven't done a stitch of work yet. Next week there'll be a place in Fresh Vegetables," and he ushered me firmly out of the office. I was absorbed into a group of workmen led by a man with a list in his hand. "Are you Cremer?" he snapped at me. "Then we're all here. If you're this late again tomorrow, it'll be deducted from your pay, understand?" We marched across the company streets, passing many similar groups, including women. The women made the most obscene gestures at us, which the men returned. "Let's go and have a fuck, baby!" one of my neighbors from the bus shouted at a woman, and we all laughed. "Sure," she yelled back, "but you'd better bring along a cow's cunt for yourself!"

It was like a concentration camp or an army barracks, the way we were marched along. I noticed a glass building. A sign on it read, *"Staff canteen. Visits must not exceed five minutes."* Below that was clearly marked the fine for anyone who stayed more than five minutes, just like in the public urinals, except there they even threaten you with a prison sentence.

We were now approaching buildings that I knew must be our destination, since they reeked of blood and cow dung. Men who walked inside wearing clean white aprons would come out again a minute later covered with bloodstains. The air was filled with the lowing and crying of animals and the smell of death. The walls were dripping with a moisture that smelled like the dead bodies we stuffed into paper bags just after the war. I began to feel sick and wanted to run away, but it was too late. "Hey!" a fat redheaded guy in boots shouted at me. "You're from the butcher shop, aren't you? Take this prodder and push the animals inside with it." He handed me a murderous-looking instrument, a heavy tube with two prongs charged with a strong electric current. As soon as a pig was touched with this thing, it screamed in terror and started to run insanely. I wanted to go home.

Huge cattle vans drove up. Hefty farmers with red eyes opened the back gates and kicked pigs down a plank and into the enclosure. The animals, reacting to the smell of death, refused to go down the plank. The farmers, helped by the factory staff, beat away at their pink, mud-covered backs with sticks, clubs, and electric prodders. Bellowing in pain, sometimes with broken legs or backs, the animals were shoved into a trapdoor that led to a long, slippery slide running down into the interior of the factory. At the bottom of the slide were large troughs of steaming hot water, which removed the worst dirt from their skins. Then the floors of the troughs were raised mechanically, throwing the screaming animals onto large steel plates about ten yards square. Every three seconds the plates were charged with thousands of volts of electricity. As if struck by lightning, the animals stiffened and shuddered in their death throes and were then moved onto other plates. There, hooks were fastened into their bleeding snouts (electrocution causes blood to spurt from their nostrils) and they were then hung on an automatic conveyor belt. Jerking and swaying, tons of pigs—their ribs and backs broken by the fall from the van and down the slide—were carried along past the butchers, men with fat red necks, heavy chins and deep-set, bloodshot eyes, wearing aprons dripping with blood. Hanging from their belts were all kinds of knives and daggers and even hatchets. With the sharpest of these they slit the animals' throats. The blood spurted into large basins standing on the floor, and was later collected for use in frankfurters, corned beef, blood sausage and bologna. The butchers, who often spit onto the floor, weren't too careful about avoiding the basins. The conveyor moved along past another row of sadists who sliced the animals in two vertically. The halves then continued on separate cables. The heads were sawn off automatically and thrown into one row of carts and the innards, which would be used in the manufacturing of meat products, went into another. The entire process of cutting up a pig into head, innards, sides of bacon and pigs' feet (which went to the canning department to be turned into soup) took less than five minutes.

There is an all-pervasive stench in a slaughterhouse, a fatty haze that clings to your skin and leaves a taste in your mouth. It was my job to push the pigs through the trapdoor, but I let plenty of them escape, pretending that I didn't notice them running out the gate. But their freedom was short-lived, for blows from clubs soon forced them back. Occasionally, one of the animals managed to jump out of the scalding trough. It would run screaming through the slaughterhouse until it was kicked onto an electrocution plate or ran into the turning wheels of a machine. Then the carcass had to be removed with a hooked stick. The workers in the slaughterhouse were a real bunch of psychopaths. They scared me, but good! When I refused, after a while, to beat and kick any more pigs, I was ordered into the Cold Storage Department—a complex of refrigerators as large as theaters. From these monstrous iceboxes I had to push carts full of slimy, foamy guts to another part of the factory. I was surprised to see, among the workers, some men who looked normal. But even they seemed as unconcerned as the others. They didn't bat an eyelash as sheep were pushed, head first, onto a circular saw, or as cows fell lowing when their heads were chopped off, eyes still open and bodies still twitching. The men then used axes to chop the heads up into eight pieces, like firewood. The legs too were cut off and tossed into piles.

A few years later I happened to see the municipal slaughterhouse in Paris, an even more disgusting place. There the legs of the cows were chopped off before they were killed. Screaming and bellowing, the animals fell onto the wet concrete floor. Without legs, they could be beheaded more easily —usually no more than a few strokes did the trick.

I walked in a daze among all the falling beasts. Every moment another life departed the earth. It seemed that soon, suddenly, a great silence must fall; but it never came. I wished I could have started crying. What else could I do? Why didn't the pigs jump at these people and tear them to pieces? Why didn't the cows form a massive herd and trample their torturers, as they could have done so easily? What prevented the horses from simply lifting their heads and streaking away? Every second another life was callously destroyed. Oh, I know, I like my steaks, bacon, chicken, chops and sausages as much as the next man!

But at that moment I wanted to run away, back home, even though I was broke. Yet I had to stay on, for keeping the job had become a matter of principle. I was repelled by everyone I saw. It was like walking in a fog, a fog smelling and tasting of death. The foreman was a tough guy, a real bastard, and he kept needling me. Every time I came off the freight elevator with a cart, he yelled at me to hurry up. I worked as hard as I could, because they really had me scared. What was to stop them from hacking me up and mixing me in with all the other bones and guts? Nobody would ever know! But goddammit, tonight I'd go to the Employment Office. Was this work for a normal human being, a student no less?

The foreman, a fat powerful man, was a special kind of monster. He had piglike eyes—one of them was blubbery as if it had been smashed by a hammer—a flattened nose blotched red and purple, pigs' ears and teeth, short blond hair and a face covered with coarse brown stubble. His stubby fingers were coated with clotted blood. All of a sudden he followed me into the freight elevator, which was lit only by a weak bulb behind wire mesh. We descended alone in the isolated cage. "Are you a Jew?" he asked me. "No," I said, astonished. He bent towards me, enveloping my face in his hot swine's breath. Half suffocated, I tried to hide my fear and the knocking of my knees and prayed for the lift to reach the bottom. He spat at me: "If you don't hustle your ass, Jew-boy, I'll stick my knife into you. Yours wouldn't be the first kike throat I cut." I thought I'd faint from fear and from the stench. I wanted to scream. At that moment the doors opened and I stood in front of the refrigerator. My knees buckled. I was scared to death of this man. I felt terribly lonely in this hell and I wanted to get out. It was like a nightmare. I quickly shoved my empty cart under a large funnel. A couple of boys opened the end and a load of revolting muck slithered into the cart.

I got back into the lift and up to fresh air as soon as I could and began to feel a little better. Who could I turn to? Nobody. They were all the same. At lunchtime I'd go to the office and ask them to transfer me to another department. Or, if necessary, I'd demand my wages and clear out. Everytime I saw the foreman, fear shot right down to my balls. Finally we had a coffee break. We walked in groups to the canteen. The women were kept separated from the men, but plenty of "fucking" was shouted back and forth. I showed my card and got a cup of coffee. It was like hot colored water, but I drank it. Even though it tasted of dead pigs, at least it warmed me up inside. The tall guy who had sat next to me in the bus came toward my table with a cup of coffee and asked if he could sit down. I was glad of company and we started talking. How did I like this work? He guessed it was quite different from math and Latin. "Well, the work isn't too bad," I answered. "But the foreman is a real son of a bitch. He's been making things rough for me all morning." "Is it Donner?" he asked. I didn't know the foreman's name, but the others at the table joined in the conversation and figured out that it was indeed Donner. "Oh, well," they reassured me, "don't mind him. Donner's just a peasant prick. He gets kicked in the ass by someone else every week. Last year a temporary workman knocked the light out of his eye." They laughed at that. "If he riles you too much, just knock him down. You're a pretty solid boy. Just pick up a piece of iron and wrap it around his head. But make sure nobody sees you. We never see a thing!"

Feeling a lot more courageous, I left the canteen when the whistle blew and went back to work. There stood Donner, ostentatiously consulting his watch. I looked him over. He was quite a big obstacle to overcome. Were the workmen trying to put me on? Were they planning to watch, grinning, while I got chopped into mincemeat? That had happened to me once in a bar. Some drunk hoodlum had started making trouble with a few of the boys. We had a conference and decided that we'd all jump him at once. But when the signal was given, only one of us jumped—me. And I got a terrible beating. The guy knocked me senseless. I saw the blow coming and then felt myself losing consciousness. He got so scared when I passed out that he sobered up and took me to a hospital in a taxi. But Donner would never do that, I thought. "Hey you, student!" he yelled at me. "Come here. I have another job for you. Load up these pigs' heads!"

Together with a little old man—who looked like he should have retired long ago on Social Security—I had to stand on an outdoor loading platform and throw the pigs' heads, which came from the refrigerators in carts, into trucks.

The heads were heavy and ice-cold. And I was frozen from the cold weather besides. After handling four heads my hands had turned blue with cold. After ten minutes my fingers had become numb and I had to pick up the heads between the palms of my hands. All the while, Donner kept watching me, looking for trouble. The heads were like brown blocks of ice. On some, small icicles covered the lashes on eyes that were still open and staring. Some heads were just a mass of blood hardened to a dark red, while others didn't have a speck of blood on them. Some had a peaceful look in their eyes, as if they had accepted their fate. Others had their mouths open, their tongues caught on their sharp, hooked teeth. They had left the world drooling, with outrage blazing in their beady eyes.

The old man could hardly go on and neither could I. Our fingers were frozen. After every five heads we stopped for a moment, rubbing our hands to warm them up. When Donner saw this he started screaming and yelling like a madman. The old man was petrified and hurried back to work, but I continued to warm my hands, completely indifferent, and let the cocksucker bellow away. Actually I was just waiting for the right moment to attack him; it was going to be him or me. But I couldn't get my hands warm. They began to itch like hell, became as heavy as lead and stung from the cold with thousands of little pinpricks. I kept staring at the big clock on the main building. The hands just didn't seem to move! I had only been working five hours, yet it seemed like five weeks and I felt I had aged five years from the misery. In half an hour it would be lunchtime.

Suddenly a cold, slimy glob of muck hit my neck and trickled down my back. I froze. In the background I heard a chorus of loud laughter, with Donner's mocking guffaw rising about it all. I saw red. The soft muck slithered down the inside of my overalls and plopped onto the floor. It was a cow's embryo. I turned around to see Donner and a group of men still laughing at me. The red mist cleared from my eyes, but my legs were shaking with anger. My face contorted and I spit out, "Just watch out, you bastard, or I'll kick the shit out of your mother-fucking head."

His face stiffened. In a sinister voice he growled, "Go ahead and try, Jew-boy!" He planted himself sideways and suddenly I noticed the switchblade knife in his hand. The other men fell back. My rage vanished and all of a sudden I wanted to run, but that was impossible. I looked around frantically for a weapon and finally grabbed a long iron shovel from the truck. Donner moved back. The old man beside me tried to calm me down and I heard the men mutter: "Lay off, kid . . . watch out, boy, he'll kill you!" But I was past all reason. Donner looked around slyly for a way of escape, for now *he* was the hunted and I the hunter. And I meant business. All the men were shouting at us to knock it off. I lifted the shovel, ready to split Donner's fat head, when I saw, in a sudden flash, a nightmarish vision of police, beatings, prison cells and handcuffs. Donner was still backing away. I couldn't just drop the shovel or it would have been all over for me, so I pushed it fiercely into his chest. He tumbled backwards against a cart full of innards. The impact dislodged an enormous coil of guts, which slipped down from the slimy heap and dropped squarely on top of his head. I threw the shovel onto the ground with a bang that kept echoing in my ears as I ran like a madman. Behind me I heard Donner yell, "I'll kill him! I'll kill him! I'll cut him open! I'll kill him!"

I ran, terror-stricken, in and out of buildings, like a condemned beast that had escaped. Workers stared at me in amazement. In my hysteria, I was convinced that every murderous butcher in the place was chasing me with knives, hatchets, saws and daggers. I finally found the dressing room and hid under the wooden staircase for about fifteen minutes. Every time somebody passed, my pounding heart jumped into my throat. Would they find me? I was sure that if they did they'd kill me or, at the very least, mutilate me horribly. I heard the lunch whistle blast, and waited until I thought everyone would be at the canteen. Then I quickly lowered my clothes, tossed the company's overalls and boots into a corner and crammed the cap—with the company emblem on it—into my pocket as a souvenir. Then I washed my hands, combed my hair and walked towards the exit. I kept looking behind me, imagining that at any second Donner would jump me and dig his knife into my back. The gates were closed. I told the gatekeeper that I wanted to leave. No, I wasn't sick and I didn't want to see the company doctor. I took my time card and clocked out. The gatekeeper sent me to the office where I had been earlier that morning. The typists were chewing on their sandwiches and looked at me in surprise. I told them I wanted to leave and they asked if I couldn't come back after lunch. I lost my temper. "Where the hell is the bastard who sent me to the slaughterhouse this morning? I'm quitting and I want my wages. I've had enough of this goddamn joint!" The man in the white smock who had put me to work that morning appeared from the next room and told me to calm down. "Christ Almighty!" I yelled. "Is this work for a human being? Taking crap from a bunch of ex-Gestapo men and animal-torturers? I want my money, I'm cutting out. If you refuse to pay me I'll go to the police." He filled out a form for me, which entitled me to draw 7.25 guilders from the cashier. As I grabbed it from his hand, he said, "If you think that we're going to stand for this kind of behavior, young man, you have another think coming. We have always had good relations with the Student Employment Office, and I intend to report you to them at once." "Shove your report up your ass!" I shouted back. "As far as I'm concerned the whole goddam factory can go fuck itself, including you!" The typists gaped at me, their open mouths full of forgotten sandwiches. White-smock wagged his finger at me and pointed to my time card. "Do you know, young man, that if I make a note on this card you won't be allowed to work here again for six months or more?" That really broke me up! Laughing in his face, I tore up the card and threw the shreds at his feet. Stamping out, I went straight to the cashier's office and collected my money. An hour later I was back in town and feeling a lot better. It felt like I had been away for months.

For more than three weeks I kept smelling the slaughterhouse smell, the stench of dead bodies, on everything. My hands seemed tainted and no matter how I scrubbed my body, I couldn't get rid of that smell. For weeks I wouldn't touch meat in any form, and for years afterwards I wouldn't buy any products from that particular factory—their odor made me throw up. Just the smell of bacon frying made me ill. It took a long time to get rid of the smell, even though I washed ten times a day and took showers before going to bed and after getting up. For a while I was afraid that when I walked down the street people could smell it on me, that horrible scent of pigs, that sickening stench of death!

71

A knock on the door woke me. I didn't feel like getting up to open the door. "He's at home," I heard the jerk next door say. More knocks. I threw back the blankets and went to the door. "Hi, Sweetie-pie!" said Helen as she came in, bringing a cold blast of fresh air with her. "Long time no see," I replied, as I slipped back into bed, where it was nice and warm. "Want me to clean up the room?" she asked after she had already begun. That was fine with me—there was a week's accumulation of dirty dishes in the sink, clothes strewn on the floor and piles of old newspapers scattered about. I watched her work, enjoying the movement of her body under her sharp outfit. She could have had a string of millionaire playboys after her, if she'd been interested in anyone but me. She came over, sat down on the bed and bent over to stroke my face. I wasn't in the mood and jerked away. She sat upright, her face now serious. She hesitated for a moment, then blurted out, "I'm pregnant!" Silence. Oh Christ, I thought, isn't that a pisser? But I looked properly contrite and, patting her shoulder lightly, murmured, "Are you sure?" I pivoted out of bed, went to the sink and picked up two glasses. "You want a drink? Some rich cat layed a bottle on me last night." She shook her head and kept eyeing me seriously and sadly. I took a drink for myself but it had such a raw, harsh taste that I spit it right into the sink. I stood there, bent over, grasping the glass with both hands. "What do you want me to do? You know I haven't got the money for an abortion." I looked into the mirror. What a handsome cat I was! But I had to get out of this mess. The dirty bitch! She had left me a month ago because I abused her—a millionaire's daughter didn't have to put up with that kind of treatment. In a small, broken voice she whined, "But I don't want to get rid of the baby." She was crying, of course. "I love you," she implored. "You love me? Who gives a shit?" I said sharply. "You don't expect me to believe that *I'm* the father!" "Oh, how could you?" she

143

wailed, breaking into hysterical sobs. I sat down next to her, put my arm around her shoulder and tried to stop her crying. The walls were very thin and my neighbors very nosey: a real loser from the drama school lived in the next room and above me were people from the art academy. All of them thrived on gossip. As it was, I was the disgrace of the town. Hadn't I already walked out on one pregnant girl? I had made my bed, and now I should lie in it! I put on my last Billie Holiday record—I hadn't been able to pawn it with the others because it was so scratched. What stupid idiots women are! They all wanted me because I looked so artistic and romantic and could fuck like a dream. But fucking meant nothing to me. I found it very tiring. But as long as I had nothing else to do, or nothing else I could do, I was willing to accept their advances. It kept body and soul together. Besides, I liked to see the faces of all those studs when I bird-dogged their chicks from them. But I had to get rid of Helen.

"I never had anything to do with that Botlek, if that's what you're thinking," she said. "He was just a good friend."

"Yeah," I replied. "A friend in bed is a friend indeed!"

72

About that time I met a new chick—Mathilde. I saw her for the first time in the all-night automat. She smiled at me and I smiled back. We went to my room and she stayed a few weeks. Mathilde wanted to be a poet. She worked as a cub reporter at the local newspaper, a bit of luck for me, because she regularly brought home blank newsprint (on which I drew nude studies—my God, what tits Mathilde had!), pencils, ball-point pens, erasers and the final edition of the paper. And she had a red Vespa. I was able to ride it all day long because, on my advice, Mathilde had switched from the city desk to the foreign desk. Now she could cozy up to the teletype all day rather than hustle her ass around on the scooter to cover crummy local fires and accidents.

The local countryside was fantastic. Pine forests alive with ants, beetles and mice creeping silently over the moss-and-needle-covered floor. Breathtaking sunsets (nobody really knows how beautiful they can be). And the perfume! It always made me think of the bath salts that bartender's wife used. What was her name again?

During this period I was really up tight for bread. At around six o'clock every night I'd fall by the home of some friends or acquaintances, just as they were about to eat. I'd let them coax me into joining them. (I was actually famished and grew faint when the dish of steaming hot spuds was brought to the table. But I couldn't appear too eager or they might think I'd come only for the grub.) Then I'd borrow a guilder and go to the all-night bar. The guilder wouldn't cover more than the first drink, but I always managed to get loaded on the proceeds from craps and poker games. Mine host's wife (what the hell was her name?) let me win because she had the hots for me. If she served me a glass of beer with two coasters under it, it meant that I could come to see her at home the next afternoon at 3. Then, if there was a pot of geraniums in her window, the coast was clear and I could go upstairs. She always "just happened" to be in her bath when I got there. I had to scrub her back—"Harder, harder!" she'd groan and try to entice me into the bath with her. But not me! The bath was heated electrically and I wouldn't have been the first to be dragged from a tub all purple and stiff because of a short circuit. She had a wild pair of knockers! When she undid her bra the pink meat streamed down practically to her navel and her nipples glowed a fiery red. All the blood flowed into them, turning them into burning volcanoes.

Her husband loved gardening and usually spent a couple of hours at it every afternoon. He lavished great care on his beans, rhubarb, cucumbers, cabbage and flowers. In the warm, pink female flesh that smelled of pine needles and rum, I always felt like I was burrowing in his garden! What a woman! She reminded me of Betty, the neighbor from the old days, so nice and warm. It was what I needed —a safe haven. Or was it safe? I was OK as long as I watched the coasters and the geraniums.

One afternoon, when it was raining, I ran straight upstairs without looking at the window. The bartender was relaxing in his easy chair and his wife was reading a magazine. They looked up at me in surprise and I barely had time to think up an excuse. "Hello," I stammered, "I wanted to ask you when I could paint your portrait." The bartender had mentioned this to me once, but I had told him that I only painted abstracts. I was offered a cup of coffee and he preened himself, obviously flattered. Every afternoon that week he posed in my studio on his big fat ass, so I couldn't visit his wife. How I painted! I sweated blood and tears to get his ugly puss onto the canvas. He had promised me twenty-five guilders and two weeks of drinks on the house if he liked it. He went wild over it when it was finished and hung it in the bar. The next time I visited my volcanic piece of pussy, she stroked my hair, bit my ear, played with my "howitzer" and took time out to say, "You

145

almost ruined everything last week! Didn't you notice that I had put a cactus in the window?"

Mathilde and I had screaming rows all the time. She kept getting at me with her poems. *"A nervous apparition, how hungrily he stalks me! Piercing my pale flesh, groaning in his orgasm."* Bullshit! Besides, I didn't like the books she gave me. She wanted me to read Freud, Nietzsche and Kant. Very interesting, I was told, but they didn't groove me. Nor did I dig the music of Stravinsky and Beethoven—unless it was very loud. But we couldn't play it loud because her radio would have blown up. If I was busy painting I'd yell at her to take her Screwitsky and her poetry and go jump in the lake. She'd get mad and start throwing things. Of course, I'd throw them right back. She carried on like a mad-woman when I threw her radio out of the window—I had to take refuge at the bar. One night I came home late and found that she had disappeared with all her things, van-ished into the night on her Vespa. I was sorry about it be-cause she was really a great chick. I'm just not easy to live with. I learned later that she married a huckster and lived happily ever after helping him write advertising copy for cocoa, bathing suits and invisible plastic bandages.

Meanwhile, Annabel was sitting in her garret brooding on her sins. I felt sorry for her and often went to see her. She was very sweet and I always planned to be very attentive and stay on with her. But it never worked. After five min-utes we'd be screaming at each other and throwing things. Then the neighbors would call the police and I'd have to run for it, with Annabel screaming and cursing after me. The landlay would spit "savage" at me as I shot through the door.

I was strictly bad news—friends avoided me and girls spit on the ground in front of me. This turned me on, and I laughed in their faces. One time, Lia—a friend of Annabel's —got so upset when she passed me in the street that she slapped my face. I just laughed. Later in the afternoon I was lying on my bed, listening to Nat King Cole and thinking about that slap. There was a knock on the door and in walked Lia. She apologized and had a good cry. Then I took her to the station so she could catch her train. For a few weeks after that she dropped in twice a day, at lunch-time and again after 4 o'clock, bringing little pans of food for me. She also mended my clothes, took my washing home and treated me to the flicks.

Suddenly, she didn't show up any more and I missed her. I hung around the academy and soon caught sight of her walking with Annabel—Annabel with the protruding belly.

When they saw me, Lia quickly turned her head away and Annabel shot me a searching look. They walked past me with their noses in the air, like I was a leper on the make. I must admit that really shook me up! Dames! I'll never understand them!

73

Winter came and I nearly froze to death. I had rented an attic right near the railroad tracks after reading in some book that Vincent van Gogh had lived next to a railroad for a while. The house, a cold and bare ruin, smelled of turnips, rancid cooking fat, stale piss and sweat. The floorboards were loose and rattled whenever a train thundered by—just ten yards away. The windows had rusty hinges and there were big holes in the roof. I ripped advertising posters from billboards at night and used them to insulate the walls. It kept some of the cold out, but not enough.

Every morning I had to shake frost and snow from my blankets before I could get out of bed. I slept on a mattress on the floor in all my clothes, including a heavy loden coat. Day and night I kept the stove going. I tore the lead from the roofs of houses in the neighborhood and sold it to buy coal and food. I kept on painting, with gloves on my hands and newspapers stuffed inside my coat. The romantic life of the True Artist! Shivering with cold, dying from hunger, I would produce Real Art. On one of the walls I wrote, *"Art is hunger!"* and *"Faster, faster. The faster the better!"*

I lived rent-free. All I had to do was mind the landlady's two kids every morning while she was at work. She woke me at 8 A.M. When I got downstairs, the stove would already be lit. As soon as she had left I'd fall asleep from the heat and lie dead to the world until the baby's screaming woke me up. I always forgot to give him his bottle. But I finally found an answer. I gave him a handkerchief with a corner dipped in gin. I also managed to get rid of the little four-year-old girl. She'd keep pestering me to draw ships and parrots for her, so I'd stand in front of the window and suddenly shout, "Look, here comes your Mommy!" Then she'd rush downstairs and sit on the steps for hours until her old lady came home. It was the only way I could get a little peace. When the attic wasn't too cold I took the baby upstairs and put him in a straw basket hung from a nail. He cooed with pleasure when I rocked the basket. And I could do some work.

Then I became an extra with a touring theater group. I

played the role of a servant in *The Prince and the Showgirl* and earned about five guilders a day—just enough to buy food and cheap paints. I did seventy-six performances altogether and had a ball.

Every week I was called to the manager's office because of my long hair. He'd bawl me out and give me a guilder to pay for a haircut. I was the despair of the makeup man because my own hair stuck out from under the nineteenth-century wig and he was constantly in hot water over it. But I wouldn't cut my hair. Nobody would be able to see that I was an artist! I reminded them of what happened to Samson after they clipped *his* curls.

One time, when the star of the show condescended to speak to me, her charming voice snapped, "Young man, your fingernails are disgusting! Why don't you clean them? Don't you ever wash?" Usually the Great Actress swept past me with her nose in the air and sat as far away from me as possible on the bus. She kept complaining to the manager that I handled her too roughly on stage—at the end of the third act, instead of picking her up tenderly from the floor onto which she had fainted, I used to walk on, grab her roughly under the armpits, throw her on my back and carry her offstage, where I let her drop onto the boards. She'd stamp off in a rage. I told the manager, "You know, Sir, a lackey is human too." Now that she'd had the nerve to talk to me about my fingernails, I decided I was being picked on, for washing and brushing my teeth are two things I do regularly and often. When I was a child, "Cleanliness is next to Godliness" was drilled into me.

"I beg your pardon, Madam," I said in my sweetest voice, "but my hobby is painting. I am working with so-called heavy materials, and it is possible that a few scraps may have remained under my nails." (I really was using pitch, rust and tar on one of my canvases at that time and I didn't feel like cleaning my hands for hours just for a brief appearance on stage.) "If you'd prefer to be picked up by someone with clean fingernails, go tell the manager."

To that she replied theatrically, "Bah! Did you know, young man, that my husband is a famous graphic artist? His hands are in black ink all day, but he always looks perfectly groomed. There's never a spot on his hands!"

"Excuse me again, dear lady," I replied, "Your 'famous graphic artist' husband may have clean hands, but as an artist—and I do a great disservice to that most noble of professions by applying the term to him—he is, to put it kindly, a rank amateur. As far as I am concerned, he is nowhere!"

That took care of her. She would have liked to snap back, but the curtain was rising and she had to swallow it. She ran onstage laughing and exclaiming, "Isn't it a wonderful day?" But she didn't get over our chat so easily. For her next line she said, "Hello, Fritz, how are you today?" instead of "Good morning, my dear Marshal." The other actors had heard the whole thing, and they grinned and winked at me. But not to her face! I heard later that they all told her how they agreed with her and how shocked they were at my rudeness. Actors!

But I did pull a few good stunts. One time, in the scene where I was left on stage alone for a moment, I disconnected the telephone wires in full view of the audience. Later in the scene, after the Marshal had been chattering away for about five minutes on the phone, I strode onstage with a satchel, saying, "Excuse me, Marshal, Your Excellency, I've come to repair the telephone!" The audience was in stitches—and so was the Marshal. That's what they call "hamming." Another time I managed to arrange it so that the majordomo walked onstage at the wrong time. He had been so tired, poor cat, that he went off to snore in a chair behind the backdrop. "Will you call me in time for my cue?" he asked me. I woke him suddenly with a violent shove and said, "You're on, quick!" So he flew onstage and spouted his piece, very beautifully too, only right out of context, three scenes too early. Every prank was fun in that business. Once I stood backstage and held the palace doors firmly shut at the precise moment when the Marshal was supposed to make a hurried exit in high dudgeon. On that occasion his anger, strictly rhetorical at first, soon turned into the real thing. He pounded so hard he brought down the whole set—a palace with the Thames visible through the windows. I was fired on the spot. Oh well, the gig was a gas as long as it lasted! Funny cats, those actors. They're always ready for a lark, but as soon as the manager comes on the scene, they tell you, "I knew it wouldn't work!" But what the hell! . . . At least I saw a lot of Holland— we played a different town every day. So I was able to drop in on all the chicks I knew from one end of the country to the other. I'd send them a postcard a few days in advance: "Get a ticket for the show, so you can catch my performance!" Of course, they always came and sat right up front!

When the show went north we got a maintenance allowance, but I slept in the bus and drank up the money. No bills, no worries, what a ball! I knew a swinger of a chick up north—Joyce. She lived in an industrial town and her parents were loaded. While I was at sea she used to enclose pressed violets in her long letters. She wrote, "When I'm twenty-one, we're going to live in a Montmartre garret. I'll cook for you and write poetry, and you can paint. Oh, I love you!" How romantic! Great!

After the performance in her town, she was waiting for me at the stage door. "You were terriffic!" she said, obviously enraptured. She told me her parents had invited me to supper the following day, and I accepted. They lived in a very expensive mansion, with acres of picture windows, like an aquarium. They had everything, all the comforts: television, hi-fi system, pop-up toaster, carpets like lawns, antique clocks, a guesthouse, transistor radios and American cigarettes in a silver box perched on the coffee table with a matching lighter. What luxury! I was almost afraid to sit down in their plush easy chairs or tread on their wall-to-wall carpets—like I might have tracked in some dog shit on my shoes. Every time her parents asked me something, I stammered and stuttered in reply. At the table I dropped my toast, my knife clattered onto my plate and I spilled a gob of sticky jam onto my lap. I remember her mother was very nice and went out of her way to be relaxed and friendly with me, but her father was a real bluenose. "From what sewer," I could hear him thinking, "did Joyce dredge this creature up?" Anyway, after watching television for a while, I was encouraged to split, because it was time for Joyce to hit the sack. She wished me luck.

Sweet shit on a pogo stick! I was overjoyed to get out into the street again, even though it was raining. It was like I had been holding my breath for two hours. What a relief! But what a disappointment—I had at least thought they'd invite me to sleep over in the guesthouse. Now I'd have to hitchhike over one hundred miles by morning, in the rain. The tour bus had left early in the afternoon and I had no money for a hotel. All that night I cursed chicks with rich fathers. I was hungry and tired and my nose was dripping up a storm by the time I finally reached my destination at daybreak. I had gotten rides from four queers, two moving vans and a truck carrying sacks of flour. Because I was soaked, the flour stuck to my clothes and gummed up my hair. Who said life can be beautiful? Bullshit! Workers of the world unite! Down with the capitalists! Down with rich girl friends!

74

Late one evening, after a wild ride with a drunk woman, I arrived in a Belgian village. I had had to get out of Paris fast, and I got good lifts as far as Mons. My next ride was with a couple of Algerians in an old Ford. I couldn't understand a word they said. They were going as far as Brussels, but right in the middle of the Belgian countryside they pulled off the road and had a row that seemed to concern me. They kept looking at me. Maybe they wanted to work me over. Finally I had to get out. And there I was. If I had known the ride would end this way, I would have spent the night in Mons! There were plenty of lonely broads there.

It was beginning to get dark, and there wasn't a village or even a house in sight. This was the countryside of Vlaminck, very beautiful and very flat, but I would rather have been in a nice, cozy bar with a pint of beer in front of me and a friendly piece of tail at my side.

Although I was standing on the main Paris-Brussels road, the traffic was pretty light, mostly trucks that wouldn't stop. So there was nothing to do but enjoy the beauties of nature for a while. Thinking over my quick exit from Paris, I wondered if anyone had gotten suspicious yet. Had they warned Interpol? No, it was still too early for that. The countryside was purplish under the twilight sky and smelled of freshly ground corn and cow dung. I thumbed all the cars that passed, but every one of them shot past me. Suddenly a huge battered Chevrolet pulled over. At last, what luck! I climbed in and immediately smelled booze. Behind the wheel was a small, dark woman who was mumbling to herself about something or other. She was loaded to the gills. I still don't know how I got out of that jalopy in one piece; one minute she'd be driving at over seventy miles an hour and the next she'd slam down the brakes and start cruising at about ten. Meanwhile we had passed through a few towns and it had become completely dark. Every time we passed a house I caught a whiff of freshly baked bread. In one village there was a trolley line running along the middle of the road. At a bend in the road we saw a trolley rushing toward us from the opposite direction while a line of heavy trucks was bearing down on us from behind. Little Miss Lushhead lost all control. Luckily she just managed to miss the trolley (for hours my head still reverberated with the clang of its bells and the scream of the trucks' horns) by passing it on the wrong side. Before I could do anything, the car was up on the sidewalk, careening toward a brick wall. On the wall was a poster of a smiling chick in a leopard skin, the word "Belga" printed across her torso. She had long red hair and was seductively smoking a cigarette. When the car had stopped, we found ourselves looking through the windshield at the radiator, which was jammed into Belga's midriff. We were stunned but unhurt. A small crowd of pipe-smoking villagers who had been hanging around in front of a bar ambled over to us. They seemed to know little Miss Lushhead—they talked to her like old friends and gently helped her out of the car. I climbed out under my own steam and helped the men lead my drunk driver to the bar, where they all disappeared. I continued on my way.

As if things weren't bad enough, it began to rain. After walking for about an hour, without getting a single lift, I arrived at the next village. *"Welcome to Soignies,"* proclaimed a sign next to a gas station. It was still pouring. What miserable weather! My blue jeans and leather jacket were soaked through. I had nothing to change into in my overnight bag because it was summer and I was travelling light. The village seemed deserted. All the shutters were closed, there were no lights, and no one in the street except nuns and dogs. I had no money, no smokes, no bed, and I was hungry and dead beat. I had started out from Paris at 5 o'clock that morning in a bakery van, hoping to get to Amsterdam, or at least into Holland, the same day. But now that would take a miracle—and I don't believe in miracles or want any part of them. I'm enough of a miracle myself!

Occasionally someone passed by walking a dog. What could I ask for, a cheap hotel? I didn't have a penny on me. A place to sleep? They'd refer me to the fuzz, and I wasn't anxious to mess with them. A smart-looking chick came out of one of the houses on the other side of the cobbled street and walked busily away. I followed her for a while to the rhythm of her clacking heels, then overtook and stopped her. "Excuse me," I said, "do you know of any cheap hotels around?" That was a good con—of course there wouldn't be any cheap hotels in a town like this, only expensive ones. So I'd play it cool and try to find out if she knew of any other place to sleep, with friends perhaps (meaning of course at her place). I could always tell her that I was only a poor medical student—that line usually went over, and it might work again. The girl licked her lips, deep in thought, and then pointed out two hotels—the only two in town. She really was a saucy-looking piece. "Which is cheaper?" I asked. Both were expensive, and probably full up besides. I asked about student hostels. There weren't any. The ploy had to succeed. Hadn't I worked it a dozen times before, always successfully? In Genoa, Rome, Nice, Metz (what a doll she was!), Luxembourg, Pisa, Lyons and God knows where else. She thought some more. She was really trying to help me, but didn't seem to be getting anywhere. I mentioned the fact that I was an actor and had made a tour of Europe . . . my luggage and all my money had been stolen in Paris, that wicked city . . . the embassy, of course, had refused to help me and I was forced to thumb my way home. She was quite impressed. No, she didn't have any friends who could put me up and her place was out of the question But there *was* a convent. It was only a little way down the road and she was certain I could sleep there if I told them I was a Catholic and explained my difficulties. She told me how to get there and I thanked her. It was a shame that I wouldn't be staying in the village long enough to knock her off.

The convent was really there, a large, cold-looking building with two high towers. It was 10 P.M. If only they weren't all in bed! There were no lights anywhere, but it was my only chance to find a bed so I rang the bell. It resounded hollowly behind the massive door. I heard footsteps and finally the door was opened by a nun holding a candle.

"C'est possible, vous avez une place pour dormir?" I asked politely. She inspected me by the light of her candle. Oh God, what if their rules were a hang-up and they wouldn't let me in? I was tired and hungry and just wanted to sleep! "Come in," she said, "I'll have to ask the Mother Superior." And she disappeared, leaving me in a pitch-black, chilly corridor that smelled of pea soup, candles, priests and cheap incense. The high-pitched voices of a choir echoed in the distance. The nun returned with her candle and the Mother Superior. She was very friendly. I told her my story and she said I could sleep there. Had I eaten? She clapped her hands and a little old man, Pierre-the-hunchback, trotted up and took me to the kitchens in the cellar. I was grateful to God for providing me with a place to sleep, but I decided to be watchful all the same. After all, I was surrounded by Catholics . . . and what if the hunchback cut off my head, while I slept, so the nuns could make soup out of me?

Catholics! Years later the mother of a Catholic girl I was engaged to got very upset over my behavior at mass and screamed at me, "Who do you think you are, you dirty heathen? Making a mockery of holy mass! Yelling 'coffee' during consecration! And calling the priest a fairy! You've put our family to shame! You dirty parasite! You don't mind sleeping in a convent when you can't find anything else! For that we were good enough! Parasite! Communist! . . ."

75

The hunchback was a nice little guy. He fried two eggs for
me and gave me a large plate full of brown bread, cheese and
sausage. While I was eating he talked about himself and guzzled a few bottles of beer. He was the janitor and odd-jobman
and not even Catholic. He told me in Flemish that he had
made the beer himself. I finished off two large bottles, one
after the other. It was really good stuff. I stayed in the
kitchen for at least half an hour. The hunchback fried two
more eggs for me and, when I'd finished them, said he'd take
me to my bed. I had thought I'd have to sleep in a cell at
the convent, but he said I'd be sleeping in another building, a
hospital across the street. Well, any bed was OK with me.
Pierre-the-hunchback said something about "a bloody mess"
and insisted that I take along three more bottles of his sweet,
convent-made beer in my overnight bag. Then, carrying an
old-fashioned lantern, he took me across the street. A faint
glow came through the windows of the wooden building.
Everything smelled of ether. Pierre quickly explained to me
that it was a hospital for seriously injured people, handed
me over to a nun, wished me good-night and disappeared.
The entire building was in semidarkness and reeked of
sickness. The night sister led me along a dim corridor to a
large ward.

76

It was a terrible situation, but I was stuck with it. I had to
stay. Badly mutilated men lay on all the beds and most of
them were attached to blood-transfusion bottles. The air
was full of screams and groans. Some of the men twisted
about in their beds, others sat up and stared at me. A few
held out their hands and forced their faces into a smile. What
a horrible scene! And the stench! Gangrene, ether, blood and
urine. My bed was in the middle of a long row. On one side
of me was an unconscious old duffer and on the other a dark-
haired young man who had no legs—the sheets lay flat up to
his knees. I undressed, and got into bed. It was still warm!
I broke out in a cold sweat, wondering how long ago someone
had kicked the bucket in this same sack. I tried to cheer
myself up but it was impossible because of the screaming
and groaning going on. Nuns kept going past with bedpans
and bottles of blood, whispering to each other. Perhaps they
were talking about me. Were they going to do away with me
as soon as I had fallen asleep? But weren't they Catholics? If

they were found out there'd be a hell of a lot of trouble with the pope!

I started counting sheep. At 573 I heard *shushing* sounds and turned around. Legless wanted to chat. He asked where I was from and I said Istanbul—Paris would have sounded so uninteresting. He wanted to know if I had any smokes with me, but I hadn't. The way we were whispering it felt like I was back in one of those awful homes. Suddenly a priest in full regalia entered the ward, followed by a robed choirboy carrying a pot of incense or something—whatever it was, it stank. A few of the patients began to retch and cough. I thought the priest was coming for me, but he went to a bed opposite where, according to the guy in the next bed, an old man was kicking the bucket. Last rites were given. For a while there was silence in all the beds while the priest mumbled on. I didn't want to watch, but after a while I couldn't help it. How else do you find out about things? Legless was very fidgety. If it was up to him, he muttered, he'd kick the priest out! He wanted me to tell him how things were on the outside. He'd been in the hospital for months now, since he'd been in a terrible accident just up the road. I couldn't tell him very much because one minute someone would throw up and the next minute we'd be interrupted by groans. Later, in the middle of the night, I suddenly awoke to see one of the patients flipping his lid. His body stiffened, he foamed at the mouth, rolled, yelled and tried to get out of bed. Nurses came running and had to hold the old man down by force. I kept waking up every half hour, for there was always something happening.

I was in the critical ward, which was filled with people who hadn't died yet but were too ill to be moved. Just outside the village was one of the most dangerous crossroads in Belgium. There were accidents almost daily and the few victims who were still alive landed in this hospital, which was run by nuns from the convent.

After the priest and the nuns had left, some of the men on the other side of the ward started calling out to me. Things livened up a bit. I entertained them with a few tall stories about bandits in Spain, pirates in the Indian Ocean and white slavers in Marseilles. Then I told them all the latest jokes and they came up with a few too, some very funny ones. Every one of their jokes was about people without legs, arms, ears, eyes, etc. After a while I couldn't stand it any longer. I wanted to sleep and not be awakened all the time, but the patients wouldn't let me. Finally, I took a bottle of beer from the bag under my bed. I gulped the whole bottle down at once, hoping to get loaded and sleepy. But they all wanted a slug and Legless slurped down most of the second bottle as if he had been lost in the Sahara for years. I got out of bed and took the rest of the bottle to a few old men on the other side who were begging for a drop. Then I began to get drowsy.

77

Later on that night Legless started yelling and shouting like a madman. The nurse came running with a needle and a wad of cotton. His legs had just been amputated and the alcohol in the beer had caused them to bleed. The sheets were dark red with blood. It was like a huge red blot on a blotter, a blot that kept spreading.

78

By the time the beer ran out the atmosphere was really gay. Legless talked Flemish to the old men, who were also high. They laughed about everything and about nothing. They started playing tag. A few of the old men got out of bed and chased each other around the ward in their nightshirts. When they tapped someone's shoulder he would be "it." It was a funny sight—all those little men, without hands and heavily bandaged, hobbling and stumbling around the room. They had a ball. I laughed a lot too and this pleased them. After all, I was their guest from Istanbul. Legless explained the game to me and asked me if I wanted to join them!

There was one little man, Jules, whose head was all bandaged up and who kept bumping into everything—to everyone's joy. There was another man without legs, who sailed under and through everything, looking like an orangutan—nobody could catch him! He slid under my bed, joking that it was much easier that way. I was astonished to see how well these men accepted their fate. I laughed a lot that night. Jules sneaked into the next ward, the eczema ward, to tell them about the "Dutchman from Istanbul." They too put on a show. Legless told me to watch the door and soon, in the flickering light, four white shapes appeared. They were shrouded in sheets and their hands and faces were covered with yellowish ointment. They were supposed to be ghosts and stood in front of my bed wriggling and wailing. Wanting to frighten me, the four bent over my bed so that I could smell the revolting eczema ointment. I forced myself to laugh. When the nurse—alerted by the shouts of "boooooh"—came rushing in, the ghosts fled back to their ward. What a time we had! God almighty, what a gas!

I finally fell asleep, but was awakened again and again by dying and screaming patients. Early in the morning, at sunrise, I got out of bed, washed at the basin and tried to disappear as quietly as possible. I had hoped that everyone would be asleep, but the entire ward was wide awake. They gaped at me and asked why I was leaving so soon. Didn't I want to stay for breakfast? I said that I really had to go but would come back to see them soon. Right at that moment I felt pretty shitty, in spite of the night's high jinks. It was awful to have to leave those poor people behind and I felt ashamed that I had invaded their ward, healthy and with all my limbs intact. I felt an indescribable pity for them. Legless asked me to come and see him if I was in the neighborhood again. He probably hadn't slept a wink all night but, with clean sheets on his bed, he looked quite fresh. I shook hands with everybody, going from bed to bed to say a few words or pat a shoulder. Then I took off.

The sun was in the sky, the earth was steaming and smelled wonderful. It was not quite 7 A.M.

Why don't they give an injection—or something to end it all—to people marked with death? Why don't they bring in beautiful whores and throw them a farewell party? They're suffering for nothing and nobody. They have to die, anyway, and soon. So why not make their last days pleasant for them?

I raised my thumb and the first car I saw stopped. The day was still young and it had started right. And I was going home!

IQ 133 ATTENTION!

79

The Foundation assigns me a new supervising guardian, the principal of a parochial school. I hope he'll be OK and not bug me too much. One evening I'm supposed to report to him at 7 P.M., but I'm ten minutes late. The man who opens the door immediately starts chewing me out. How dare I be late? He's a very rude man with stiff white hair and a face you could crack rocks on. He speaks with some kind of northern accent and is so reserved that I doubt he knows how to smile. But he'll force me onto the straight and narrow! What do I want to be? A painter or a writer? Not a chance! When I become an adult I can choose an artistic career if I still want to, but until then he'll tell me what to do. I'm too shocked to protest, and besides, what good would it do? We just don't communicate. He sits behind his desk like a grand duke, surrounded by books on penal law. He's just like a character out of Charles Dickens. I've read all of Dickens' books in the prison library. Also Jules Verne, Karl May, history books, a world atlas and The Bible—Old and New Testaments. The Bible was the most interesting of all. There was almost nothing left of it, though, because everybody kept tearing out pages to roll smokes with smuggled tobacco.

The supervising guardian's wife brings in a cup of tea for her husband. Nothing for me. She shakes hands with me like I had shit on my fingers and then disappears again. It's as if I'm an animal. After hours of talking to and fro (more fro than to for I'm not allowed to reply to anything) the old prick shuts me up as though I'm in his classroom and tells me I'll have to get a job. I don't know what kind of work to look for, because I don't know anything. He says, "You should join the navy. There you'll become an enterprising and lively lad. You won't have the chance to pull any tricks. They know how to deal with boys like you!" I tell him that I have no desire whatsoever to join the navy, that I want a creative job, perhaps as a commercial artist or a potter. Then I'd show everybody that I was really fit for an art academy. My former guardian, Ruggers, had told me that if any authority on the arts told him I had talent, he would not stand in my way. If I could prove that I had talent he'd see to it that I got a chance to develop it. So I had hoped that this new bastard would be willing to help me, but he was obviously anti-Jan Cremer. He kept insisting that I join the navy but I kept saying no. He became irritated. If I wouldn't even consider the possibility of enlisting, he'd change my mind for me. Telephone in hand, he said. "Now listen to me, you pigheaded snot-nose! All I have to do is make one call to the police station and they'll pick you right up. Then you can think it over all night long. And if you're still stubborn in the morning I'll see to it that by tomorrow evening you're back in the correction home. And you know what that's like, don't you?" He got my wind up, all right! Was he just bluffing, or would he really call the police? I retreated. What could I do? I could see Ruggers' face in front of me, saying reproachfully, "You are a difficult boy, Jan. Why can't you ever cooperate with the people who have your best interests at heart?" Longingly I looked outside and finally asked, very meekly, "Could I think about it at home, Sir?" Yes, that would be all right. But within three days, at the most, he wanted to hear my decision. If my answer was yes, he'd see to it that I was examined at once and sent to an induction center. He had already sent four or five boys like me to the navy and every one of them had been happy in the service. He told me how great it was in the navy, how I would find myself there, and finally learn a trade. It would be better for me to forget all about my artistic inclinations. He hoped I'd see the light soon. I left. When I heard the garden gate shut behind me I stopped for a moment and turned around. Then I rang the bell again. When he opened the door I said, "Sir, I've made up my mind. I want to join the navy!"

And so, two days later, I was examined at a navy hospital. The next day I boarded the train, with a free ticket, for the induction center. Within an hour and a half I had converted from an anti-militarist to an enthusiastic navy recruit, thanks to my worthy Christian guardian who had forced me to choose between a return to life in chains at a home and "voluntary" naval service. I chose the latter. My mother was pleased, and so was Ruggers. Finally someone had been found who could do something with me! Long live the Rehabilitation Office! Three rousing cheers!

Twice a week in jails, correction homes, military camps and other government institutions, they serve, by Ministerial Decree, *nasi-* or *bami-goreng* as a gesture towards our Brown Brothers. It looks and tastes like dog food and is made with raw acorns (*"Those are peanuts, buddy!"*) and lumpy rice. The *sambal* shakes like a pot of red jellied soup (*"What's wrong with a couple of thousand worms, maggots and eels!"*). "If you're hungry enough, you'll eat it! In our time they didn't serve such exotic foods. It was half-raw potatoes and mashed turnips. And if we didn't like it we could lump it!"

80

When I arrived at the training center, late in the afternoon, the sun was setting and casting its last rays on the houses alongside the trolley tracks, bathing them in a reddish yellow glow. In front of a gate with a large golden anchor stood two sentries, rifles over their shoulders. I fished papers from my inside pocket and was allowed to enter. I had to sit on a hard wooden bench in a wooden shack. An officer entered, sniffed eloquently and looked at me condescendingly. While he was inspecting my papers, a girl in uniform came running in with a file. "At what time were you ordered to report?" asked the officer. I wondered what his rank was. He had a few silver stripes on his sleeve. I should have looked at the instruction book more carefully "At 10 A.M., Sir!" "Right," he said, "and it's 5 P.M. now! The offices are closed. Not only that, but we don't accept recruits who arrive drunk! You can try again tomorrow!" Crazy, I thought, I'll go right back into town. But the officer rang a bell and two MPs entered. "Take this recruit to the brig," he commanded, looking at me coldly. Surprise written all over my face, I started to protest. . . . "Shut up and snap to attention!" he shouted. I was marched off between the MPs and spent the night in an underground cell, a screw standing guard in front of the bars. My first night, and already I was on bread and water! And I *wasn't* drunk! They sure were hot to teach me discipline. What a crock of shit!

For three months I was at boot camp. I learned to handle carbines, Sten guns, pistols, machine guns, hand grenades, daggers, bayonets, bullets and all kinds of new automatic weapons; to dig foxholes, crawl under barbed wire, wiggle through muddy trenches, salute, shit in the latrine (two rows of holes in a bare cement floor) with a dozen other recruits and not give a damn about the lack of privacy, and jump across high-voltage wires; to shave, wash and comb, make my bed, change my uniform and gulp my rations, each in three minutes flat; to run on the double carrying a one-hundred-pound pack, jump off backwards from a truck driving at forty-five miles an hour, memorize ranks and salutes, strangle a man with my bare hands, march in step, stand at attention (but no heel-clicking, for we weren't Krauts) and fight with sabers; to take poison if I fell into enemy hands, morphine or belladonna if wounded, shots against nerve gas, shots against torture, shots against pox, scurvy, typhus and syphilis; to down fifty-six beers in one hour, dive with oxygen tanks to pick magnets from a ship's bottom, shoot bottles off a pole; how to act when an atomic bomb, hydrogen bomb, gas bomb, phosphorus bomb or nitroglycerin bomb is dropped; karate, judo and jujitsu holds: strangle hold, leg hold, hip hold and shoulder hold; how to cut throats, gouge out eyes, smash noses, combat mosquitoes, kill without making a sound, dig a field latrine, rig a tent, sabotage a motor vehicle, throw a shiv into someone's back from a distance of fifty feet, fell trees, prepare a hangman's noose and so on and so on.

81

After three months I made the grade: third-class marine. *Attention!* I had become a full-fledged member of the elite, the Marine Corps. I was now a seagoing soldier, ready for landing operations and for police and guard duty on land, on sea and in the air. We were responsible for the maintenance of Peace and Order and, in case of war, we'd be the first ones to be sent into enemy territory. From landing craft we'd occupy the beaches, shoot down the enemy, burn down forests, throw grenades into houses and organize an orderly evacuation of the civilian population. Some profession! But at least I had qualified for something! And who wouldn't be proud to serve with such an elite group? Boy, were we elite—we drank our tea with pinkies in the air!

Because I could throw grenades farthest and fastest, never got tired, excelled at calisthenics, didn't have nude pin-ups over my bunk, hadn't caught the clap yet, was good at climbing poles, broad jumping and racing, and always politely said, "Yes, Sergeant," I was chosen, together with three others from the battalion, for the Naval Intelligence Service. My

IQ was 133. Before the assignment became definite, I had to go through weeks of tests and trials. I sat in a pitch-dark room for seven hours without uttering a word or a sigh; large microphones were installed in the room and officers in the next room listened carefully. I had to stand at attention and not even shift my feet while an officer held a burning cigar in front of my eyes or placed a razor-sharp dagger against my throat. I had to talk to an officer—small talk—but had been warned beforehand of one word I was not to mention, like "yes" or "night." What a ball-breaker: you really have to pay attention to what you say. If you stop concentrating for one second, you're lost. After going through another series of shots and vaccinations, I was appointed on a trial basis for training as an agent of the Naval Intelligence Service. *"Semper Fidelis!"*

"The aim of the Naval Intelligence Service is to obtain information about the enemy, the terrain, the expected weather or other conditions, in order to provide the military commander with a basis for the deployment of his troops. This service uses the facilities of the regular troops for reconnaissance, radio receiving and surveying. The Intelligence Service is responsible for the interrogation of prisoners of war, deserters and resident civilians, the interception of radio, telephone and telegraph messages, the investigation of confiscated documents, the gathering of data from newspapers and other publications and the deciphering of codes. This branch will be afforded all possible privileges and otherwise assisted in the execution of its functions. In time of war, the Naval Intelligence Service will devote itself to espionage and counter-espionage as well as sabotage."

82

I liked it. It became a kind of game, and I did have all sorts of privileges. I was transferred from the barracks sleeping 260 men to a wooden hut with 6 beds. The food was better —we ate steak or sausage every day. We got more rest—sometimes we even slept during the day, lying in the sack and then falling to for ham-and-egg sandwiches. It was like a crossword puzzle and I knew the answers to the most difficult questions. Among the regular troops I wouldn't have been allowed to open my mouth, but here I could ask or say anything. The officers were intelligent people, mostly young men with cadet training. It took five years to become a noncom, but I wasn't going to be in that long, that much I knew. The chow was good, I had everything I needed and the war was already ten years past. I regarded my Intelligence Service training as a matter of prestige. Most of the others had college degrees, but I had never even finished the first year of high school. If I hadn't made the I.S., I would have had to become a specialist—a radio operator, a navigator or a driver —or I would have had to go on submarine service: in other words, learn, work and sweat. We were trained for the I.S. in camps all over the place. But first I was given a week's leave because for the next two months I wouldn't be allowed any contact with the civilian world. When I got home I quickly changed into civvies. I reassured my girl friend that I would only be in the service a few months more, that they were treating me great and I could leave whenever I felt like it, but she didn't believe me and carried on plenty. At least my guardian was proud of me. When my week's leave was over, I could feel the butterflies in my stomach. As the train started to pull out, I wanted to jump back onto the platform. For two long months I wouldn't even be able to see a flick, except about Hiroshima, concentration camps and men with their guts hanging out of their bellies.

83

I wouldn't see my girl friend or my pals again for two whole months. Boy, did we raise the roof that week! The moment I was wearing civvies again, off I went, with Tibbe, Fritz and Kees, to do the town up red. There were all kinds of new girls around. In one whorehouse, we played one of our old tricks on a young, black-haired chick. The four of us took her upstairs to her room and waited while she undressed. Then we pushed her onto the bed, the three of them holding her down while I stuffed an egg up her cunt. How that broad screamed and yelled; for she couldn't remove the egg without breaking it! *If* she could even reach it! Otherwise, off to the hospital. Her pimp, a young guy with a small black moustache and long hair, came after us in a rage. But he didn't dare touch us. If he did he'd get a good beating —the whole neighborhood would have turned on him. Every night I got loaded to the gills and ended up in a brawl— military training had put my muscles in great shape and I could really hit. We broke the glasses after every round of drinks, for I had plenty of money and I hadn't seen my pals in years. They all seemed much older and stronger.

Fritz was a docker and had hands like shovels. Tibbe was in business and had a car. He had just turned eighteen and his mother had died. Frankie was pimping, in partnership with Kees, and they had four chippies working for them. As soon as he was eighteen he wanted to open a bar or a luncheonette. My brother Jackson had come out of jail and was working his ass off as a bartender in the Hula-Hula Club. The girls I used to run around with were now either selling in dress shops, working in candy factories or hustling at Auntie Sjouk's. Wart, good old Wartie, had been killed by a trolley. He had smashed right into it on his motorcycle. Dead as a doornail. Perhaps it was just as well, for we all knew that he had had cancer.

84

Everyone was doing what he wanted to. And I? I didn't really go for the sailor-boy bit, but I would hang on for another month or two and then cut out. I could go abroad or just hide out somewhere. I had signed on for six years, but no one was going to keep me in for six years! It did seem like a good idea to stay in at least a bit longer, if only for the chow! I had a very good-looking girl friend, although I didn't really care for her. But I had to have someone to send cards to, saying "much love!" and letters saying, "I'm crazy about you!" She was still in college, studying domestic science. She didn't dig my military career, for her father had said, "Soldiers? They're just cannon fodder! All poor idiots! I don't want you associating with that Cremer. He's much too rough for you!" The old bastard should have seen me with my pals. For I always took Lenie home before the fun really began. She was a beautiful girl, tall, with plenty of firm flesh on her, very solid tits and pubic hair that was still stiff and curly. A nice dish. We used to go for walks in the park at night. I'd meet her at school and we'd go to a milk bar to drink shakes and play the jukebox. On nights when her parents were out visiting relatives or at the movies, I'd sneak in the back way and she'd prepare a feast for me. I was sorry when I had to leave—the week seemed so short! I was no longer interested in painting and whenever I passed a gallery I'd force myself to look the other way. I even insulted one artist in a café, a bearded cat who was sitting in a corner talking to his girl friend. I called him a lousy beatnik. Even as I was doing so it seemed to me that my voice sounded strange, far away, like it wasn't really me. How long ago was it that I'd been insulted in exactly the same way? But the laughter of Fritz and Kees brought me around and I thought no more about it.

85

I was taught how to do many other things: memorize maps quickly, recognize the main characteristics of various races, learn the geography and languages of England, France and Germany, split the enemy's skull with a bayonet, rip open a man's belly and push his guts right out his ass, cut the jugular vein in one clean swipe (always remember to clean off the bayonet to avoid infection), break a collarbone with my bare hands, kill a man with one kick in the kidneys, perform the "flying scissors," tie up prisoners, build pontoon bridges, plant explosives, do spins in a centrifuge without throwing up, jump into a sandpit from a height of ninety feet and climb back up the same distance on a rope, send and receive Morse code, go for five days on water with a little sugar in it, simulate death, use a mirror to send messages, drive a car, ride a horse, parachute, stalk unnoticed through the grass like a tiger, remain underwater for five minutes without oxygen (that trick I'll always remember, so when they drop the atom bomb I'll be ready for it!), ride new recruits, play tiddledy-winks, canasta and blackjack, search for hidden objects in forests ("Hey, look, I've got it!"), look for missing persons in the morgue (my God, what a stench!), conduct night patrols, fire patrol-boat and submarine artillery, drive in the snow, saw through steel cables with my teeth, jump from moving trucks and planes, and hoist a flag (we had to know the flags of every country in Europe). We studied the physical characteristics and behavior patterns of the peoples of Asia. I know exactly how they eat, talk and act—even how they shit.

86

At one point I decided that I'd learned enough. If I wasn't careful, I'd become a prodigy or something, so I stopped. I began by falsifying leave passes, losing my copy of *The Marine's Manual*, hitting a sergeant, turning left when I was told to turn right, manning a machine gun under the influence of alcohol, loitering in the latrines, talking back to superiors and cursing them, and running the flag up the pole upside down. That last caper got me two week's confinement to quarters. When I was freed again I remained in the mess after the bosun had piped "Clear tables!" I fought with the officers and finally was handed over to the psychiatrists. I told them a different story every day. One day I was a member of Jehovah's Witnesses, a conscientious objector, and I refused to touch another rifle because I had received a message from *Him*. The next day I begged the psychiatrist to give me a machine gun, for God's sake, for I just had to shoot. I'd mow down the enemy if only they'd give me a gun. The following day I announced that the dark clouds in the sky were a sign that war had begun and that the commander would be the first to go over the hill to the enemy. The day after that I begged the medical staff to give me an injection, a lethal one. "Destroy me!" I cried dramatically. "Please! Destroy me! I have betrayed you! Close the windows! Don't you know there's a war on? The bluebirds are going to fly in! Quick, close the windows, quick!" When they finally put me in sick bay, I behaved quite normally, nodding and smiling at the orderlies and officers like a poor soul. I snitched some benzedrine pills and swallowed a handful of them: for three days I didn't sleep or eat. During the day I just stared straight in front of me and at night, when they thought I was sleeping, I suddenly leaped out of bed, screaming at the top of my voice, "Look! Blood! There's blood on my hands!" They tried to calm me down and at last I allowed them to put me back to bed. All the while I gazed in wonder at my palms. Then I yelled, "It is the Day of the Lord! Can you not see it? Here is the proof. I am Jesus Christ! Hallelujah and Hosanna on the Highest!" The Jesus Christ bit really got them. They had a Napoleon, a Prince Bernhard and an Honoré de Balzac, but I was their first Jesus. Honoré tossed and turned in his bed all day long, and once an hour he wailed plaintively, "I shouldn't have jumped from the Eiffel Tower!" Next to me lay a marine who had shattered the neon lights outside the supply depot with his rifle butt and had reported to the sergeant of the guard, "General, I have downed two enemy planes!"

The medical staff thought I was overworked from all the intensive training I'd gone through, so they allowed me to rest up. But I was jailed a week later because I said to a chaplain who came to inspect the sick bay, "Listen to me, prick! Stand at attention!" The chaplain turned white. "Listen, you cocksucker," I continued, "don't you know who I am? Recite the Ten Commandments one hundred times! That will be your punishment!" The orderly came running with a piece of cotton drenched in chloroform and, after I had bopped him in the face, pushed it under my nose. When I came to an hour later, with a terrible headache, they made me dress and I was sent to the brig. There I had a real bad time. I was in solitary confinement and I thought that would really drive me nuts. I was taken from hospital to hospital in ambulances with barred windows. At each one I told a different story, until the psychiatrists held their heads in despair. When I promised to behave myself, I was allowed back into sick bay. There I didn't say anything to anybody. But in the middle of the night I'd start singing *Roll out the Barrel*.

87

After a while I was sent to see the commander. We talked for two hours. I told him exactly what I felt about everything: that I had been forced to enlist, that I felt I had to get up too early in the navy, that I wanted to become a painter, and so on. He thought he'd crush me by telling me that because of the psychiatric reports I could no longer be in the I.S., but that meant nothing to me—the whole setup had started to drag. Two days later I received my discharge papers from him. He said that if I ever wanted to, I could apply for reexamination. So everything was fine. For a while, when I was in solitary confinement, I had doubted that things would work out so well. The guy on guard had told me that every day spent in the brig was without pay and would have to be served over again. Luckily that wasn't true. I handed in my gear and got back my civvies, which I had outgrown, especially around the shoulders. I picked up my pay, which amounted to quite a wad, and went to the canteen to stand my ex-comrades to a few rounds. I was a free man again. Long live freedom! I caught the first train home. First class, of course!

88

I visited Portugal, the land of Amalia Rodriquez, for three weeks, two of which I spent in an internment camp. The trip back by sea was wonderful.

89

Corrine, the daughter of a pastrycook, was a student at the theater academy. After our short-lived affair she joined a travelling circus as a lion tamer, married a clown, and is still living happily ever after. I met her on the street and she asked me to come to her home on Christmas Day. This was very dangerous, for Corrine's father kept her and her two sisters strictly under his iron fist. Any deviation from the path of virtue, any disobedience was settled by the old bastard with a razor strop or a rolling pin. And it worked. His business flourished and so did his daughters. Two of them, as a matter of fact, blossomed under my personal supervision. On

Christmas Day I sat in an easy chair with coffee and a pastry in my hand and watched TV while Corrine and her sisters ran around frantically preparing orders, packing them in boxes with special yuletide ribbons and delivering them to clients in a small truck. Daddy was off playing Santa Claus at an orphanage.

At an opportune moment I knocked off one of the girls—on the floor among thousands of almond cookies and assorted cakes. She was only seventeen, but she had the ripe body of a full-grown woman. What a gas! But how the hell are you supposed to fuck a broad on the floor? Even with the mat, the floor was hard as nails. And the easy chair wasn't any more comfortable. I finally figured out a solution. That evening Corrine and I tried it out: we put the cushions from all the chairs on the floor. We were laying there, writhing around, when suddenly her father burst in, Bible in hand. That was it! I had to split, my trousers fluttering behind me like a kite! I ran through the kitchen, got onto the roof and from there jumped across the neighboring houses. I watched that cursing pastrycook stamp about, brandishing a club in his hand, peering here and there. At one point he stood, breathing heavily, just in front of the chimney I was hiding behind. It was close to an hour before I got the chance to slip down a drainpipe. I felt pretty rotten, because all the while I could hear Corrine's screams. Since there was nothing I could do about that, I decided to take in late mass. After about half an hour I couldn't stand the sweaty smell of the place any longer, so I cut. As luck would have it the pastrycook got smashed up by a milk truck a few weeks later, and that was the end of the old bastard. The shop was sold and the girls went to live with relatives. Corrine was able to devote herself to her calling, show business.

90

I had some connections in the local underworld who kept me supplied with tubes of paint, canvas and food so that I could work. In return I had to build boxes for them, anti-cosmic-ray boxes. They were little wooden affairs painted black, decorated with big nailheads and metal tape, filled with electromagnets and nuts and bolts, and finally wrapped in thin, black barbed wire. The more vicious it looked, the better it was. After a while, when business was going well, I went along to help sell them in the country, because I knew all about farmers from the time a buddy and I used to visit farms every weekend. We'd ask the farmer if we could do a painting of his farm. He'd give us lunch and supper and, if he liked our work, we'd swap it for an "old kettle" or "that old kerosene lamp over there." Those farmers were pretty cautious, and very critical. The first thing every one of them looked for in the painting was the small detail, like the little hearts cut into his wooden shutters. If we'd caught that kind of thing, everything was jake and he'd usually want to keep the painting. But he didn't want to pay for it, at least not in cash. So we'd just happen to notice a copper kettle and say, "Well, perhaps we'll take that. It might come in handy as a pisspot, if nothing else." The farmer, suspicious, didn't go for the idea of his treasured heirloom being used as a pisspot. But we had planted the seed of doubt, and he wasn't sure any more that it was really so valuable. We sold those kettles, kerosene lamps, doorknobs and ornaments in town as genuine antiques. A kerosene lamp, for example, usually brought about one hundred guilders.

Selling anti-cosmic-ray boxes involved quite a ritual. They'd be left for two weeks on approval. After that, the farmers could pay whatever they thought it was worth—they were assured that we were not interested in money, but only in serving humanity. We'd arrive in an impressive American station wagon and our lead man would go right into his spiel. Meanwhile, the rest of us would be fooling around with divining rods, sound lines and TV antennas. Even the most suspicious farmer would end up by taking a box on approval. Over a cup of coffee the farmer—who was always complaining of backaches—would be convinced that with the box in his possession, his entire family would soon be tingling with health and full of energy. A few benzedrine pills secretly dropped in his coffee soon made apparent the beneficial effects of the box.

Luckily, I quit the racket just a few weeks before I happened to read in the paper of the arrest of a shocking gang of con men. Dealing in anti-cosmic-ray boxes, they had cheated local farmers out of thousands of guilders. Although my cut had only been enough to keep me alive and working, with an occasional bonus of a side of bacon or a chicken, I felt badly all the same. Those poor hayseeds!

91

So I lay low for a while, holed up with a sculptor, a nice guy who carved nothing but Christ on the Cross—in marble, sandstone and granite. I became his assistant. I sanded and smoothed the rough edges and wedged the clay. In return, I was allowed to live and work in the studio. The sculptor brought me a pot of hot stew every evening. It was such greasy slop that the first bite always made me gag. So I asked him for fifty cents a day instead of the food. Late at night I'd slink down to the automat and buy raisin puddings, two for fifty cents, a mixture of stale bread and pastry with raisins and sugar. They were very heavy on the stomach but at least they were nourishing and edible.

The studio was infested with rats. They'd even crawl over me while I slept. I'd wake up with a start and shake a hairy body off my face. Only when the first light of dawn filtered in did I manage to fall asleep. The entire studio was filled with figures of Christ. When I started to wake up my first sight was a roomful of vague and menacing figures—in my half-awake state I saw them as detectives armed with pistols, gangsters with stilettos, priests with lancers and sometimes even the sculptor brandishing a large scythe. The slightest sound caused me to lie frozen and deadly quiet, as I waited in terror for them to hurl themselves at my throat. Sometimes I'd be almost beside myself with fear, and I'd leap off the divan and run headlong into the street. In my haste I often crashed into one of the figures, toppling it over onto the cement floor, where it smashed to pieces. Whenever that happened the sculptor got good and pissed off, for he thought I didn't dig his work and that the destruction was intentional.

Every night, after he'd left the studio to return home, I'd begin to work. I drew and modelled nothing but figures of Christ. I even saw Christ with my eyes closed. Christ was everywhere. I, you, he, we, they, everybody! One day I painted Christ on a canvas seven feet high and five feet wide, a real beauty. It was all bloody. Jesus Christ with his eyes gouged out and his limbs cut off, reaching out in four directions with his stumps, which still spurted blood. Barbed wire was stretched across his distorted face. And I painted him with absolute realism: a bearded face on a clump of bloody flesh, strung to a wooden cross with barbed wire. Blood dripped even from his crotch. I had worked all night, painting feverishly, dripping with sweat and bursting with enthusiasm. It was great! After twenty centuries, Christ had finally been painted for real! Blood, sweat and tears! I had made the Supreme Sacrifice, and I was satisfied. My masterpiece was finished!

A couple of hours later I was awakened by the sculptor. He was so mad he shook with rage! He spat at me, and even though I wasn't quite awake yet, I knew he wasn't kidding. "Get out of here, you blasphemous pig! This is too much! You've mocked our Savior for the last time! You'll be punished! You'll burn in hellfire! How dare you, you ingrate!

I won't stand for it a moment longer! It's a wonder you didn't drop dead in the act! Desecration, that's what it is!" Seizing a large poker, he rammed it through the canvas and then began to beat it as you would a burning mattress. It was an incredible sight: in the dim light of dawn the small bearded man stamped about as if possessed, ripping the painting to pieces with the poker. Our Savior's head was the last shred to go. At that point I decided to get the hell out of there before the lunatic thought I was Satan himself! I really hadn't wanted to hurt anyone's feelings. And I thought the painting was just great! Oh well, our Savior has been through so much in the last twenty centuries that a few poker blows won't make any difference.

92

All day I trudged through the streets of Marseilles without a penny in my pocket. It was miserably hot, and I'd had a bellyful. My clothes were sticking to me and I felt clammy all over. I was about ready to beat my head against a wall or something. I drank some water at a fountain and then splashed it over my face and neck. By the time I reached the bottom of the Canebière I felt like I'd been walking for days. I just wanted to make it to the youth hostel and get some sleep. That was all I could think of, just sleep, sleep and more sleep! The bitch they called the "housemother" looked at me poisonously from behind her thick glasses, but I was far too tired to react. I simply mumbled something about sleep and staggered towards the stairs. The old bag began to holler . . . about regulations and payment in advance. I knew, of course, that a youth hostel is not meant for daytime sleeping, the daylight hours being properly spent in seeing the sights and in enjoying the fresh air. But I had hoped she wouldn't see me come in. "You can sit in the recreation room," she shouted at me in a shrill voice, "but no one is allowed upstairs before 7 P.M.!" I had to make do with that. In the recreation room there were long ping-pong tables, various games and stacks of the uplifting literature you always see in such places. On the walls were all kinds of faded posters portraying the beauties of France. One of them, advertising the Foreign Legion, had a strip of paper pasted on it listing the various recruiting stations in Marseilles. A Legion official visited the hostel every morning to drum up recruits and the housemother was always glad to accept such applications. In return for their passports, the recruits got one hundred francs and the address where they were to report before midnight—some camp or other on the outskirts of town.

At least three or four guys signed up every week. Not everyone was accepted, of course, for the physical examination was very strict. That was no life for me, I thought, remembering the marines. But on the other hand I wouldn't mind having a C-note! It would buy me a decent meal and pitchers full of ice-cold beer, and there'd be plenty left over for the flick. I hadn't been able to turn any tricks for two weeks now. I was just about ready to die of hunger—whatever grub I'd had, I'd begged, borrowed or stolen in the dining hall or on the street. I didn't know a soul in Marseilles and I already owed for two weeks at the hostel. I was hoping to bump into some rich broad who was looking for someone just like me. She'd pay for everything and invite me in her red sports car, into Spain or Italy for a month or two where we'd live off the fat of the land. Unfortunately, the broad never materialized. Nor, for that matter, did any broad. If a girl had so much as nodded or smiled at me in the street, I would have gone after her on my knees.

I found some empty beer bottles in the dining hall, and stuffed them into my shirt. There was no one in the building except the housemother and her daughter, an ugly little snot. I didn't feel like just sitting in a place that reminded me of an orphanage, so I went out, cashed in the empty bottles and brought some tomatoes and grapes with the change. I walked into a small park and gulped them down. That made me feel a bit better.

Children were playing all around, a cop was standing on the grass picking his nose, and a really beautiful chick was sitting on a nearby bench reading a book. She was a good-looking piece, about twenty, very stylishly dressed—like most French city girls. She had a beautiful tan and perfect red lips. Before long I was quite excited with the possibility that here, at last, was my big chance. I began to give her the eye, trying to catch her glance. Several times, when she happened to look my way, I smiled at her, but she didn't seem to notice. Finally, I got up and walked over to her. Just to sit with someone and have a chat would have been great. I started the conversation with "Do you speak English?" She looked at me like I was something the cat had dragged in, her eyes flashing irritably above the book she was reading. She quickly sized me up, her eyes moving from my head down to my shoes and, with a contemptuous look, she ended the conversation with "No!" With that, she slammed her book shut, got up and walked stiffly to the exit, her nose in the air. She slammed the small iron gate behind her on her way out. Well, there I was, left standing there like a goddamn fool. I was so furious that I shouted after her, "Cocksucking

172

whore! Fucking snob!" Suddenly I came to my senses and saw that everyone was staring at me—the knitting housewives, the kids and, what was really bad, the cop, so I decided to take a powder. On the way back to the hostel I thought about what I might have done to the girl if I didn't feel so down-and-out. Knife her, maybe? Or rape her right there in the park? Something with a touch of melodrama, for sure. How about joining the Foreign Legion? Yes, that would do it! And besides, I was flat broke and one hundred francs seemed like a small fortune. So I told the housemother of my decision. All of a sudden she became very friendly and said that it was the best thing for me, they'd surely make a man of me. When I asked her if she would mind advancing me a little money until the following morning, she laid twenty francs on me. As far as she was concerned, there was no risk—she had my passport. I felt better immediately and made straight for the corner bar, where I downed a few steins of beer and gobbled a bunch of hard-boiled eggs. When I got back to the hostel it was nearly 8 P.M., so I sat down in the dining hall (after all, I was a paying guest now!) and started to gas with some cats from California. I decided not to tell anyone about my plans, because I didn't want to spoil a pleasant evening. Then I decided to sack out for a while before making the rounds of bars and cathouses to get loaded and laid. But by the time I opened my eyes again, it was very late. Most of the others were already in bed sleeping or reading, so instead of going out I slipped off my clothes, rolled under the blanket and slept like a baby.

93

I was awakened around 6 A.M. by the general clatter. I felt pretty depressed. I washed and dressed, knowing that, short of a miracle, I'd had it. There was no way out—unless I dug up a hundred francs somewhere so I could buy back my passport and settle my bill at the hostel. Maybe I could borrow them from an old crony who'd just happen to show up out of the blue. Miracle is right! At breakfast I got into a row with a German who pulled the pot of jam out of my hand. I was thinking about my next move when in pops the housemother to tell me that a gentleman had phoned and would be arriving at any moment. My morale was rising and falling every few minutes. I couldn't make up my mind whether to be happy or sad, so I went off alone to have a smoke in the recreation hall. There I bumped into an American chick who, for some reason or other, was very friendly. It occurred to me that I might take off with her, that she might lend me the money if

I explained the fix I was in. But suddenly I realized that I was grasping at straws. I was still wondering what to do when the housemother reappeared with the gentleman who had called. He had in tow another volunteer, a young cat I had seen for the first time the day before. The four of us went into the office. I was asked to sit on the bench outside and wait until I was called in. I could hear the other guy being questioned through the door. He was a Kraut and didn't speak French very well. Then it was my turn and I felt a sudden panic. The gentleman was nice enough and tried to put me at ease. He offered me a smoke before he pulled my passport from his pocket. The housemother, of course, had given it to him. He talked of how-good-things-were-in-the-Legion and told me that sea duty would do me a world of good (he must have noticed my shaking hands). Then he gave me the address I was to report to at 2 P.M. and said he'd take care of my debts. He finally asked if I had enough money to last me through the day and then wished me luck. I went up to the dorm to get my gear together. The Kraut was also up there packing. We chatted nervously and then left the hostel together and went into town. His name was Klaus and he too had to report at 2 P.M. We went to a café where we drank some coffee and I tried to crap the butterflies out of my system. We shot the breeze about this and that. I dug from the beginning that Klaus, who must have been about twenty-four, was a tough cookie. As a matter of fact he was a real hood from the streets of Hamburg, and this made me feel a lot easier. We left our gear at the café and went to pick up some toothpaste and socks. Klaus bought a lot of garlic sausage and we ate in an Arabic restaurant. Then we got into a cab, picked up our bags and were soon on our way to the address we had been given. It turned out to be about three miles outside of Marseilles, a camp surrounded by guards. They had been expecting us: a soldier was waiting to take us to the office. Squads of men were exercising on the parade ground and trucks kept moving in and out of the main gate. While we waited we told each other jokes, and I began to feel better about things. I even found myself looking forward to my coming adventures. The same gentleman who had been at the hostel that morning ushered me into the office. I was asked to sit down in front of a table. Four officers were seated on the other side and my passport lay on the table in front of them. They began to question me. Did I know what the Foreign Legion stood for? Did I know what an honor it was to serve in the Legion? The bullshit flowed fast and heavy. Had I ever been in trouble with the law? Officially, I wasn't really old enough, but if I were serious about joining

174

they could make an exception in my case. I found myself answering the questions in the way that would make me look best. It had become a challenge and I was determined not to be rejected. Then I was asked to sign some forms and was given a manual of regulations and a book of coupons for beer and coffee. They took a lot of pictures of me and gave me a quick physical. Then one of the officers took me into a separate room. His uniform was covered with fruit salad and he had gray hair and a moustache. I cottoned to him right away. We sat down and he stared at me for a while through his glasses. Did I really know what I was about to do? He wanted me to know that I could still withdraw. On the other hand, if I still wanted in, there would be plenty of chances for promotions and higher pay for a lad like myself. When all the details were settled, he opened my file and read off something I didn't understand. I finally realized that my name was being changed to Bok, Jan Bok, and that they were making me two years older. I didn't like the name and told him so. Couldn't I change it to something else? He said that he couldn't make that decision himself and that he didn't see what difference it made in any case. I explained that Bok means "goat" in Dutch. He grinned at that but still insisted that it hardly mattered.

Then he informed me that I'd be kept at this camp for three days for examinations and inoculations. Afterwards I'd be sent for three months' military training in Algeria before I got my permanent assignment either to a commando unit or to a ship. I was given vouchers for the quartermaster and told to pick up my uniform and turn in my civvies. Then I'd be free to hang around the mess hall until 4 P.M., when I was to report back to him for my papers and further instructions. After I turned in my old clothes—they were put into a numbered box just like in the clink—I asked what they were going to do with the rest of my gear: books, an alarm clock, a dagger, snapshots, and so on. I was told that they'd all have to be examined, but that I'd probably get them back later on. The uniform was stiff and smelled very new and the cap hurt my head. But all in all I was quite pleased with the dashing figure I cut.

The mess hall was like bedlam, with everybody speaking a different language. I went over to the bar and ordered a beer. I heard someone behind me yell, "Hey, Dutchman!" It was Klaus, who was sitting at a table with a group of uniformed men. They all waved to me and I joined them. I soon noticed that German was the main language. I was accepted immediately like an old-timer, in spite of the fact that one of them had been in the Legion for ten years and

the others between one and six. They all told wild stories of
their adventures. We discovered that Klaus would be going
to Algeria with me and we celebrated that by using up all
our beer coupons. I got a bit drunk and we both laughed
like fools at the veterans' jokes. Then Klaus was called away
by an officer and I went to buy a carton of Camels.

Someone started walking around the mess hall shouting,
"Bok!" I walked over to him and said, *"C'est moi!"* "You
are to report to building 2 *tout de suite!"* and he showed
me the way. At building 2, which turned out to be the barracks, I was met by a sergeant, who assigned a bunk and a
locker to me. While I was making up my bunk, a voice
came over the loudspeaker, "Bok, report to building 1, *tout
de suite!"* This was repeated twice and I said, under my
breath, "Shove your *tout de suite* up your ass!" I was still
a bit high and didn't feel at all like hurrying. When I finally
arrived at building 1, the nice officer with all the fruit-salad
led me back into his office. I plopped down on a chair and
answered his questions politely, signed some sort of form,
took a cigar from a box on his desk and was given a green
identification card. There was a picture of me on it and
underneath that were my new name and vital statistics.
"Hello there, Bok old boy!" I said to myself, and departed
with my orders and papers and the officer's best wishes. As
soon as I got back to the barracks I hit the sack. A minute
later I was shaken by the orderly. "What the hell do you
want?" I blurted out. "Don't you know the rules around
here?" he demanded. I looked at him contemptuously and
was about to argue when I noticed the wooden club he was
carrying. So I offered him a smoke instead. "You're not
allowed to smoke in here during the day," he said. I then
called him every name I could think of—in Dutch. His grip
on the club tightened and he asked, "What did you say?"
With a friendly smile I answered, "I don't understand what
I'm supposed to do. My French isn't so good. Perhaps you
would be so kind as to help me with these papers." And I
thought to myself, "I'll get you later, prick!" He snatched
the papers from my hands and thundered "You're supposed
to report to the medical office and then to building 6."
I shuffled over to the medical office. The doctor, another
German, asked me all kinds of questions: Did either of my
parents have cancer? Or TB? Did I have the clap? I answered no to everything and signed more papers. Then I
was dragged around to four or five other buildings by
different officers. By the time I was finished it was supper-
time. The food wasn't bad, but there was a fight at the
table—about broads, I think. After supper all the Legion-

naires took cabs into town, but I wasn't allowed out of camp because I had just been inoculated. So I went back to the mess hall, soaked up cheap booze like a sponge and played cards and checkers. When Klaus started a chess game with an Italian sergeant, I got bored and went back to the barracks. When I got there, some of the guys were playing blackjack, so I introduced myself and joined in the game. I played until I was cleaned out and then decided to go to bed and think things over. But I was so worn out that I fell right asleep.

94

I was rudely awakened by what I thought was an attack on the barracks, but it was just reveille blaring out of every loudspeaker in the joint. It was a goddamn awful racket and I caught the worst of it because one of the speakers was right over my bunk. I decided that I'd have to get another bunk. The thought of being jolted out of sleep like that every morning gave me the willies. I met Klaus in the showers and he didn't look too bright-eyed either. We were both still half-looped. The corporal came in to tell me to report to him before parade, which I did.

Parade was held in the inner courtyard, which was surrounded by the four barracks. I saw General Charron, the commander, for the first time. He was an elderly, gray-haired man with a huge moustache and bags under his eyes. With his brown, wrinkled, humane face, he looked like a general in an American movie who is outwardly a tough disciplinarian but kneels, with tears in his eyes, at the side of the wounded man and encourages him to bear up. Then, when the soldier dies, the general's tears flow, but are bravely brushed away. General Charron looked sympathetic to me but the others who were standing with him—lieutenants, majors and sergeants—had the look of bullies and shitheels about them, and fanatical gleams in their eyes.

Later that day we heard that General Charron was being transferred to Sidi-bel-Abbès, the largest Legion outpost in Algeria, where every Legionnaire was automatically sent after being recruited into a combat unit. This meant me, and I would be leaving the next Monday on a troop ship bound for Oran. From there I'd be sent to Sidi-bel-Abbès and it was comforting to think that the humane old general would soon be there too. As far as the other officers were concerned, I had heard that you only had to fart to land in front of a firing squad.

We spent the next few days eating solid chow, going to

the flicks and getting plastered in the canteen every night. Then on Monday afternoon, about six hundred of us piled into large green trucks and, escorted by motorcycle police with sirens blaring, drove through Marseilles to the port. I felt like a real hero and hoped that lots of chicks would see me on the truck and wonder who that handsome, young, tough-looking Legionnaire might be. I was really sorry there wasn't a photographer around to take my picture, for I'd have loved to send some photos back to Holland to impress my guardian and my many girl friends. On board ship we were assigned to sleeping quarters, had some good grub and were left on our own. I played cards all evening with Klaus, had a few drinks and went to bed. I felt like an old salt again and laughed at the poor bastards who were hanging overboard heaving their guts out.

We were at sea for a day and a half. In the morning we had calisthenics and sports, in the afternoon we slept or read and in the evening we could choose between a movie and church services, followed by fun and games in the canteen with jukeboxes, one-armed bandits and cheap drinks until midnight. We dropped anchor in Oran very early in the morning. After about one hour and four inspections, during which numbers were stuck on our caps, we were allowed ashore. We were assigned to groups, according to the numbers on our caps, and loaded into trucks by big, suntanned MPs, real heavies with scarred faces who kept their clubs handy. As we drove through the gates of the port I noticed that it wasn't quite 7 A.M.

Oran was miserably hot and crowded even at that hour in the morning. We drove through all kinds of markets swarming with slum life and past large department stores and skyscrapers, escorted by MPs in jeeps with sirens. At the busiest intersections the traffic stopped to let us pass. Natives leading mules scurried on to the sidewalks, jostling crowds of white people who were on their way to work. Once out of the city we passed a large lake and residential suburbs where dapper men were getting into large American cars to drive off to work in Oran. Buses full of black workmen, donkeys pulling vegetable carts, and veiled women with baskets of fruit on their heads scattered to the sides of the road as we drove by. Some of the children waved at us. There wasn't much room in the trucks so I rode standing up all the way. The cool breeze on my face was beautiful. It was already sizzling hot and the sun hadn't even reached its zenith yet. Some of the Legionnaires in the truck, who were returning from leave, told us that we hadn't seen anything yet. "When it's really hot, boys," one of them said, "you might as well cut off your balls because they're too hot to carry!" We eventually got to Sidi-bel-Abbès and drove into the shadows of the huge walls of the fort. Two enormous flags hung above the big gate where we were admitted by guards armed with carbines. "That's 'The Gate of Hell,' " joked the same soldier who had made the crack about the heat. The trucks stopped in the central yard, we jumped off and were marched, baggage on our shoulders, to a large hall. We revived ourselves at the drinking fountains while tanned Legionnaires with lists in their hands pushed through the crowds. One of them walked up to me and asked, "Bok?" When I nodded he pulled the number from my cap and shoved me toward one of the groups of waiting men. Officers milled around, looking over the newly arrived suckers as though we were cattle at an auction. Everyone was chatting and joking and I suddenly felt all alone.

95

The first group marched off, accompanied by shouting officers. Fifteen minutes later we followed them to the mess hall for breakfast. It was exactly 9:30. The food was good—fresh meat and onions and cold milk. The officers with lists were still moving among us, giving orders. A young Algerian corporal tapped my shoulder and asked, "Are you Bok?" I nodded. "Wait here after the exit whistle. You'll be called." I took a peanut-butter sandwich and more milk to pass the time. Just like in the navy, they blew a whistle meaning that everyone should stop eating and give thanks for what he has received. There were a few seconds of silence, during which you could hear the birds outside and a bit of appreciative lip smacking. Then the exit whistle sounded and pandemonium broke loose. Dishes and silverware were piled up in clattering heaps, benches were pushed aside and men shouted their way out of the mess hall. Those of us who were left behind killed time smearing butter and jam on the table.

96

Months of heat, drought and exertion followed. Reveille was at 5 A.M. and each day was filled with boring maneuvers, lousy chow and brutal heat. Worst of all was the monotony! As soon as the tricolor was hoisted (it never even fluttered because there was never the slightest breeze), the orders of the day were read and we went off with our battalions. We were driven to the shooting ranges to practice with pistols, rifles and machine guns. Liberty, Equality, Fraternity! I kept wishing I was back home, painting or writing again. But here I was being trained to kill again! If that's all it took, they might as well have made me a general on the spot.

We were trained for service in the desert. There were Germans, Frenchmen, Senegalese, Danes, Norwegians, Turks, Italians, Poles, Belgians, Dutchmen, Englishmen, Americans and Swiss; in short, almost every country and every race was represented. I saw camels, mules, aardvarks, hyenas, beautiful Moorish girls, Arab huts, sunsets, Moorish towns, black dancing girls, veiled women, mountains and burned-out villages. All over the barracks were lists of instructions and posters warning us against everything. I learned to smoke hashish and opium, to eat snake meat and drink turtle soup and to fight with sabers. I discovered that the word "assassin" is derived from *"hashshashin"* and mastered the snappy Legionnaire's salute.

I had hoped to get some relaxation in the Legion, but forget it! I became scared of my own shadow. On patrol I never wanted to bring up the rear. I wouldn't look at the women. We were warned almost daily against messing with Moorish women. We were told that they'd entice us into their back alleys, poison our drinks, steal our clothes and cut off our tongues. They also were reputed to have leather rings, lined with razor blades, inside their vaginas. We were even warned to beware of small boys. If you're walking along and an Arab snot-nose asks you for a light, don't stop or chances are that he'll cut you open from top to bottom with a razor-sharp knife.

It was a great life if you didn't weaken! Dysentery was common because the food and the water were contaminated. I suffered a mild case of malaria but recovered with the aid of large doses of quinine. After a while I didn't care about anything any more. As they say in Islam, *"El Mektub Mektub"* ("What will be, will be") and I just took things as they came. I had a few buddies and we all usually went on leave together. When we went to the city, we all felt safer if the four of us stayed together. The Legion wasn't too bad. War is a craft and like other crafts it had to be learned. The principle we lived by was that we had no country but the Legion. With this thought we were able to trudge through endless miles of burning sand, tired and sick from last night's heavy red Algerian wine. Then I'd remember how cold and crisp winter is in Holland: the beautiful frost flowers gleaming on the windows, the wonderful hot stews and sauerkraut and smoked sausage. To hell with Holland!

97

I had a girl friend in Oran. She was a whore in the Casbah, a real beauty. Her name was Halima. I was shy—almost speechless—the first time I went to see her. Besides, I was afraid that an armed Arab might spring from behind the curtain at any moment, in spite of the fact that Klaus, Davis and Azzizig were standing guard outside the door. She was as sweet as "the girl next door," but I still had to pay. So I made a deal with her. On weekends when I wasn't on guard duty or in the clink, I'd come to her place, stay all night and have breakfast with her, all for thirty francs. I always brought along whiskey, cigarettes and canned meat from the commissary. I felt like a family man, slipping through the Casbah at night in my uniform, carrying a large paper bag full of goodies. Halima always welcomed me like her husband. She'd throw her arms around me and then undress me. Her body tasted of cloves and fresh butter. While she was cooking I'd take a shower, wrap a robe around my body and lie down until dinner was ready. What a cozy love nest. Then we'd eat, drink a little and listen to the radio—usually the English broadcast from Gibraltar. When I heard Elvis Presley or Fats Domino it felt like I was back home in my studio with an Arab piece I'd picked up on my travels. Halima didn't speak English and my French was rusty, so we never argued. I'd give her the thirty francs just before I left in the morning. She'd always snatch them and spit on them, her eyes glistening with greed. Halima was crazy for money.

When I got back to the barracks, I had to tell Azzizig all about the weekend. Azzizig was an Algerian billeted in our barracks with his outfit. He really knew his way around. I'd often go out with him and it was he who first took me to Halima. "Did she satisfy you?" he asked every time. "Was it all right? If she doesn't fuck you just right you must let me know, and I'll go and tell her that she isn't making you happy." That apparently was the most insulting thing you could say to a Moorish woman. But I had nothing to kick about.

98

I was still half asleep and my head felt two sizes too big, so I tried to keep my eyes firmly closed. But the man who was shaking me wouldn't stop. "Take it easy," I finally muttered, and sat up. The rest of the guys in the barracks were already up and out of their bunks, dressing and cursing, and some, with towels over their shoulders and toothbrushes in their hands, were on their way to the can. "What's the action, anyway?" I asked the guy next to me. "What in hell's going on?" Then I noticed that it was still pitch-dark outside . . . so I wasn't hung over . . . I just hadn't had any sleep. My neighbor, who was, as always, having trouble zipping up his fly, finally answered, "We have to go on a punitive expedition, clean out some Berber village or other somewhere up in the mountains. Everything's snafu here too. I hear that orders from HQ came too late and the Old Man is shitting bricks. So you'd better get a move on." A few minutes later I was dressed in fighting gear. I hadn't bothered to stash away all my gear the day before after field exercises, so everything was handy. Everyone, including me, started griping his ass off about the chicken-shit mission. What a drag!—Saturday morning, and I'd just applied for a three-day pass to go with some of the other cats into Oran to paint the town red. Of course that was all fucked up now! Those goddamn Berber camps! They're always way up in the mountains or way out in the desert, a day's drive at least—if you can drive there at all.

Sergeant Reaumour stormed in carrying a sheaf of papers and yelled at us to move our asses. Then our own sergeant, Silecy, came in, took the papers from Reaumour and shouted at us, "Get a fucking move on!" Meanwhile, Reaumour was moving around the room, taking everything in, glancing here and there at the feverish activity all around. He and Silecy were acting so nervous that I could tell something very special must be up. I sat down on my bunk and got so involved trying to figure out what we were in for that I didn't notice Reaumour had come over and was standing in front of me. All of a sudden he bellowed in my ear, "Bok! What the fuck's wrong with you? Thinking again?" He nearly burst my eardrum, and with my splitting headache I could have done without that. "Fuck off, Sarge, can't you see I'm taking a crap?"

"Cut the clowning, Bok! And get that bed of yours made!" Then he turned to one of the new men and yelled at him, "What the hell did I tell you? Combat gear, you prick! Asshole idiot!" The rookie nearly burst into tears. The poor bastard had put on the wrong uniform, his parade gear. Naturally, he was the laughing-stock for the rest of the day. I decided to do without a wash and had a smoke. My mouth tasted rotten, like I had eaten the ass end of a maggoty dog for dinner the night before . . . which might have been true, come to think of it.

Within ten minutes the entire company was standing in formation in the dark yard, which was lit only by four large spotlights. Whispers ran through the ranks: "Something's cooking, *Kameraden*. . . . It's for real this time. . . . It looks like bad news. . . ." It sure did. Everybody, including all the highest brass, was there: General Charron, his adjutant, a major or two, a whole batch of lieutenants and three companies of troops. The roll was called quickly and the sergeants reported all present and accounted for. Then they received their orders and returned smartly to their units. The General made some kind of speech that no one listened to. "More bullshit," a voice said somewhere behind me. "In a few minutes those fat-assed brass will be back in their beds, hard-ons in hand, ready to engage in cock-to-cunt combat with their wives. But that jazz ain't for the likes of us. . . ."

Then Silecy read out our marching orders: together with the men of Reaumour's and Martin's companies (Klaus was in the latter) we were to proceed to El Mahfoura, about three hundred miles away somewhere behind the Atlas Mountains, and from there we were to continue on foot to a village where some kind of skirmish had taken place.

"Any questions?" Sergeant Silecy demanded. "Can we have some music on the way?" somebody piped up. "Yeah, the Death March," the sergeant replied. "OK now, boys, go grab some breakfast and pick up your combat rations, and then get over to the munitions stores. Fall in at Communications in fifteen minutes." We moved off to the mess hall. There were three massive food parcels for each man and large aluminum pails full of piping hot soup were on the tables. The cooks, sleep still in their eyes, were running around like mad with coffeepots and fried eggs.

"Do we have to take all this shit with us?" asked Davis, pointing at the rations. "No, you can ram it up your ass!" said the cook. "My ass! Fuck that noise! Shove it up your own!" Davis was a real intellectual! "Some more coffee, Bok?" the cook asked me, shaking the pot up and down under my nose. I saw that there was only mud left in it. "I don't need any of your dregs," I said. "Just listen to his ladyship! Kindly excuse me, Madam!" the cook said, and started to walk away. I stopped him. "Don't you have anything stronger?" He smiled, "Sure, but at the usual price. What'll it be?" I ordered a bottle of cognac. A minute later he returned with it, very stealthily. "Put it on my bill," I said, and filled my canteen. I passed what was left along the table and the bottle was soon empty. Some of the others followed my

183

example and in a few moments there were empty bottles all over the place.

At the munitions stores we were given cartridges and hand grenades. Because I would be manning a machine gun, I also got two full belts. "Couldn't I have a bag or a cart for these, grocer?" I asked. "Or better yet, why don't you send them to me COD? How much extra will that be?" But the sergeant wasn't quite awake yet, had a hangover, and was in no mood to be put on. "You ain't dry behind the ears, prick!" he snarled, and naturally I lost my cool. "Get off it, you fuckhead," I snarled back. "We're going out there to get killed while you drag your fat ass back and piss in your bed!" Without waiting for an answer, I grabbed my ammunition and beat it. Later, I thought, I could make it up to him by buying him a couple of cigars or a drink in the canteen.

Over at Communications, the officers were assigning their men to waiting trucks, and I, along with six others, wound up in the back of Silecy's Landrover.

It was still pitch-dark, not even 5 A.M. yet, when the vehicles started to roll out through the main gate. I counted twelve Landrovers led by a jeep carrying the ensign. I was surprised at the strength of the force, because they normally detailed only about twenty men for a job like cleaning up a small village. So I asked Silecy, "Are we going to wipe out a band of Berbers or invade the United States, Sergeant?" "We're only going with Martin and Reaumour as far as Brézina. Then we go on alone. They've got their own orders to follow."

A few hours later, after it had become light, we were driving through small Moorish towns and villages. Sometimes the entire population was out, waving at us, including beautiful dark girls carrying baskets on their heads. We shouted obscenities at them in a dozen different languages. What a ball! Later, lulled by the monotonous sound of the wheels on sand and on gravel roads, I pulled down the top and we dropped off to sleep. We didn't wake up again until the vehicles stopped, well into the mountains past Mechéria. It was about 11 A.M., time for lunch. It was so eerily quiet in the mountains that it was a relief to get moving again. But after a while all the jolting and bouncing began to make me sick. The next time we stopped, I threw up my lunch—cognac and ham sandwiches. Most of the others did the same. Then we guzzled more cognac—hardly anyone had water or coffee in his canteen. The scenery began to change. We were now climbing steeply through woods, past large fields of yellow and red earth. Felled trees and chalky yellow boulders dotted the roadside. Then, for an hour or so, we rolled on through a valley with towering cliffs on both sides. High above us, at the top of the canyon there were blackened tree stumps and charred bushes. Since passing through the last village, much earlier in the day, we hadn't seen a living soul, not even any animals.

"You know what I'd like now?" one of the men asked. "A real nice black broad! I'd fuck her forty times without stopping once to come up for air."

"You're out of your skull, buster! Moorish chicks stink like limburger from their cunts to their mouths!" said Fells.

"Oh, yeah? You must have kissed their cunts and fucked their mouths to be so sure," added Kramer. This was the kind of talk we'd all heard a thousand times before, but at least it was a diversion. Just staring at the road would have driven us off our rockers.

"Anyway," continued Fells, who obviously hated blacks, "those that'll let you fuck 'em have cunts as big as buckets. And those that won't, you couldn't get it in without a quart of axle grease! Why, I once fucked a black bitch in Oran and you could have marched a whole damn company through her cunt, it was that big!" Fell's face twisted in disgust at the memory.

"I once fucked an Arab widow," said Olsen, "and, goddammit, she hadn't washed her snatch since her husband died. You should have seen the thing, all caked up with shit. Yecch! And she was a good-looking bitch, too. Took me back to her place, she did. I was loaded to the gills, but not so bad that I couldn't get a hard-on. Anyway, I lay down on her bed and she starts getting undressed. Everything is swell so far and I think to myself, What a nice piece of tail! And free too! She has a pair of tits like pumpkins, full, firm and erect. Then she puts the light out and takes her panties off. I get on top of her and man, what a stink! I can't begin to describe it. But I'm drunk, you see, so I get to thinking, maybe she just farted. But then, when we get around to a sixty-nine, goddammit, it's like sticking my face in a tubful of manure. And as if that wasn't enough, just then she lets out a long, juicy fart. Brother, that did it! I jumped up and threw on my uniform. And she just lies there, all dazed and cross-eyed and asking me what's wrong and where am I going. So I tell her I'm going out for a smoke and out I split. The first bar I came to I bought a pint of cognac just to wash my mouth out. But things worked out OK because I bumped into an air force sergeant and I sold her address to him for a carton of Camels."

"Who wants a piece of chocolate," I asked, "to wash down the shit?"

We had been driving through the same valley for over an hour now, with steep white rocks rising at either side of the narrow, winding road. Suddenly there was a lot of honking from the cars in front and we lurched to a standstill so suddenly that we were all thrown onto the floor. After the first shock we were ready for anything. We expected shots, but none came. Then, through the dust clouds, we saw the car behind us pull up. A sergeant and a few men jumped off into the road. We followed their example, in spite of the fact that we had strict orders not to leave the car unless instructed to do so by the sergeant. Sergeant Silecy climbed out, cursing wildly, his hands clutching his forehead. Blood was streaming between his fingers: when we stopped he had gashed his forehead against the windshield. We went forward cautiously toward the first car and finally realized what had happened. Reaumour was grunting and fuming like an angry rhinoceros, at a funny little Arab man, dressed in brightly colored wraps and a beaded cap, who was wailing and pointing to a small gray donkey that lay under the car bumper. It was a horrible sight. The donkey, loaded down with straw baskets, wasn't dead yet and its gray belly, all sticky with blood, was still rising and falling as it wheezed its life away. You could see it was trying to rise, kicking feebly in the dust, braying weakly and rolling its large staring eyes in a silent plea for help.

The driver of the car told us that when the little Berber —probably an itinerant merchant who wandered the roads for months at a time—saw the car coming he had eased his donkey over to the side of the road against the cliff to allow us to pass. When the first cars had gone by, the animal had suddenly taken fright at the blast of a horn and jerked in such a way that one of the big baskets he was carrying snagged on the rear bumper of the vehicle in front of Reaumour's. The poor beast was sent spinning right under the front wheels of Reaumour's jeep. The little Berber fell but just got scratched up a bit. Reaumour, when his jeep was stopped short, banged his head on the windshield. Serves the bastard right! The arrogant prick was always ready with his fists and his men feared and hated him. My own sergeant, Silecy, a Hungarian, was a hard man too. But at least he was reliable, loyal and friendly, probably the most popular sergeant in the outfit. Reaumour went on yelling at the dazed little Arab. He, of course, didn't understand a word and finally kneeled down beside the donkey and tried to untie its load. Reaumour interpreted the man's turning

186

away as an insult. So he really blew his top. I've never seen him so excited: his neck swelled up, his face became purple and his whole body was trembling, stuttering and spitting with rage. The rest of us were standing around wondering why the son of a bitch was kicking up such a row. I felt sorry for the poor little Arab. After all, it wasn't his fault that the donkey had shied. And it was obvious that the poor beast was dying. These Berbers have to work and scrimp for years to save enough money to buy a donkey and start a business. The man patted and stroked the animal, trying to coax it to get up again. But it just licked its master's hands and its head dropped lower and lower. We were all thinking it would be best simply to kill it out of mercy. There was obviously no hope and the beast's terrified eyes seemed to be begging us to put an end to its misery.

Sergeant Silecy, whose head had meanwhile been taped up by his driver, came over sporting a large bandage over one eye. He saw the animal suffering and pulled out his revolver. But the Arab pulled at his arm, bleating all the time in his staccato language. Silecy tried to calm the man down in the best Algerian he could muster, but the man became completely hysterical. He must have been afraid he was going to be shot too, or left behind here two hundred miles from the nearest settlement. Again Silecy tried to aim between the donkey's eyes but the Arab kept pulling at him, making him lose his aim and his balance. Reaumour jerked the little man away by his collar and Silecy aimed and fired. The animal shook its head for a moment and twitched in its final spasm, and then it was all over. The Algerian escaped from Reaumour's grip and threw himself on the ground in front of Silecy. We all felt sorry for the little guy. I knelt beside him and patted his back but Reaumour pushed me aside and then hauled the Algerian to his feet by the collar. He held him at arm's length and spit in his face, snarling, "I'll teach you some manners, goddammit!" I came damn near emptying my machine gun into Reaumour. What right had he to shove me around? I wasn't under his command, and besides, he had no right to lay his hands on an enlisted man. I hated his guts. Silecy tapped me on the shoulder. "Forget it," he said, and his steady eyes calmed me down a little. But I was still seething inside. That bastard Reaumour! Who the hell gave him the right to treat the little guy that way? We weren't at war and it was his own damn fault that he banged his head against the windshield. The Arab, still in Reaumour's viselike grip, was baring his black, rotten teeth and shouting the most terrible insults at his captor.

Reaumour had been in the Legion for twelve years, during which time he had been demoted more than once because of his temper. He had fought in Vietnam and there acquired an unreasonable hatred of anybody with a black or brown skin. And one of his best friends had recently been tortured to death in an Algerian camp. Now he was releasing all his pent-up hatred—and perhaps fear, as well. Silecy told him to control himself but he knocked the Algerian down and out with one wild swing, yelling at Silecy to mind his own fucking business. The men muttered and started moving forward, but Silecy shouted authoritatively, "That's enough!" Noticing the ugly mood of the men, Reaumour pulled himself together and went back to his car, looking defeated. His men spat on the ground contemptuously. We loaded the Berber and his straw baskets into three of the cars and continued on our way. In spite of Silecy's efforts to justify what his colleague had done, we all hated Reaumour. Any officer who can't control himself is disgusting!

99

July 16—El Mahfoura. Searing hot again today. Davis has yellow fever. 115 degrees and I can hardly stand it much longer. The heat burns right through your cap and scorches your head. Five men are in the hospital with sunstroke. Once you get delirious, you've had it. The heat is so intense that even the birds are too dazed to move off the road, so we've run over dozens of them. They can't find shade anywhere; in what little shade there is, the Berbers are lying in wait for them. The Berbers eat birds raw. All they do is pluck them and then pop them into their mouths whole. They eat everything but the heads. Azzizig eats them that way, says they taste good. Come to think of it, Dutch farmers do the same, but I'd rather have fried chicken any day.

July 19—Had to get up at 5 A.M. again this morning, goddammit. I hardly have time to keep up this diary. You just about get to sleep when you're told to get up again. But at least at this hour it's not too hot in the woods. We have two teams of dogs along with us, Alsatians. They're good-looking animals, but highly unpredictable. One time one of them shot out of a farmyard with a chicken in his mouth. When Martin tried to take it from the dog, it went for him. The trainer had to come and call the dog off. The dogs ate the chicken. Even the dogs are crooks in Algeria.

July 20—Today I had to carry some baskets of fruit to the

pantry for the colonel's orderly, which meant going through the mess hall. Two Algerians stood guard at the entrance. They're the scum of the earth. While their countrymen are being killed they sit in the shade scratching their balls. Inside the mess hall, three officers were holding an interrogation—an Algerian boy who had been picked up during a raid last night. He didn't make a sound when they knocked him down, but as I was putting the baskets down in the pantry I heard him start yelling. They had pinned him to a table with bayonets through his hands and ears. His screams were hideous—they made me want to throw up. I heard one of the officers say, "Cut off one of his ears—as a warning." The screaming became even worse but I was outside by this time. And the guards made me move on.

July 28—Went on patrol in the woods with machine guns and flamethrowers. We were ordered to burn down a hill covered with greenery. "Why?" I asked Captain Defosse. "To stop the damn Berbers from ambushing all our convoys," he said. "But they wouldn't be in the middle of a forest, would they?" "The bastards are everywhere, even up a sheep's ass." With a roar, the flamethrowers spewed jets of fire through the undergrowth. Every minute I was expecting to hear sudden screams and see men staggering forward to surrender, hands and faces singed black, shreds of blistered flesh dangling from their bodies. Behind every bush I pictured a barbecued Berber. I didn't want to shoot anyone, so I prayed there weren't any Berbers around. I've never seen anyone burned. The worst I've ever seen was the boy pinned to the table in the mess hall. And three hours later we were eating at the same table. The blood had been removed with bleach.

Last night we marched twenty miles with full pack to our exercise in guerrilla warfare. At a signal from the sergeant, we all had to hide ourselves in the woods, then stalk the man designated as our "enemy." We had to locate our man by the sounds he made or caused in the woods. That was great. Once in a while a bird that was awakened chirped, and the forest smelled clear and fresh. One time, in Holland, when I really had to take a shit, I ran into the woods. It had just rained, and the fragrance of the foliage was so strong that I couldn't smell my own stench. Of course it never rains here, but there's a heavy morning dew. How childish people can be sometimes! As soon as they were hidden, our highly trained soldiers began acting like kids, deliberately making weird noises, mostly imitation farts. I found my man pretty fast.

August 4—This evening there were two deaths in barracks 8. They were playing *"tirez-le-chien."* (The "games" here always have hundreds of francs riding on them. Two soldiers, A and B, walk into the room, A armed with a pistol. The lights are turned off and A has to shoot the gun six times—three bullets are real, three blank. B, by watching the flashes of the gun, has to try to get it away from A. Whoever has the gun after the sixth shot is the winner.) I saw Tosca, the Dutch nurse who works in the hospital. She's still trying to make me. But she's so fat and tough-looking and besides, I don't like red hair and freckles. Except Mai Britt's freckles. Tosca was called to give first aid last night, but there wasn't much she could do. A corporal had been killed instantly by a bullet through his heart and a Pole (his name was something like Szabokirski) had got it through the eye—his brains were blown right out. The bullet had ricocheted off the blackboard. What a bloody mess! I wonder if it's hot in Holland now too. I wouldn't mind lying on the beach at Scheveningen with a few nice chicks.

August 5—Went on patrol into the woods. It was deadly quiet, so quiet that you could hear the silence. My stomach was rumbling and sounded like a stuttering motorcycle engine. The silence quivered and hummed. Broad beams of sunlight filtered through the green branches of the trees. The rays of light were so round and clean that you could have sat on them. Rembrandt should have seen it.

August 8—Awakened at 5 A.M. for duty on the firing squad. My first time. I don't know why they had to choose me. I guess it's part of the training. They want to harden us. All day long they shout at us, "You have to be tough!" One minute I sort of like it, the next I'm so frightened and desperate that I could die. If I'm left alone for a moment I become hysterical. I see Algerians with rifles everywhere, even perched up trees. At night, with everyone asleep, it's so quiet that I'm afraid to go outside to the latrine. I'm having terrible dreams again, too. I keep on the run all day and get drunk at night. That way sometimes I can sleep without dreaming.

I dreamed that I was back home. It was winter and I was stoking the stove. When I opened the lid I suddenly saw my mother in the white-hot fire. She looked at me reproachfully. Her arms, legs and lower body had been burned away—all that was left of them was black spots. Her breasts were on fire, too. Only her face was still whole. I screamed and wanted to pull her out, but when I tried to grab her I felt a terrible wave of searing heat on my face. Desperately I looked for a poker or a piece of iron. She looked at me mournfully and said, "Close the lid, Jannikins. It is too late to save me now." I didn't want to do it, but her eyes forced me to. All the time I was closing the lid, very slowly, her eyes kept staring at me.

When I woke up I started crying very softly. It was still early. By the time the orderly came to call me I had recovered somewhat, and after some strong coffee in the mess hall I was OK again. I wonder why they needed twelve of us. "Fall in, firing squad!" I was really afraid but I forced myself not to show anything. Wasn't I a man? Hadn't I seen death before? The execution was awful. The condemned man, a Frenchman, was a lieutenant, a young guy, and very good-looking. An intelligence officer and the field chaplain were present. It was just like that film I'd seen in Algiers. At the order "Fire!" I purposely aimed wide. I felt so sorry for him. What a goddamn mess it was! His brains came spurting out in a bloody spray, but he still wasn't dead. He fell to his knees, blinded, screaming hideously for the *coup de grâce*. What confusion! Everyone started milling around and I just turned away, feeling sick. The captain and the field chaplain cursed and yelled; the intelligence officer just stood and looked. The captain's pistol jammed and he threw it away in a rage. All this time the dying lieutenant screamed and screamed. He finally got the mercy shot from one of the MPs and writhed on the ground as if he was nestling into a nice, warm bed. Now I can believe those stories about executions that get screwed up because of faulty rifles. I know for sure that I didn't hit him. My bullet went into the wall just above his left shoulder. We were all shaken up, even the captain. Nobody said much at breakfast and I didn't touch a thing. I still felt sick.

By this evening I was fine again—I even went back for seconds on stew. So much happens in one day. But if you think about it, it really was rough on that poor cat. Maybe he left a beautiful chick behind. Frenchmen, especially the officers, are pretty hot stuff with women. What would happen to his girl? She probably lives in Paris, in a large apartment with a view of the Eiffel Tower. . . . When you go there, she asks you in very graciously. . . . You make her in the first five minutes, fuck her all night and stay for weeks and weeks. . . . Maybe she hated her lieutenant because he had four other women and never wrote. . . .

Whatever could that lieutenant have done to deserve such an end? I didn't know him, and they never tell you anything. All I know is that there's a firing squad almost every morning. Condemned men from all the camps and prisons are brought here. They're driven into cells with bullwhips, just like at the slaughterhouse!

August 14—Next week I'll be sailing on the *SS Constantine* to Marseilles and back, on guard duty. I'll try to desert. I'm so homesick for Holland! I know what I'm risking, but it's worth it, even if I won't be able to leave Holland again for the rest of my life. I'll stay there and write a book, or start painting again and have exhibitions. I wonder how my friends are, and all the other people I know. I can see myself standing in the local bar. "Two beers, Joe!"

There's something new now: guerrilla training. All you get is knives—knives to tie to your shins, knives to tie to your arms, to your chest and back. You have to crawl through the swamps and over the sand and then swim underwater and attack the "enemy" with your knives.

The mosquitoes are driving me crazy. We had lice in barracks 7 and had to burn off our iron bedsprings with gasoline. We couldn't smoke because the legs of the beds were standing in cans full of gasoline. The mosquitoes aren't so bad by comparison, even if thousands of them zoom around like torpedos. They're really out for blood! And who can sleep inside netting? It's like sleeping in a steam bath! Yesterday I hurt my thumb on the sights of a submachine gun. It was a minor wound, but it hurt like hell! I don't believe those war films that show courageous men fighting on like heroes after they're wounded. A small scratch could make a soldier surrender.

I've got to get out. I don't feel at home with these desert fighters. But where would I feel at home? For four years I've been trying to find myself. I don't feel at home anywhere. What if I get back to Holland and immediately get into more trouble? I'll just have to take off again. I don't even know who I am any more. When I'm on guard duty at night, and things are quiet, I like it. The world is so wide. Sometimes I wonder if we live on the globe or in it.

August 18—Now it's definite, I'm going to Marseilles on the *Constantine* to escort troops. I wouldn't be J.C. if I didn't take advantage of it. Of course, it's very dangerous, but I feel like I have to leave. I'll just disappear. On the other hand I might come back. I don't have leave this weekend so I may never see Halima again. Just as well, for in my enthusiasm I might talk. And my rule is: Don't trust anyone, not even yourself!

These last few days we've been in Ait Assad Kemach, helping the engineers repair the command post there. The post was destroyed by Algerian *moussebilines*—suicidal saboteurs like the Japanese kamikazes. Not one of them was killed, but they were all wounded. All day long I have to help tear things down and build things up, and at night I stand guard. We're just outside the village and last night the caid, the head of the village, invited our commander and the commander of the engineers to dinner. I went along as part of the security squad. We had to stand guard outside and make the rounds every hour. We got fed too: a dish of soft, silvery stuff with little chunks in it. The other guys threw theirs into the bushes, but I ate it. It tasted like meat. I asked the girl who had brought it what it was. "Snake and dogmeat." Shit! Was I sick! In the Casbah there's always that disgusting stench of singed meat. And in every house there's the sickly odor from the dogs. But I didn't let the girl see how disgusted I was. I'm not one of those people who travel around the world and insist on eating only cabbage, smoked sausage and oatmeal wherever they go. A little later the girl came back with another plate, on which there was a very small piece of brown meat in an awful reddish sauce. I asked what it was, for I wasn't about to eat a turd in a pool of menstrual blood—and that's what it looked like. And Arab women use that sort of thing to put their lovers under a spell. Maybe this girl had her eye on me. She grinned and said something in Arabic. She pointed at the palm of her hand and gestured to show me how good it was and the way to eat it. It was a small piece so I swallowed it whole without even tasting it, a trick I learned at the homes where we were forced to finish every bit of the greasy bacon and slimy oatmeal. I asked one of the guards, a Swiss who knew some Arabic, to thank the girl for the delightful tidbit and ask her what it was that I had eaten. He did so. The girl started explaining with gestures and shrill sounds and the guy turned white. He looked at me with disgust, belched and said in a shaking voice, "She says it was human meat, the palm of the hand of an old man who died last week. It's been under the ground for six days. She says that seasons the meat!" I ran down the wooden steps and threw up my guts into a big potted plant.

August 19—There's a new rage here. Everybody bets money and cartons of American cigarettes. Then, at night, when the men get back from patrol duty in the woods, tired and still camouflaged with mud on their faces and foliage on their helmets, they report how many guerrillas they've killed. The Algerian liberation forces are shot out of the trees like sparrows. An American from Chicago, Mike, almost always takes the jackpot. He averages three Algerians a day. His winnings come out to about fifteen francs or three cartons of Camels for each dead guerrilla.

We've been given special pills, because dysentery is spreading. We have to put them into the drinking water and our soup. Some wise guys discovered that they're great as pep-up pills. Even if you're hopelessly drunk, as high as the Eiffel Tower, take one pill and you're fit as a fiddle. Now we can drink ourselves into a stupor every night. One pill in the morning and we go through the day like a breeze. Those pills are a gas! Almost every officer here uses narcotics. They sniff benzedrine, smoke hashish and shoot cocaine, morphine, and belladonna. But it all goes on under cover—it's strictly prohibited. When an Arab dealer is caught, he's shot on the spot. Users receive heavy punishment. But nobody can keep us from smoking a water pipe in a coffeehouse. That's what it's there for!

August 20—We're at Fort St. Thérèse, near Oran. Tomorrow morning we sail at 6 A.M. I walked around Oran today. It was very pleasant and I suddenly felt much better. Something's going to happen. Oran seems like part of Europe. It looks so European: large boulevards lined with big department stores, banks and cafés. Scattered throughout are large, white marble mosques with gleaming minarets. At twelve noon the voice of the muezzin resounds: *"Allah allah Akbar allah Lah illah lah lah illah il allah!"* I saw half-naked Negroes, expensively dressed Arabs, French officers, beautiful French chicks and praying Muslims kneeling on their mats facing the East.

100

Early that morning we shipped aboard the *Constantine*. The sun was already high in the sky by the time we set sail. It was a good trip. There were nurses on board, and the decks were always jammed with couples fucking. After forty-eight hours, Marseilles appeared on the horizon. Armed guards were watching the railings, because on previous trips dozens of men had jumped overboard. Those that were caught were later shot. But there were other ways of escaping; in the Arab villages you just had to give the password, "allaman," and you were safe. This password was on all the posters pasted on the walls by the FLN. As it turned out, on this trip nobody jumped overboard. Just as well! At 2 P.M. I picked up my pass, which allowed me to stay ashore until 6 o'clock. I wandered around, met a bunch of guys from the ship and then managed to lose them. All the time I kept thinking feverishly about what I should do. I made up my mind I'd had enough. No borders or guards could stop me now. On to the next stop! Everything went so smoothly it was almost unbelievable. I thought back to my friends and Halima. But I liked it better on this side of the ocean. And I'd see to it that I remained on this side. I had to succeed, I Jan Cremer.

101

Brigitte, my friend in need, my gorgeous whore! She took me in, the wandering adventurer, off the streets where I walked hungry, cold and sad. I stopped a nameless passerby and asked for a handout. Clutching a briefcase, and with his head sunk deeply into the collar of his coat, he had been hurrying down the street, occasionally glancing through the windows of the red-lit dives at the heavily painted whores. Hands trembling—terrified of being rolled—he gave me a guilder. I hurried into the nearest bar and bought a drink to insulate myself against the cold.

I was sitting alone at a small table in the corner, nursing my drink, when one of the girls came and sat down next to me and asked me to buy her a cocktail. I refused and she started calling me names. I was feeling too cold and miserable to start a fight.

Then She came, gliding from her stool like a panther. I had seen her enter a little while earlier, a beautiful piece still damp from the icy cold outside. Sitting down at the bar next to some old prick, she had smiled at me—not a professional smile, but a sympathetic, sensitive, encouraging smile. She came over, got rid of the screaming slut with a few words and a push, and sat down next to me. I smiled at her sheepishly, not daring to say anything, afraid she'd find out that I had no money and just walk away. She was beautiful (only later did I find out just how beautiful she really was), dressed in a fur coat that reached to just above her knees, beautiful knees descending to well-shaped, slightly heavy calves, half-hidden under black nylon stockings. Occasionally she looked up at the men coming in and called out a greeting.

"Don't you want to offer me a drink, sailor?" she asked me.

"I'm not a sailor."

"Are you a student, then?"

I laughed. "Not a student either. Do I look like one?"

"How should I know? Well, are you or are you not going to offer me a drink?"

"I'd love to, but I haven't any money," I said. She looked at me and called to the bartender, "Two beers, Joe," and Joe brought us two beers. We started talking. She told me her name was Brigitte and that she originally came from Germany. I told her that my name was Jan, I had no money and I felt terribly poor, deserted and dirty.

"Do you have a place to stay?" asked Brigitte.

"Not really," I said. "A friend lets me sleep on the floor at his place."

102

I was staying with a casual acquaintance, the only person I knew in town. I slept on a moth-eaten blanket over the cold linoleum, covered by my heavy loden coat. At the crack of dawn I had to get out of the place by way of the drainpipe, because the landlady didn't allow guests. She started puttering around in the kitchen at 5 o'clock and brought breakfast up at 8, so it was impossible to get past the kitchen door without her noticing. Once, when she found out that this guy had brought a girl home with him, she threatened to throw him out for endangering her good name and so forth. I couldn't stand all that crap—it was such a drag! But the nights were so cold I just couldn't stay in the streets. It was freezing on the floor too, but at least I had a roof over my head. My friend gave me a guilder every morning and I'd spend the whole day in a coffeehouse or café.

I didn't know a soul in this impersonal town full of impersonal people, except a few bums. One was a hunchback who played a harmonica during the summer to entertain the rich as they sunned themselves on their terraces. All he ate was peanut-butter sandwiches. There was also a fat man who had been dubbed "Count Loafer," because he was a down-at-the-heels aristocrat. He spoke in a refined voice and drooled whenever he saw a woman. He came in for a lot of teasing because he had been castrated by order of his family to keep him from fucking away the entire family fortune with his insatiable lust for women. He was now living on a healthy allowance, so he was generous with drinks and smokes. I used to earn quite a bit of money supplying him with dirty books and pictures. I'd go off to pick up a batch and bring them to him at the coffeehouse, where he waited impatiently with the usual bunch of cronies. He'd grab them, then disappear into the john—to give it one more try. After a while, he asked me to find him a girl and promised she'd be well rewarded for a few unusual tricks. But she had to be a "nice, fresh cherry." That ruled out the town tarts, who were all pretty well reamed out and, since I didn't know any of the local society belles, I gave up after a couple of days.

The hunchbacked musician was a very friendly character, full of jokes and tricks, although most of them were pretty sick—about invalids and deformities. At lunchtime, he unpacked the sandwiches he'd brought from his boardinghouse and shared them with me, which was great, only I don't dig peanut butter. After I had known him a few days, he took me back to his boardinghouse. I met some friends of the landlord, underworld characters who, I was told, might have a job for me. Sure enough, I was offered "work." They told me to meet them at 9 o'clock on the second floor at 13 Wilhelmina Street, keep my trap shut and do what I was told. I realized that the "work" was probably breaking and entering and I didn't feel very enthusiastic about it. My release papers from jail were still in my pocket and I was enjoying my new freedom. I pretty much decided to forget about the job. That was the night I met Brigitte. I walked up and down Wilhelmina Street until 9:30, then took off for the other side of town, the red-light district. I felt at home in the anonymous crowds of salesmen, clerks, laborers and unemployed that thronged the streets there.

. . . And now here I was in a nice, warm place with a tall, beautiful girl beside me, gazing into my eyes as I talked. Before I knew it I had fallen in love with her.

"What a beautiful voice you have," she purred at me. That really embarrassed me and I just shrugged my shoulders, although I've always known that I do have a beautiful voice. I had a very pleasant glow on by the time Brigitte asked me if I'd like to come and stay at her place. After all, I was all alone and homeless and there was always plenty of food at her place. Besides, I could run errands for her. I don't remember much of what happened that night, but the next morning I woke up in a heated room, in a large double bed under soft blankets. Sunlight streamed through yellow curtains and soft music was coming from a radio near my head. I lay there trying to remember what I was doing there, and then I remembered Brigitte. She was gone and there wasn't a sound from the other room. Reluctantly, I got up to have a look around. The gas heater was going full blast and the floor was littered with a pair of high-heeled shoes, stockings and lacy panties. Desperately, I tried to remember what Brigitte looked like. Then I found a picture of her on the dresser.

I went into the small kitchen, got washed and brushed my teeth with her toothbrush. While I was dressing I heard the clatter of high heels on the stairs and in she came, her cheeks flushed with the cold.

Desire overwhelmed me when I saw her standing there, her

lips parted in a smile that radiated sex. I took her in my arms and soon entered the luscious warmth of her body. We writhed, struggled, heaved, bit, and cried out in the heat of our orgasm. It was heaven after being without a woman for so long.

Swinging high as a kite in the clear sky . . . falling into the depths of a blood-red hell . . . those first days I became bitterly jealous whenever Brigitte took one of her customers into the little hotel. I could hardly bear the thought of those lechers, toothless old men, fingering my Goddess, touching her sacred body. I hated them. I hated her. I hated myself. I was mad with jealousy.

There were times when my anger welled up in me like a tide of blood. Blood! Blood! I cried out for their blood! But I repressed these feelings, always somehow managing to control myself. After all, I was her protégé and she was my benefactress, so I had no right to complain. I soon became familiar with the scene and met all kinds of sharp cats, guys it was better to have as friends than as enemies. They were like my brother Jackson, fast with their tongues and faster with their knives. With their pretty faces and sharp-looking suits, they were the terror of the neighborhood. I felt right at home hanging around and playing cards with the pimps, having nothing to do with the square pricks, the Good Citizens who had always put me down. Mine was the world of the sneer beaten from a face, a knife pulled, a chair kicked from under your ass and a threat—a threat, but never a grudge held. Grudges and lectures belonged to the other world of holier-than-thou, to all the lousy teachers, the lousy bosses, the lousy police, the whole lousy, no-good mess called Society.

In the beginning, I fucked Brigitte four or five times a night. What wild nights! Later, when I couldn't manage more than once a night—and that with difficulty—she called me a rotten intellectual. She was nice, she was beautiful, she was sweet, but all the same I couldn't be at it like a pile driver all the time. I gave her a pair of parakeets, but she wouldn't keep them in the cage. She let them flap around the apartment all day. "You wouldn't like to be in a cage, would you?" she said. They flew about freely and they shit freely, too, on our dinner, in our eyes, and on the slicked-down and bleached heads of our friends. We had some awful rows with people over those damn birds.

I tried to wake Brigitte up to a few of the finer things, but she wasn't buying. I gave her a book, *The Black Light* by Mulisch. She tried to read it but had to stop every other minute to ask me what was this and what did that mean. I tried to keep her interested but finally, after getting through only a few pages in an hour and a half, she threw the book at me and yelled, "So this is what you like, you dirty bastard! This filthy trash, this dirty, horny crap full of fucking blacks! Is that what you like?" Give her Superman or Tarzan, though, and you wouldn't hear a peep out of her for hours. Whenever I left to go into town, she'd call after me, "Honey, get me some Tarzan comics, will you? And some bubble gum?" And I would. I loved her, her and her unspoiled mind.

When she came home, tired from the evening's work, I'd be waiting for her with a nice pot of hot tea. The stove was lit and a record was playing on the phonograph she'd bought for me—on condition that I'd play Elvis Presley for her once in a while. The small table lamps cast a cozy glow over the room. I'd lie on the bed reading poems by the Experimentalists—Lodeizen, Andreus, Vinkenoog, Achterberg, Hanlo, Campert or Kouwenaar. When I came to a poem that I understood I'd read a few lines to Brigitte, while she stared intently at my moving lips. When I asked, "How do you like it?" she'd come across the room and plant a smoky kiss on my mouth. "I think it's just darling," she'd say, although she hadn't understood a word of it. The fact is, most of it threw me too. Only when I read Achterberg to her did she listen with a glimmer of understanding, maybe because he was the one I understood best. I read his *Past the Last Town* dozens of times, in bed at night, my body pressed against hers under the blankets. One hand under my head and the other holding the book of poetry, I'd read and then stare at the ceiling for a while, the thoughts running through my head and damn near making me dizzy. I once illustrated a copy of *Past the Last Town*, covering the pages with drawings. It was a good piece of work, and it's a shame that I've lost it.

Everyone said Brigitte and I were made for each other, and we were as happy as a couple of lovebirds. It was nice, too, wearing the good suits, the gold bracelet, the gold watch and the gold ring she bought for me. And when we walked down the street together, people turned to look at us, for she was a beautiful piece of tail. I liked that. She was like a goddess come to earth for the sole purpose of making my life a pleasure. I wanted to marry her, to stay with her forever, but I knew, in my sober moments, that it would never work. For one thing, she was older than me, and though I didn't mind it at the time, I guess I worried that it might matter later.

Brigitte had a list of regular customers who would have me locked up for five years if I printed their names here. But I can tell you that they were all VIPs—all from the top of the social ladder. One of the VIPs—let's call him the Ambassador—sent his big black Rolls around every Thursday evening at 8 o'clock to pick up Brigitte and bring her to a place he had set up for their dates. The Ambassador himself, an old, graying gent, stiff and rheumy, would greet her. First they'd have some champagne. Then Brigitte would take off all her clothes except the pair of high black leather boots worn especially for the occasion, sit down in a black leather easy chair and throw one booted leg (what legs she had!) over each side of the chair. The Ambassador, wheezing and groaning from the strain, would kneel down on his creaking knees, place a handkerchief over her cunt and lick for a few minutes. Then he'd pull out his fat wallet, pass her a hundred guilders and bid her adieu. The chauffeur, who'd been waiting in the Rolls, would then return her to her door, less than an hour after he'd picked her up. When she got back we'd go to a bar and Brigitte would treat everybody to a drink "on Fido," which was her nickname for the old guy. She considered Fido her easiest john, neat and quick and he paid top price.

Another regular was the Professor, a well-known personage (he would have been a perfect patsy for a blackmailer) who had Brigitte fall by once a month. She'd call on him in the middle of the night, and in the pitch-blackness would hold his nervous, sweaty hand while he fucked his own wife on their bed. This one paid a hundred guilders too, plus little extras like genuine pearl necklaces, rings, dresses, stockings and a copy of the *Kama Sutra* for her instruction and edification. On Christmas Eve he gave her a huge roast turkey, which we finished off with our friends Lex, Annette, Andy and Lucy, with lots of laughs at the Professor's expense. We already had two turkeys!

Brigitte wouldn't take on any really unsavory clients, but passed them on to her girl friends. That was the case with Pete the Pisser. Pimples took him off Brigitte's hands (as a matter of fact it was Pimples who named him) and went to see him every week. He was a little guy with glasses who looked like a minor official or a clerk. Actually he was very high in the Army, something like a brigadier general. Pimples had to stretch out full-length on the big sheet of canvas he had spread out to protect the Persian carpet in his living room. Then he'd pull out his peter and piss all over her face, after which, groaning and heaving, he'd come. Then he'd pay her and send her on her way, all very proper and businesslike. We once ran into him, the miserable sneak, and really gave him a hard time, putting him on about his sex life. He was flabbergasted!

The small hotel where Brigitte plied her trade was called the Hotel Buddha. It was run by a low character by the name of Charley, with a slick black moustache, who looked like a Spaniard. I never liked the guy. Rooms were rented for twenty guilders an hour. There were about twenty small rooms and each had a built-in loudspeaker and microphone, so that if one of the girls had trouble she would be heard at the switchboard. The switchboard was in a cubbyhole next to the lobby, and Charley always sat there on guard duty, playing cards with his cronies. I never actually caught Charley cheating during those games, but I knew for sure he was doing it. Playing poker or twenty-one in the cubbyhole, we could hear exactly which rooms were in use, and once in a while a chick would call out, "Hey, Charley, can you change twenty-five guilders for me? Would you bring it right up to number 14?" Charley would swear and slam his cards down on the table: "Goddammit, just when the luck's running my way! I'll be right back, boys." And we'd wait for him. The pimps never stole or got into a fight they could avoid; they stepped lightly where the law was concerned. The trick was to take it easy, play it cool and keep making money. That's just what they did and so did I. I had my housekeeping money, pocket money, money for smokes, money for the flicks and money for drinks. I lived well but after a while this kind of hanging around began to be a drag.

I'd been thinking for some time about getting back to painting, ever since the weekend Brigitte and I went to Amsterdam to visit my mother. We'd seen an avant-garde exhibition at the Stedelijk Museum. Brigitte didn't much care what I did, as long as the chow was ready on time. She even seemed pleased at the idea of my doing something I'd enjoy, so one day I went out and spent a pile of dough on paper, paints and canvas. I made a studio for myself in a corner of the room by placing the double bed diagonal to the walls. Then I spread some newspaper on the floor to protect the rug (Brigitte had said, "I don't care what you do, just don't get any paint on my rug.") and I started smearing. Paint got on the rug, anyway, and on the bed and on the blankets and on everything else within range. Eventually I left paintpots simmering on the stove next to the soup, and paint-smeared brushes lying on a crocheted doily on the dresser. The whole place stank of turps. Brigitte got really pissed off a few times and I always apologized, although I didn't really give a shit about the mess.

I decided to paint a portrait of Brigitte in the nude. At first she said she'd have no part of it. She'd never allowed anyone to photograph her in the nude and she wasn't going to be painted in the nude either. After much gentle persuasion, though, she finally gave way—on condition that, when I was famous, I'd never exhibit the portrait unless I made her face unrecognizable. So on one of her nights off, we turned away all visitors, saying that we wanted a night to ourselves for a change.

. . . The evening was filled with atmosphere. Dark, smoky clouds drifted through the candle-lit room, and from the distance came the humming of thousands of ants. On this moonlit night I met Kikiras, Son of the Black Moon. He asked me to witness the Battle of Night and I watched, for I could not keep my eyes off the Form of the Female (I had died a thousand deaths under Her and wanted to die another thousand times and thousands of times thereafter), the Form of a Goddess from the *Kama Sutra*. I watched the movements of perfect grace as her shoes slipped off her lovely feet and her skirt crept up (I had seen this so many times, but found it more enchanting each time), revealing the spot where her stockings ended: the beautiful white flesh, the fragrant flesh, the asking flesh that bulged ever so slightly where it emerged from the stockings, then rolled under pink garters up to the mound of Venus, where a black, luxuriant bush grew, curling and beckoning from the edges of her cream-colored panties. Then the skirt went over her head. Her golden hair, her soft, wonderful, sweet-smelling angel's hair fell down over her bare shoulders. Deftly she unbuttoned her brassiere and the firm spheres of flesh, the inviting spheres of flesh softly rolled out, pale pink breasts with nipples tasting of honey, wonderful, ripe, light-ochre nipples ending in buttons like ice-cream cones. With a smile on her sweet face she stepped out of her silk panties, the Valley of Heaven still half-hidden by the garter belt. Then the stockings were rolled down carefully by her slender, graceful hands with the long, jungle-green nails. I stood up and threw her on the bed. Sweating and sighing we descended into the deepest crater of the sun, her vagina agape at my command, my moonseed streaming into her ravaged but virginal body. Our feet burned in the ferocious heat and on our stumps we hopped through the lilac twilight. I watched the flight of the sun, a racing red ball, through the moon-night cosmos. I met the corpse of a Crater-Creature that wanted to sacrifice my testicles to the Bird-Demons.

We suddenly awoke and Brigitte posed for me. I wanted to immortalize her on the canvas as I saw her, surrounded by on-lookers dribbling sperm from their mouths, my Goddess of Erotic Joy.

After hours of steady work I finally had a nude woman on the canvas, but a woman like every run-of-the-mill artist paints, a cold hunk of meat with two red points and a black spot on her crotch.

103

It was a winter night, cold as a witch's tit, and we were all hanging around the Buddha. Brigitte was upstairs. A half-hearted card game was going on at the table near the switchboard, but I'd arrived too late to join in, so I was watching without much interest. We had lit an extra oilstove and a nasty, humid smell hung over the room. Tom, Big Hans, Lex, Charley, Andy and I were seated around the table. After every hand, the cards were shuffled and slapped down in a hypnotic rhythm. Suddenly there was a violent crackling from the loudspeaker. We all looked up, but there was no further sound, so the game continued. Then a scream, a hideous gurgling screech, ripped through the amplifier. They dropped the cards on the table, and Charley yelled half at us and half into the microphone, "Goddamn mother-fucking cocksucker—what the hell is that? Who's up there? Annette, Brigitte, Annie, Laura . . . who else? What the hell is going on?"

We all made a rush for the stairs. It was Friday night and a lot of broads were working. Everyone began knocking at random on the doors, pounding and shouting and making a hell of a racket. I made straight for Brigitte's room. She opened the door, dressed in her robe. "Upstairs," she said, her face pale from fright, "it's upstairs! Jan! Stay here! Come back!" Carried along in the general excitement, I was tearing up the stairs. I'd had a vision of Brigitte strangled with a silk scarf, a knife jammed between her lovely breasts, and now I was acting the hero for her sake. Everywhere doors were flung open and girls in various stages of undress were running around, yelling hysterically, while in the background several little men, ridiculous in long underwear, slipped their glasses back on and disappeared quickly behind doors and screens. Andy was just in front of me. The girls from rooms 16 and 17 stood in front of their doors, but the door to room 18 was closed. Andy began to hammer on it, shouting, "Lucy! Open up!" When this got no results, Andy stepped back a few paces and crashed through the door, straight into a knife wielded by a huge, scar-faced bruiser. Andy groaned and collapsed to the floor.

Lex threw himself into the room and began to attack the guy with his iron fists, beating him mercilessly to the floor. The landing was full of people, all yelling "Help!" and "Police!" Red-faced Charley was weaving in and out among them, shitting in his pants and whining, "I told them! I told them not to bring in just any old piece of shit they run into! Damn sluts!" I had seen Andy collapse and I myself was scared to death, but I was crowded in on all sides and couldn't get away. Lex had beaten the guy unconscious but went on kicking him in blind fury, and there was blood all over the guy's face. The push of the crowd behind me forced me into the room, and I saw Lucy lying on the bed, stark naked. Everything was bloody, sheets, blankets and clothing. I figured she must be dead. The girls were bent over her with wet rags. Andy lay on the floor, his clothes slit down the middle. Then I felt Brigitte's soft hands on me. Andy came to and tried to get up but we held him down to the floor, where he was lying in a pool of his own blood. His big brown eyes opened wide with fright when he caught sight of his bloody belly. He mumbled, "Christ, it hurts! How is Lucy?" They'd been together for years. I looked at Lucy again, lying lifeless on the bed.

The bastard responsible for the whole mess began to come around and a couple of guys began kicking him again. He passed out. Just then I caught sight of some john from one of the other rooms. He raised his fist over Big Hans' head and brought it down with force. Hans disappeared from sight. The crowd fell on the goon and began to pummel him and the guys he was with—a bunch of beered-up Norwegian sailors. The girls used their spiked heels to clout them in the eyes. Even Brigitte joined in. It was madness, with people breaking out into private fights in the midst of the confusion, settling old accounts that had nothing to do with the present fracas. Everybody was belting everybody else. Two nasty-looking little guys, detectives, began to shove their way through the battle, and that was the moment I decided to split. I let myself be swallowed up in the crowd and slowly made my way to the door, stopping only to give one of the detectives, who was trying to arrest Big Hans, a good kick in the ass. Downstairs I looked around for Brigitte, but couldn't find her. Annette told me Brigitte had gone home to wait for me. I cut out, and not a moment too soon, for a minute later police wagons pulled up, sirens screaming, and those stalwart servants of the people, the cops, stormed the place with drawn sabers and truncheons.

When I got home, Brigitte was in the shower. She shouted to me, "Thank God you're back!" I undressed and joined her. Her body was steaming from the hot water and we embraced under the spray. Later, in front of the mirror, I discovered that I hadn't been too successful at trying to stay out of the fight—I was bruised all over, one of my eyes was swollen shut and my lips were puffed up like a couple of marshmallows. Brigitte, dressed only in a bra and panties, began to dab tenderly at my wounds with ointment. Her breasts spilled out from the bra every time she leaned over, and my tongue darted out to caress them. We made love, beautiful love.

As it turned out, Lucy's knife wound hadn't been fatal, and after a few weeks in the hospital, both she and Andy were back at the Buddha. The Norwegian sailors were locked up for assault with intent to kill.

104

My painting was going well and I made up my mind to enter the academy. So one morning Charley drove me there in his Ford, my portfolio in hand, my best suit on, and my face still smarting from a close shave. Brigitte and Nanny had insisted on coming along. I didn't like the idea, but I couldn't change their minds. They looked great to me, but I could imagine how they'd impress the head of the academy in their flower-splashed, low-cut dresses, their breasts bulging out and a heavy odor of perfume trailing along behind them.

We entered the building just at the break between classes, and the hallway was jammed with students, all ogling us as we proceeded to the Director's office, the girls' high heels clattering on he marble floor. The Director received us with some surprise. "Yes?" he said, looking us up and down. "What can I do for you?" Brigitte was chattering away before I could say a word.

"Look here, Mr. . . . uh . . . Mr. Director. We have a boy here who wants to enroll in your academy."

"Oh?" said the man, looking at me rather strangely. "I'm afraid we don't accept pupils in midterm." Another penetrating look in my direction: "Have you had any formal training, young man? What were you planning to study at this academy?"

Brigitte beat me to it again. "Study? Study? My good man, this boy paints so well he should be *teaching* here. You should be proud that he's chosen your academy. You understand? He is an extraordinary talent. I don't know much about art, but one thing I can tell you, Sir, he knows it *all!*"

I could see how the Director must be sizing me up: a slick young pimp who wanted some new blood in his stable and thought the academy, with its abundant supply of young students and nude models, would be a fine place to shop around. I was about to start telling him about my art background when he said, "I must warn you that the fees here are quite high. If you find you can manage the fees we could then consider registering you for the next semester. First my staff and I would have to examine your work——"

"What's all this crap got to do with it?" Brigitte shouted. "Look here, what we want to know is can he or can he not get into the academy!" She was leaning over him, both hands on his desk, her enormous breasts exposed to his nervous glance. He sputtered something, but Brigitte didn't give him the chance to speak. "Or aren't we good enough for the academy? Is that it? Isn't our loot clean enough for you?"

"Madam, you must realize, I don't know you or what your relationship is to this young man" (with a nod towards me, standing there like a damn fool). I could see Brigitte getting more and more excited. She'd placed her hands on her hips and was staring bitterly at the poor man. Nanny stood near the door, her red umbrella raised for battle.

"You listen to me, Daddy-o!" Brigitte screamed. "Don't think you can impress me with your snob act! I've been around, you know, I've seen your type before. You uppity bastards have pricks in your pants like everybody else!"

That did it! They guy looked like he would explode. And the way Brigitte was standing over him, he couldn't even get up from his chair. Well, so much for the academy. "Come on Brigitte," I said, "let's go!"

"Come on, Brit," Nanny said, "let the asshole drop dead! I told you it wouldn't be any good. All these rich cocksuckers—they're a bunch of parasites!"

Brigitte finally turned to go. "You wouldn't want to be caught dead in this hole, Jan. Let's go!"

It was time to go, all right. I could imagine what would happen if we didn't. Brigitte would let loose at the man with everything she had, including those long, venomous nails of hers. Then Nanny would let fly with her red umbrella and before we knew it we'd be hauled in. I wished to hell I'd come alone, but it was too late now.

In the hallway the two of them muttered obscene remarks at the gaping students. I was relieved when we finally got outside. Brigitte was still fuming. "They think they can treat you like a dog just because you work for your money. And why? Because your father isn't the Ambassador to the

206

United States or a girdle manufacturer! Screw them all!"
She spit on the pavement behind her "And he had the nerve
to call me a whore! The asshole! Let's forget the whole thing!
We'll go and have some coffee at Aunt Sjuul's."

TABI NORA SOPHIA
JOSEPHINE
JUDITH ALLEGRINA PASCALE
DALIDA

105

I wound up one of my journeys at La Camargue, in the south of France, where I became a cowboy. It was a wonderful life: lots of horses, and the only kind of horseshit around was the real thing. But I was caught in bed with the daughter of the ranch owner. She was engaged to the foreman at the time, so I bid a hasty farewell to my four-footed friends and left at full gallop on the back of a mustang.

In Germany I got a contract to paint theatrical scenery. I hired six employees, who painted the sets while I tinkered with an old motorcycle in the courtyard. Journalists came to ask me questions, for I was a hot item in the gossip columns. I tried to give them an interesting story, hinting that I'd been something of a motor-racing hero. Next day a long article appeared in the *Neue Ruhr Zeitung* with the headline: *"Well-known Racing Driver Paints Theater Sets."*

In Spain I was a bullfighter. What else was there to do? I became a nightclub porter, joined the other porters in their football games and went fishing with them at 5 A.M. I always brought along my portable radio. I dreamt that I have to parachute from a plane. I jump, but someone has cut the cords and the parachute won't open. Fortunately, we're flying over the ocean, so I shoot down like a rocket and hit the water with terrific impact. I sink lower and lower. I try to surface, but I'm as heavy as lead. Around me it gets darker and darker ...

Eeny, meeny, miney, mo. In Naples I saw the cruiser *Garibaldi*. In Genoa I stole 10,000 lira from the cash register at a fruit stand. In a Swiss village near the St. Gotthard Tunnel I slept at a hostel in a bed made to hold thirty-six people, the women below and the men above. That night there were only two of us, myself and a British girl who snuggled up to me because it was so cold. I had to wear two pairs of socks because my feet sank in the snow every time I took a step. I bought a bottle of ninety-proof brandy for insulation. A day later I was photographed in Lugano, standing under a palm tree in a bathing suit.

I hailed a lonely cyclist on a long, dark road and asked him for a light. "I'll have your bike, too, Mister, if you don't mind!" But he wouldn't give, so I had to knock him down. I hated to do it, but I'd been wandering for three days and three nights without food or sleep. The man sat up but didn't say a word. I grabbed his bike and started off. When I came to a bridge lit by yellow neon lights, I got off the bike and pitched it into the water. Then I tried to hitch a ride but no one would stop to pick me up. Whenever I saw sparks flying back from a car window, I ran like a fool to pick up the cigarette butt. The couple of drags tasted great.

106

I awoke with a start. The peppermint in my mouth (compliments of KLM) tasted bitter. I asked the stewardess for a beer. Through the window I saw below the plane a pile of clouds you could have walked on. I found my place in the book I'd been reading, Henry Kane's *Armchair in Hell*. Soon they instructed us to put out our cigarettes and fasten our seat belts. Paris was below us, lying at my feet. The city was clean, clear and fresh—it was wintertime. In the summer, flying into Paris, you're enveloped in a thick fog of exhaust fumes, dust and factory smoke, and only the tip of the Eiffel Tower is visible.

I had a drink at the airport, took a taxi into town, had another drink (plane trips always make me thirsty) and made for the office on Boulevard Raspail where I was to report. I had received a study grant from the French Government for a year of looking around, a bit of work and lots of "enriching my horizons," as it said in the letters of recommendation from the museum directors who had selected me to benefit from this friendly gesture. *Vive la France!* Every month I received invitations for receptions and for excursions to Versailles (I had seen enough tulips in Holland). And there were always reams of forms to be filled out—"*Formulier de déclaration.*" I just kept filling them out and harvesting sheaves of banknotes. Such pretty lettuce: yellow paper with a picture of a man in a brown goatee and a skullcap—probably the pope.

I had four different identity cards: one to pick up my money, one for meals, one for admission to academies and museums, and one for nightclubs. I had become a number again, but this time I didn't mind it. I felt I had successfully adapted myself and was on the road to success. What poverty I had known in Paris in the past! But that was all behind me now.

The first hotel I lived in was clean and pleasant: double bed, bidet, toilet, roses on the wallpaper, large balcony and a view of the Observatoire. But I discovered that they prohibited visitors after 11 P.M. and the view of the Observatoire began to bore me. So I found a place more my style and lived there for quite a while, a small hotel in the Latin Quarter, just across the street from the Sorbonne (who said I never got within a mile of an education?). The place had an international clientele—Negroes, Chinese, Japanese and some American beatniks who later whined a record of *Holy, Holy, Holy.*

Now I was really swinging, with a nice Spanish chick friend for my leisure hours, a chick who worked in the office where they gave out vouchers for meals (I pocketed plenty of them). When I came down with a serious infection of the lungs and throat, the university medical department gave me free treatment, and even put in two gold teeth. I only had to pay the price of the gold. I became a regular hypochondriac, with some new complaint every week, and I managed to get prescriptions for all kinds of pills—benzedrine, tranquillizers, sleeping pills and pep-up pills. In fact, the only time the medical department drew the line was when I tried to get an abortion for a Filipino girl. That I was supposed to handle free-lance, and I had to turn over one entire month's allowance to a Chinese doctor. Another time, I knocked down a cabdriver who called me a Kraut. He absolutely refused to go into the university clinic (his brother-in-law had gone in once with a sore throat and come out again with both legs cut off at the knee), so I had to pay the private doctor who treated him. The first few months

I was supposed to take it easy and acclimatize myself to the City of Light. Paris is a nice town, and expensive, but I wasn't stingy with myself. I'd lived long enough on dry bread and turnips in fat with onions. I'd already had my seven lean years, now it was time for the fat ones. After all, if you haven't hung around the Moulin Rouge, the Lido, Pam-Pam, La Tour d'Argent, Maxim's, Les Deux Magots, the Bonaparte, La Coupole, the Select, Le Dôme, the Monaco, Madame Arthur's and La Reine Blanche, you haven't seen Paris. And I had to have my inspiration! I had already seen the Eiffel Tower in 1956 when I shared a room in the Cité Universitaire with James O'Hara, a Negro student from Michigan. He used to attend the Sorbonne during the day while I stayed in the room and messed around with pastels. I once painted a prick and asked James how he liked it. He thought it was great and wanted to buy it, but I wouldn't sell it. I gave it to him. Then we knocked off for the day to see the town, including the Eiffel Tower.

Now I went back to see it again, this time with a girl friend's three-year-old daughter. We sat in the little park under the tower. No one else was around so I told the little squirt that the tower was a huge iron monster and had eaten all the other people in the park. She started screaming and raised a hell of a racket. I had to take her right home. On the way, every time she caught a glimpse of so much as the tip of the tower she broke into hysterics. I bet she'll never send anyone a postcard with a picture of the Eiffel Tower!

Despite the beauty of the city itself, my main inspiration came from the galleries on the Rue de Seine. I saw so much shit there that I felt I had to paint something good. I went to the Academie de la Grande Chaumière, run by the white master Ossip Zadkine. (I remember sailing up the Nieuwe Waterweg into Rotterdam. Three American ladies pointed to the *Maritime Monument* towering above the rooftops and asked the captain what it represented. "That? That's Zatopek's sculpture of a city with its heart torn out," said the captain, proudly. Enraptured, the ladies threw up their hands and exclaimed, "Oh, it's perfectly charming!") I made some rough sketches, good ones, of a nude Negro chick with nipples like giant strawberries. But I found the academy too commercial for my taste. American ladies sat mixing expensive tubes of chrome yellow and cobalt blue, their bracelets jangling, their marten-hair brushes resting on their palettes. The Great Master Himself hardly ever showed his face. Shinkichi Tajiri worked in the garden studio. A few doors down from the academy was Chez Wadja, a good restaurant that was popular with the students. They served great fried potatoes, crisp and tasty new potatoes. If you were out of cash you could pay for a meal with a drawing. Ah, *la vie bohème!*

107

I met Gabo, a Hungarian, who was the founder-owner-manager of an academy. He fucked his way through his entire female student body, laying two to six different chicks a week. A lot of them stormed out of the academy in a rage because they didn't want to overpay for their art instruction. His appetite was insatiable. Somehow, he'd got hold of a large old house, boarded off a few floors, chucked in a few stands and easels and a divan for the model, and called it an academy. It was a howling success. The rich came, eager for a taste of the artist's life, anxious to suffer— for them it was a lark, and they paid through the nose for it! The serious students came too, because they liked Gabo and they liked the atmosphere. If you didn't want to work, you just stayed away—as long as you paid your class money, six francs an hour. Every student got a large registration certificate, on which the Director personally put his signature right across a large stamp. Gabo had once been a customs official in Hungary and had a mania for stamps. He stamped everything. I developed an interest of my own in Gabo's mania, for every week it was he who stamped my declaration forms. We made them out for thousands of guilders worth of paint. He took his cut, of course—business, after all, is business. He was quite the businessman. For a night's lodging on the model's divan in the academy he asked five francs; you could sleep on the floor in a sleeping bag for four. With the profits from the academy he bought old studio buildings in the Rue de Tombe-Issoire. Out of every room he would make eight cubicles and rent them to Chinese and Japanese students. He couldn't accommodate Swedes or Germans in the place, for they couldn't have stood up straight.

I worked in an annex to the academy, in the Rue de Montparnasse, a bare, wooden shed in the middle of a storage yard for granite. A bunch of newly arrived Japanese students boarded in the place, sacking out at night on lumpy mattresses under straw mats. They paid five francs a day. There was no light, no gas, no water, and at night they were locked into the yard by the people who ran the granite business. Gabo had made a virtue of each deficiency in his sales spiel. "Sure it's inconvenient! But what beautiful inconvenience! You have to know deprivation to become an artist, you know that! Besides, you should only work in daylight. Electric light ruins the eyesight. Only daylight! Daylight!" So the Japanese went to sleep at 5 P.M. and rose at the crack of dawn. They worked incessantly. Gabo kept pigeons in the place too, another hobby, and he was very proud of his flock, which included all sorts of expensive species. To the Japanese they were merely a bunch of birds. I ate lunch with them—rice with pigeon.

108

My Negro chick from Mozambique had tattoos on her face. Tabi Urual Casi Buru Inhambane Bent was her name. I called her Tabi. She was a striking creature, with the grace and beauty of a Bengal tiger. She didn't walk, she slinked, her tall, strong, muscular, supple body swaying slightly. It didn't take her long to initiate me into the customs of her people, the ones you don't read about in the textbooks, for I was an avid pupil. Tabi (and I, after a while) lived in a crazy little room in a small hotel, with lots of pillows thrown about the place and spears and shields on the walls. She was studying psychology at the Sorbonne. She always dressed in her native costume, for she was the daughter of a tribal chief. I toyed with the idea of adopting tribal dress for myself, but I decided that a bright orange scarf, a yellow caftan and a beaded cap wouldn't be too becoming. I picked her up every night at school and we'd go to eat at one of the students' restaurants, then to the flicks or a jazz club, and finally back to her place for a night at home. Those quiet evenings at home with her were great.

The students' restaurants we ate in were always packed to the rafters and everyone slurped and chirped away like so many sparrows. They threw bread balls and whistled when I walked in wearing my tiger-striped jacket. It revolted me, all those mouths chewing, chewing. I pushed one bastard's face into his soup when he refused to pass the bread. The food was good, but I couldn't stomach the place: rows of people sitting and chewing at long tables—it reminded me of starvation, war and sorrow. None of my friends were allowed inside because they didn't have student meal vouchers, and a couple of self-important little twirps stood outside the door checking every card over before you could get in. They acted like *gendarmes* from the Sûreté. I once threw one of them downstairs at the Odéon.

Tabi had a brother, Danga. The three of us used to hang out together at the Blue Note or Storyville. Danga could

213

roll a joint in one turn of his hand, without spilling any of the pot. He told me about the customs of his tribe. Little girls are sewn into lion skins. Their toe and finger bones are broken and reshaped into claws. The corners of their mouths are cut and their teeth are filed to points. After six months of training inside the skins—all the while kept on drugs—they emerge Lion People, scratching, crawling on all fours, downing red meat and ripping humans apart at a command from their master. I planned to go with Danga to Mozambique during the summer, but at the last moment I vetoed the idea. I had seen myself in a dream, stark naked, a tusk through my nose and my spear glistening with poison at the tip, dancing wildly around a white man tied to a totem pole.

109

One of my girl friends, the daughter of a Belgian Minister, was writing a dissertation on *Birth Control and Childlessness in Rome at the Time of Giambattista Piazzetta*. It was at her home that I met Manuel, a Spanish painter, who became one of my closest friends. One time he took me along to a party at the home of Monsieur Dupont, a millionaire manufacturer of beer, lemonade and soda. Madame Dupont, a very beautiful Madame, spent her time painting and buying art. Once a week Dupont went bowling with his friends in the Bois de Boulogne. That was the night chosen by Madame for her weekly soiree. And Madame was an extravagant hostess ("Do call me Nora!"). There were all kinds of meats and hors d'oeuvres and gallons of beer, wine, whiskey and champagne. The place was jammed with custom-made suits and expensive gowns. The most successful and well-known artists were always there, clutching drinks and admiring Nora's work, which lined the walls of her massive studio. Every one of them could find imitations of his own style among her efforts, for when Madame bought a Foujita, she began to paint like Foujita—and on real linen, with marten-hair brushes.

After supper we sat in easy chairs and discussed Art. The conversation eventually bogged down into gossip about personal feuds. Aided by the flowing booze, tempers flared. I kept out of things because I still didn't speak French too well. Manuel had introduced me to Madame as "an exceptionally talented and famous painter from Holland." She looked at me, obviously enchanted, clasped her hands together and cried, "Oh-la-la! But you must come and take a look at my paintings. I should adore having a famous Dutch artist judge my work!" So I trotted along after her, not saying a word. I couldn't very well tell her how bad her paintings were, nor was my French good enough for lying. She took my silence for overwhelming approval and produced a portfolio. I wasn't in any mood for art, much less her pale imitations. Besides which, I was loaded to the gills. So I just muttered a few unintelligible comments, nodded my head once or twice and managed to slip my arm around her waist, which she pretended not to notice.

She didn't leave my side for the rest of the evening. The discussions, which continued to rage, grew less and less coherent, so I settled myself on a large, comfortable couch and Nora came galloping over with a stack of expensive art books. She tossed one in my lap, nearly rupturing me. She went through every book with me—*Expressionism, Impressionism, Gauguin, The School of Paris, The Life and Works of Vincent van Gogh, Rococo Art* and so on—never failing to tell me how much each had cost. The prices, always over one hundred guilders, did impress me. Obediently, I leafed through each of them, exclaiming at appropriate points, while Nora kept hopping up to refill my glass and bring me tidbits from the table. She must have been about thirty-five, and looked good to me. She was dressed in turquoise velvet, her tits overflowing at the top. A king's ransom in ice flashed from her throat, ears and fingers. God knows what I said that evening, but Nora kept staring at me, apparently entranced, pausing only occasionally to toss a comment into the group discussion. She wanted to see my work . . . "If only I might!" I told her I didn't really have much to show because I hadn't yet found a studio. I really poured it on heavy. "I'm not sure how long I'll be staying in Europe, so I just can't make up my mind whether to buy a studio apartment." She was impressed. "But does it not hurt you terribly—inside, I mean —not to be working?" "It's unbearable," I assured her. "Everything conspires against me. Those real-estate agents take up all my time, trying to push houses on me that really won't do at all. All I really want is some place where I can get on with my painting in peace and quiet."

When I'd had all I could take of the drink and conversation, I nudged Manuel and we got ready to leave. Nora thanked him profusely for bringing me along and asked me for my address. "I'm slumming at the moment," I said, as I wrote it on a slip of paper. "But I mean to put all the lowlife on canvas. And now I must go. I thank you for your hospitality." And with a reverent bow, I departed.

In the taxi, Manuel complained. "Why would a woman

like that fall like a ton of bricks for you? You didn't open your trap the whole evening!"

"We Dutch geniuses don't say much," I said. "We're too busy creating!"

I had to throw up before I could fall asleep that night.

110

Killing time one day on the terrace of Le Mabillon, I was jolted by a rude waiter in a blue apron who suddenly slapped a folded napkin on my table. He was after a fly. With the arrogance peculiar to French waiters, he asked me what I wanted. I wanted hot wine, but every time I had tried to order it, I always got a glass of milk or a sweet liqueur instead. As I was trying to figure out the proper words to get my point across, the waiter walked away to the next table. The man there ordered something that sounded good, so I shouted, *"Moi aussi! la même chose!"* A few minutes later the waiter brought me an ashtray.

111

Nora telephoned me at my hotel. She had just finished a new painting that she wanted me to see and she had a surprise for me. The painting didn't interest me, but the surprise did, so I hopped a cab to her place. She greeted me with kisses on both cheeks and immediately gave me a whiskey. I looked at her new painting, making a few well-chosen comments, wondering all the time what the hell the surprise was. One thing certain, it wasn't bed, because her husband was there, a nice old guy with wrinkles and a white goatee.

She had spoken with Monsieur Dupont about me, she said, and they decided that if I cared to, I could move into a little flat they owned. She thought it would be perfect for me, but of course I must see it for myself, and if it pleased me, *voilà!* I could live in it—no charge, *naturellement*—until it was sold, and they weren't in any great rush to sell it. She explained that Dupont had bought the flat for her while he was waiting for a divorce from his last wife and that she'd lived there herself before their marriage. Smiling, they handed me the keys. I told them I'd let them know if it met my requirements. "In any case," I said, "thank you most sincerely."

I made straight for the place, a well-cared-for eight-story building behind the Gare du Montparnasse, and went right up to the seventh floor. The "little flat" was actually a tremendous layout, with a big balcony and a great view of—I don't remember what. There was a TV set with remote controls, a stereo system with records, lush modern furnishings, a bar crammed with half-full bottles, inch-thick blue carpeting dotted here and there with handwoven rugs, two guest rooms, central heating, a radio, rows of bookshelves packed with things like a first edition of *Mein Kampf*, a large kitchen (there was a plate of dried-up spaghetti sitting on the table), a luxurious bathroom and, of course, Nora's paintings all over the walls. Later on I found some old nude photos of her—very appetizing indeed! After an hour or so, I telephoned the Duponts. "It is a bit small, but it will do nicely," I said. "Thank you again." Nora said she was delighted and would drop by soon to see that I was properly settled in. "You'll find sheets in the linen closet. If you have any questions about anything, the cleaning woman will be in twice a week—she'll show you where everything is. And now, my dear, toodle-oo!"

112

I had calling cards printed at once, with my new address and phone number, and sent invitations to everyone I could think of to visit me at my new place. I bought myself a Harley Davidson (750 cc.) and, with the rent money I saved in the next few months, I fixed it up with a siren, a walkie-talkie and a saddle studded with copper nails. When I found that the Harley was uneconomical and impractical in the heavy Paris traffic, I bought myself a Vespa too. But the H-D was my baby. I painted it silver and sped along like a bolt of lightning. The police confiscated the Vespa after I had collected twenty-eight tickets, so I bought another one. I had a black leather outfit made for myself long before it became standard gear for the bike-brigade boys. And I spent most of my time driving around in my black leather suit, black leather boots, black leather gloves, a black leather cap and black sunglasses. Everyone called me the Black Super Hood. *Heigh-ho Silver, aw-a-a-a-y!*

I got to know Paris inside out. Occasionally I'd shoot out to a village fifty miles or so away, because I liked the onion soup at a certain inn there. I used to scare hell out of chicks, who were always glad for the chance of a spin, perched on the back seat behind me. I'd drive out of the city, onto Route Nationale 7 and go so fast that they'd scream for mercy. Then I'd go faster. For the tougher cases, I saved my *pièces de résistance*, like taking my hands off the handlebars at ninety mph, or wriggling the front wheel at sixty-five, or standing up on the saddle or putting my head down between my legs. If that didn't do it, I'd get it up to a hundred and then, put both legs on the handlebars and both hands in the air. Sometimes I'd go after motorcycle cops for kicks. It was a matter of honor. In town they'd tear past me at the stoplights, but on the open road they might as well have been riding bicycles.

113

I had no time for painting. I had girls coming in all the time to cook and clean for me. I'd canned the cleaning woman because she always showed up too early and got in my way. When Nora phoned, from time to time, to make a date to see me, I'd drop what I was doing, take off to the Rue de la Grande Chaumière for a framed canvas and some paint and empty the tubes onto the canvas. When she came she always brought something for me, a cake, an art book or twelve tubes of Paul Veronese green. We'd review my latest effort, and she'd always exclaim over it. But I'd say, "No, I'm not pleased with it, not pleased with it at all. But it is, after all, only a preparatory study."

Once a month I went to dine at her place and to look at her work. She was now painting in my style of *Peinture Barbarisme*, but that only lasted until she discovered that she'd ruined the carpet and a couple of her favorite sweaters. Then she switched to another style. We never slept together. I couldn't tell how she stood on that score and I didn't want to risk my setup by molesting my patroness. Besides, I already had all the broads I could manage. How they dug my pad, with the TV, the big soft bed and me!

Things went beautifully. I bought myself a swing and attached it to the roof of the balcony. When it rained I'd swing all afternoon. Once a week I threw a party. Everyone had to bring his own booze and a little grub, and the girls took care of all the preparations while we guys watched TV or listened to my favorite records—Bach, Wagner, Rimski-Korsakov, *West Side Story* and the Everly Brothers. A friend of mine had married a girl who was making it big in the movies, so there were always a lot of movie and theater people hanging around—Pascale, Dalida, Emanuel, Allegrina, Jean, Rita, Claudia and Aki fixed my grub. We played roulette with a wheel I had picked up at the Flea Market, danced, gossiped, played our guitars and sometimes took in film premieres on the Champs Elysée.

218

114

After a while I found myself badly in debt to garages, cafés, paint shops and various buddies. I let my apartment for two weeks to a pupil of Marcel Marceau, a girl who spent most of the day hopping around the place with a baton. She paid me one hundred francs a week. I figured I'd let my place for a couple of weeks every month. I spent my nights in bistros, occasionally got a bit of work in the monstrous market at Les Halles and slept by day at a girl friend's place. It got pretty tough at times in Les Halles. The foremen would appear and toss a handful of numbers into the crowd of waiting men and then there'd be a vicious scramble to get hold of one. When I'd had my fill of that, I used to walk aimlessly around the red-light districts, watching the cops stage raids or shoot down Algerians. I was run in on three occasions because I'd left my ID card at home. Each time I was set free with profuse apologies when it was discovered that I was a guest of the French government.

Josephine was a dancer with the Bluebells Girls. When she found out she'd be going on tour to South America, she promised me the use of her room for three weeks. I made a date to meet her at Popoff's before she left, but, exhausted from three nights without sleep, I had taken a hotel room, sacked out and overslept. So I missed her and she took her keys with her. When the Marceau pupil left, I moved back into my own place.

It looks so simple, when you're sitting in the Luxembourg Gardens, just to lie down on the grass and have yourself a snooze. Surely nobody will even notice. But just try it! You've just shut your eyes when you feel the nudge of a cop's nightstick—"Okay, son, move along now." Or else some brat's ball bounces off your head and you start up, thinking the bomb has been dropped. There's no place like home.

115

When my grant had expired and the Duponts had finally sold the apartment, I found myself flat broke. So I worked out a crafty little con to solve the rent problem. I'd enter a hotel late at night and nine times out of ten the desk clerk was dozing, with his legs up on the counter. Without making a sound, I'd look over the keyboard and find myself a room number with the key still on the board and no letters in the slot. Without quite waking up, the clerk gave me the key I asked for. Then I'd go upstairs and get a good night's sleep in a comfortable bed. I'd leave early in the morning, whistling as I strolled past the desk. Only once did things go wrong, when I'd come in really late and overslept the next morning. When I awoke I heard the chambermaid shouting and rattling the door. I jumped out of bed and threw on my clothes as quickly as I could. She moved on to the next room with her clanking pails and, nervous as a cat, I washed and brushed my teeth (Mother's lessons die hard!). The chambermaid returned, muttering and grumbling and turning the doorknob back and forth, then walked away again, no doubt on her way downstairs for the key. I grabbed the key to my Vespa from where it had been lying above the sink, but in my frenzy I dropped it right into the drain. I tried to pry it out with my fingers but it had slipped into the pipe. There wasn't time to get it any other way, so with a few good yanks I tore the sink from the wall. Water gushed all over the floor. Inserting my fingers into the pipe that was left sticking up from the floor, I managed to get a grip on the key, but after I'd carefully edged it along a little bit, the damn thing slipped out of my grip for the second time, down into the pipe. I started to sweat. Any moment the chambermaid would be back with a key. I ripped the whole pipe out of the floor. A geyser spurted up and water cascaded to the floor. I was going to have to start swimming in a moment, but I had my key! Feverishly, I tore a curtain from the window and stuffed it into the hole. Then I slipped out of the room. There was no one in the corridor, but I heard a racket from the stairs. So I hid behind a heavy curtain. When the chambermaid and a man had gone past me, I ran down the stairs three at a time, pulled to a halt and walked calmly past the front desk. I never looked back until I was safely on my Vespa, speeding away.

116

My friend Carter had a neat little ploy, which we used on an international basis. We worked only three-star hotels, Carter, myself and another cat. Carter, dressed to the teeth and really looking sharp, would enter the hotel about four in the afternoon and, using one of his many authentic-sounding accents, would ask for the key to a room—which he chose when he saw the key on the board and a letter in the slot. This meant, of course, that someone was staying in the room, but was out. With much obeisance the guy at the desk would hand him the key and the letter as well. "And by the way," Carter would add, "I'm expecting two gentlemen. Please tell them to come right up." Shortly after, we would arrive, ask for Carter, and be sent up to the room. Upstairs, Carter would be waiting for us. We'd take everything we could get our hands on. Or, if there wasn't anything worth carrying out, we'd phone room service for a bottle of Scotch and three glasses, guzzle down the booze when it arrived and take off.

Carter was cool as ice. Once he spotted a flashy American car in front of an expensive hotel, loaded to the roof with luggage. He drove it to his place, unloaded everything, the whole works, and returned the car to the exact spot where he had found it.

117

I caught Edith Piaf at the Olympia Music Hall. *Paris Soir* had hinted that any performance might be her last. I thought I'd see her drop dead on stage. But she didn't. What a gyp!

Some nights, I slept in a cemetery in neat, warm, cozy little homes for the dead. They provide well for the departed in Paris: everything except hot and cold running water. In the morning I'd be awakened by guitars: American hipsters, street singers from Alabama, who managed to live by making the rounds of the suburbs with their Rhythm and Blues songs. Some of them slept at the cemetery with their chicks. During the day we dropped in at galleries that had new shows, where there was always a load of free booze and tasty tidbits of salmon, caviar, *pâté*, camembert and champagne. This ploy entails some knowledge of art and the ability to look like you belong; the Order of Freeloaders, of which I became an active member, is not without its responsibilities. I stayed for some time at the Grand Hôtel des Sports on Place Contrescarpe, where, in the square, the tramps lie, shaking and groaning in a constant delirium. They all suffer from syphilis and they've got filthy gauze rags tied around their legs and arms. I became infested with lice, so I slept for days on the floor in the middle of a circle of gasoline.

During my Paris period, I produced some good lithos and got a lot of publicity. I appeared on a French TV show and on Dutch radio and was widely talked about in Holland. I stood them on their heads, acclaiming myself "probably the best painter alive." I was working hard and had a little money. In the Rue Santeuil, where I lived with a sculptress, jealousies and animosities were forever flaring up among the other artists, but I kept to myself. Evenings I trotted round to the Rue Mouffetard with a little pail to fetch my soup, twenty-five cents a quart.

My luck improved with a series of paintings I did. Paris hailed me. Galleries offered me five-year contracts against delivery of two canvases a month and I was promised a pile of gelt and a car. I was invited to exhibitions and salons and the prices of my paintings rose by the week. But I told them to shove it! I was a painter, not anybody's pet. I've seen what they do to painters.

I returned to Holland in a white leather suit. The suit cost me so much that I had to get a ride in a butcher's truck, for ten guilders. It's a family tradition. The Cremers always return in better style than they left. Even if we haven't had a meal for a week, we come back in a new suit, with rings on our fingers and smelling of success. Otherwise we don't come back at all. I made a big hit in the old neighborhood and it wasn't long before everyone was telling everyone else, "Hey! Jan Cremer's back!"

118

I get up from my seat. I have to go. I can feel a large turd trying to push its way through my asshole. A guy and a girl in glasses across the aisle look me over. If only the lock on the door reads "Vacant"! I make my way through the swaying bodies in the corridor. I'm in luck! The lock does say "Vacant." Pushing past a soldier who is just about to enter, I hurry inside and bolt the lock so that the "Engaged" flag pops up outside.

The air inside is fresh, cold as a matter of fact.

I plaster the seat with toilet paper, for hygiene's sake, and hastily pull down my pants, watching my face in the mirror. I remember other johns, the one in the youth homes, bare and sterile, with signs: "Please wash hands before leaving." And they taught us to cover the seat and to wipe our asses properly. But in all my time there, I never saw anyone wash his hands before leaving.

At one time I worked in a bakery. The baker was a tyrant, an ex-boxer who once gave me a terrific wallop on the head —I couldn't hear anything for two days afterwards—all because I hadn't washed my hands after a piss. The bastard never bothered to wash his own meaty mitts and used to come out of the toilet, go straight to the pastry board and squeeze the dough through his hands like so much shit.

In Morocco they never wash their hands, or anything else for that matter. One time, in a Moroccan restaurant, a waiter set a dish of fish in front of me. I had just seen the guy come out of the shithouse. He had hitched up his trousers with one hand, picked up the plate with the other and brought it to me. I saw brown streaks—shit—on his hands and when I examined my plate where he had touched it I noticed the same brown muck. I'd had a hell of a time scraping together enough dirhems for a meal, but I wasn't about to scrape shit off my food too.

A very rich gay boy I used to know once invited another queer (who happened to be a spastic) to his pad, tied him to a bench and then shit on his head. After that he massaged the crap into the guy's face until he'd had his kicks and then threw him out into the street. The whole town was up in arms over the incident and some guys ambushed him one night and beat the hell out of him.

The Dutch countryside rattles away underneath my asshole. I had to maneuver pretty deftly to keep the paper on the seat (the draft from below kept blowing it off), but I finally managed and was thankful for the little insulation it provided. There's still a cold wind stinging my buttocks. I open the sluices and the turds go thundering forward and down, while the water sprays hot steam against my backside.

I wonder why the railroads don't make things more pleasant for their customers. There isn't much atmosphere in this rolling shithouse: a mirror that can't be unscrewed and a window. But the glass is opaque so you can't see anything of the countryside. And who the hell is going to see anything inside a train going like a comet? Who the hell cares anyway? The only removable items are the toilet paper and the paper towels. And there's always a wastebasket brimming over with all kinds of crap.

I imagine I can hear the turds fall with a dull slap between the rails. Sometimes, on a bet, guys used to lie down between the rails. I can picture some cat squeezed flat against the ties down there. His friends, who encouraged him and put up money, squat on the grassy grade, holding their breath as the train rumbles past. Just as my car runs over his body I open the sluices and a great pile of shit flops onto his face. When he rises, with a face full of shit, his friends gape at him for a minute, not realizing what has happened, then burst into insane laughter.

These automatic drainpipes could be dangerous. What if a pebble, sucked up by the speed of the train, jumped through the pipe and hurled violently into my asshole at such terrific velocity that it charged through my guts right up to my gullet like a dumdum?

In crappers on trains there are always signs: "Please do not use toilet while train is standing in station." It doesn't take much gray matter to figure out why, so for that very reason I always make a point of doing just that: when the train stops at a station I deliberately have myself a nice crap—if I can possibly manage it.

I think of a mournful family group—father, mother, a

young girl and a chaplain—waving a sad good-bye to someone, the son of the family. They continue to wave until the last car has rattled by the iron rails. Then sudden quiet. And, on the spot where their loved one ascended, a large, healthy, steaming heap of shit. When I run into a heap of shit between the tracks along a railroad, I stop to ponder. Where was this one going? To the front? To jail? Maybe he or she will never return and all that will be left behind is a dark, steaming, impersonal heap, unidentifiable, unnoticed, disintegrating after a few days into nothing.

What a pleasure it is when your guts demand your whole attention: to sit and have a crap, quietly and voluptuously, reflecting or looking at a magazine or just staring at a mark on the wall that suddenly becomes a face or a monster or a cunt. Crapping is an entirely personal pleasure, and one should allow proper time for it, with everything calm, steady and, above all, controlled. In the army you can't sit quietly; you've always got to make room for somebody else, cursing him under your breath for disturbing you in the one place where you want to be alone. Personally, I can't understand people who take a quick shit in a couple of minutes. They must have no spiritual life at all—they're the sort with nervous, unhealthy looks, who are always in a hurry. Crapping should be a completely selfish act, involving not another soul, just being wonderfully oneself, surrounded by one's own stench within four walls.

A guy I know has the habit of sitting down on the pot to take a crap with the door wide open, so that he can take part, in a low and ecstatic voice, in the conversation going on outside. It's just like having everybody sitting on the crapper with you.

In the john your mind takes flight. In your imagination, you can say and do exciting things to the broad you've just seen on the train, and you can wonder about the guy who warmed the seat before you.

Men's rooms in public places are usually cold and businesslike affairs; ladies' rooms, though, are different. The air is full of delicious smells and perfumes. The wastebaskets, admittedly, are pretty unpleasant, chock-full as they usually are of bloody rags, but the rest of the atmosphere is pure heaven. I remember having dinner at Maxim's during one period when I was flush and catching sight of a famous Italian movie star seated with some friends not far away. She rose, excused herself and undulated past me towards the ladies' room. I hurried after her. I ducked into the men's room and out again in a flash, then stood at the foot of the stairs, waiting. She came out of the ladies' room and walked past me, so close that I could smell her perfume. As she swayed up the stairs I stood looking after her from below. Her thighs were full-blown, wonderful to behold, and her calves were round and firm. When I bent down—to tie my shoelaces—I could see the dark edges of her black silk stockings, and above them her garters and the bulge of her buttocks. As soon as she had disappeared from sight, I whipped into the ladies' room. Ah! That exotic mixture of odors! One stall was in use, so I slipped into the other one and locked the door. Immediately I recognized her perfume and I sat down bare-assed on the seat. It was still warm. What joy! What paradise! I felt her perfect body under mine. I imagined myself peering up through a glass window at the bottom of the bowl as she sat on the seat. I pictured how she would ease herself onto her lush backside, how her fat, purple pubic lips would open and spread, how I would break the glass and wallow with my face against her wet cunt.

I snapped back to reality when someone began to shake and rattle the doorknob. I came out of the stall. It was the attendant and she began to abuse me in French. I shrugged my shoulders—the helpless foreigner—and vanished.

When you're walking in the street and you've had too much beer and you suddenly feel that you've just *got* to piss or go blind, you have to be in good shape to stay in control. You want to sit down with your legs crossed to keep it in, but at the same time you've got to force your legs apart so they can carry you to the nearest john. Your whole being is propelled by one desire, to get rid of the burning load inside your bladder. Finally you find a bar, enter as casually as possible, order a beer and then, as if the thought had just occurred to you, you stroll in the direction of the men's room. Noble are they who step in quiet dignity to the crapper. You shoot inside, bolt the door, unbutton your fly, grab your hot rod, rip it out and throw it over the side of the trough. Just in time! The urine explodes onto the metal like a hand grenade, your swollen bladder subsides, and you know the bliss that comes with piss.

119

In the army they issue thin balloons that look like rubbers. But these are different. They're impregnated with some kind of acid, and you're supposed to piss into them while on maneuvers or at the front. Let's say you've been up a hayloft for days, machine gun at the ready, while the enemy patrols outside. You deposit your offering into the balloon and seal it by pinching it closed. Then you just drop it. The urine combines with the acid and destroys the evidence of your humanity. The only thing they've invented for shitting, so far as I know, is: "Sergeant, I have to go sit on the soup kettle for a minute." But you can't always depend on a soup kettle at the front—just shifting the lid might draw enemy fire. So you undo your belt and buttons, slide your pants down to your boots, roll away a short distance and then go, thinking, "In a few hours we'll be gone, before the sun gets too hot." If you are gone, fine! But if you're still there the next day the stench is almighty, because, due to the tension, everyone has been crapping constantly. If you know you won't be pulling out for God knows how long, you just shit in your pants. After a while you feel the hot mess oozing at the edges of your shorts, itching and irritating your buttocks. And the longer you stay that way and the more you move, the more unbearable it becomes. You begin to feel raw skin under the heavy, scratchy khaki. But then, when you finally do pull out, how delightful to find a stream and soothe away the filth and the pain in the cold water; to crouch down among the bulrushes, ass spanking clean, listening to the chirping of water birds, covered by the high shadow of the rushes; to wipe your ass by sliding it along the cool, clean grass; to stretch lazily in the hot sun and then dive into the water again, opening your asshole and letting the clean water rinse it out.

120

You should always flush your own turds yourself, for, like the length of your tool, they're nobody's business but your own. Cats who don't check to see that everything has been properly flushed away are shameless bastards. When I go into a john, full of anticipation, and see a bowl full of shit, the romance is gone. I'm disgusted. Anybody else's shit is repulsive to me. My own, on the other hand, never fails to delight me. I examine it with interest and a certain pride and, after it has whirled around and disappeared with the churning waters, I retire from the john with a sharp sense of satisfaction.

When confronted with someone else's turds, I find that I can judge the character of the manufacturer simply by looking them over carefully. I have delved deeply into scatology, the science of shit. O-shaped dung denotes a quiet man, one who sits down with deliberation and calmly allows nature to take its course. He doesn't have to read a book or concentrate on anything other than the job at hand. He's a person who thinks ahead, a businessman or such. Shitting doesn't particularly interest him, but what must be done must be done.

Then there are the X-shaped turds of the quickies, the two-faced types who push both ways at once, straight and on the bias. Pointed shit is the sign of the real snobs, the tax collectors, the judiciary, the moralists. They are the pinchers-off, the ones who go out of their way to keep things from taking their natural course. As for me, scatologist that I am, nobody ever sees my shit. Like the junkie, I keep my addiction private. People with individuality and personality never leave traces or seek publicity.

The first time I went to sea, I set out as an apprentice seaman on a coaster. The entire crew slept in the fo'c'sle. An able-bodied seaman and I shared a cabin in the back part, next to the pantry and directly below the head. It was a very small and narrow cabin and some damn fool of a designer had put the drainpipe in our cabin, right through our berths, a pipe with a diameter of fifteen inches. Sheets and blankets had to be cut in two at the bottom so they would fit over the pipe and we had to sleep with the pipe in our crotches. There was one advantage: when the ship rolled in rough waters, you only had to clamp your legs around the pipe and you could snore away in peace, while everyone else was being pitched onto the floor. The trouble was that the drains from every sink and toilet led to this one pipe and if someone had taken a hot bath and pulled the plug, you woke up screaming, your balls damn near burned off. When someone took a crap we could hear the turds plunge and rattle between our legs. That could be an unpleasant sound, especially if you were just planning to have the little snack you pinched from the pantry. In the end we could recognize everybody by the sounds they made on the toilet. Loud farts, groans and heavy *flups*—that's the bosun. *Pfffwwaauwwwgrrrrrksssssjt!!! Bloooeemmmbss!!!*—that's the first mate. And a short *krrtsjttrrr-plomp-plomp*—that's the cook.

You can tell a lot about a person by his john. I like artists' toilets, which usually have pornographic bits and pieces hanging around, or beautiful nudes cut out of girlie magazines. Intellectuals tend toward a strange kind of exhibitionism, with cute sayings and sage advice like you find on the walls of every bar between Amsterdam and the Cape. Sometimes there are collages and newspaper clippings, which can be very entertaining as well as instructive.

A john has always been for me a hallowed spot! My ideal shithouse is completely black—walls, toilet, sink and all—with a few erotic prints pinned up to capture the interest of the visitor: a little world of its own, where each shit is an adventure. I always use pastel toilet paper and have a special hook on the wall for pictures, cut from newspapers and magazines, of people I loathe: I get sweet revenge by wiping my ass with them. Afterwards I take a look at the faces, ridiculous with the slimy mess covering them. Then I flush them down the toilet, having finished off with soft paper to save wear and tear on my ass.

I always make a ritual of visiting the bathrooms in homes I visit, as well as hotel bathrooms and men's rooms in bars. Once, staying at the home of a wealthy Lord of the Manor in the south, I counted forty-six bathrooms, some of them like mausoleums. I really had a ball there!

121

There was an ambassador in Paris who used to throw the kind of parties that separate the men from the boys. Joseph, a rich buddy of mine, always told me about these affairs and one evening I went along with him. The crowd was mixed: some very cool characters who looked like they'd seen and done just about everything, some very respectable types, lots of important people and lots of gorgeous broads—models, starlets and the like. They were mostly chicks who worked as extras in films, chicks who couldn't get their panties down quick enough for anyone involved in movies, even if he turned out to be a studio porter. They all wanted to be "discovered." You couldn't talk to them; their conversation never went past their new fur coats and their "important connections." Any attempt at a worthwhile discussion was regarded as worse than rape.

I downed a few drinks and looked around for a suitable companion to pass the evening or, hopefully, the night with, but I didn't have much luck at first. There was plenty of material to choose from, but most of them already had cats with them, and the unattached ones weren't paying any attention to me. I wasn't having a very good time. I shuffled around, stood up for a while and sat down for a while. Then I noticed a lovely creature, with the dusky good looks of a half-caste (she turned out to be Egyptian), giving me the eye. Her delectable tits, long, pointed ones that drooped a bit, could be seen almost to the nipples in her low-cut dress. Although she was with a slick-looking guy, she kept sending me long, deep glances. But I stayed put. I didn't want any trouble.

After a couple of hours, most of the official guests had gone and a small coterie of professional partygoers, playboys and lushes remained. Joseph disappeared into one of many bedrooms with a beautiful Japanese chick. Somebody put an Art Blakey record on the phonograph and the atmosphere became sensual, with bodies swaying moodily to the music and coming together in the half-light. I was still alone. The Egyptian girl kept looking over at me, but every time I decided to go over to her, some guy or other would join her first. If I could only get to her, I thought, we'd take off for my place and hole up for a few days with the blinds down. Joseph appeared and gave me a big hello. He looked as if he'd been through the mill and back. "Man!" he said, mopping his forehead, "I just came down for a refill. She's not finished with me yet."

"Up to your old tricks, Joe?"

"Yeah, and a lot of new ones! Listen, man, why don't you get hold of one of these broads and have a ball? That's what they're here for!"

I told him I was shopping around.

The ambassador himself was quite a character. He had been the soul of respectability while the other members of officialdom were present, reserved and proper as a bank clerk. But the minute the door closed behind the last of them he dived onto a monstrous couch with three broads and started digging in. I could see the red lace panties on one of the chicks, a dark-haired girl—her skirt was up that far! He was humping her right there in the middle of the room. Whenever someone called his name, he'd emerge, groaning and sweating, from the pile of flesh, like a wolf with blood on his fangs. The horny bastard!

Meanwhile, I was examining the showcases full of his collection of precious stones and toying with the idea of pocketing a few. A couple of queers were moaning and rolling around in one corner. Then a voice, thick with whiskey, announced that a striptease was forthcoming: *The Firebird*, danced by the one and only Miss Judith!

Miss Judith swung into our midst wearing a leopard-skin dress and dangling three-inch earrings. Her lips and nails were painted green. There were loud shouts of approval. She looked saucy, exciting, vulgar and full of promise. The Mexican combo that had been playing off and on through the evening swung into a tune. I didn't recognize it, but if it was Stravinsky's *Firebird*, it's a good thing he wasn't around to hear it. Miss Judith, who could have been a pro from the Place Pigalle, began to weave and pose in front of us to the slow, tantalizing rhythm. One by one, she tossed her clothes into the audience, each flick of her wrist accompanied by enthusiastic roars. When her sheer panties had slipped from her rosy hips she stood before us like a nude goddess. She bent over, picked up the panties and tossed them playfully in the direction of her host. The greedy old pasha rose, grunting, from his harem and pulled her down onto the couch with him. After much squealing, jostling and giggling, she managed to disengage herself and disappeared into a side room with a little bundle of clothes under her arm.

I couldn't take my eyes off the door that she'd vanished through. I wondered what would happen if I just walked through the door and took her, but I couldn't bring myself to make a move.

Earlier I had smoked a few joints of tea and, high as a kite, hadn't minded just watching the scene. But now I felt like fucking. A girl sat down beside me and started to talk. She was a dead loss and I told her so. When my little Egyptian gave me the eye again I beckoned to her, no longer caring if I had to fight off the bruiser she was with. She circled the room and came back to me, settling her beautiful ass on the sofa beside me. I liked her face even better from close range—the lines were strong and she looked independent. She exuded an odor that made me want to get her into a bed. We chatted a bit and I told her I was a Dutch movie star and had just flown in from America. Gradually we inched closer together. I fingered her smooth back. She didn't object. Then I slowly slid my hand down and placed it firmly under her fanny. Still not a murmur. I was on the point of suggesting we retire upstairs when she said, "Let's look at the moon."

We walked out onto the patio. There were people in the garden and an occasional hoarse whisper could be heard from the darkness. "My name is Laila," she said, guiding me to a secluded corner. I perched on the railing right next to her and I could feel every snakelike movement of her body. She plucked from her sleeve a cigarette case that caught the reflection of the moon. "For the two of us," she smiled, handing me a cigarette. I took it and discovered that it was a joint. I laughed out loud. Laila laughed too, puzzled. I pulled her to me, embraced her and gave her a long cool kiss that made my cock jump up like a spring. Still laughing, I delved into my pocket and pulled out one of my joints, which I offered to her. "And this bomber is for the two of us, too," I said. She was delighted.

After we'd smoked the two joints, I wanted her more than ever. I asked her about the guy I'd seen her with. Maurice was just a friend, she assured me, but a great cat. "Come, I'll introduce you!" It wasn't what I had in mind but I allowed myself to be presented to him. The three of us smoked and chatted for a while and, when he handed Laila a small cube of hash, I decided he must be a pusher. When he had gone, she and I shared the joints that were left, chewed a little hash and popped a couple of bennies. I was out of my skull again and walked back into the house on all fours, amid gales of hysterical laughter. I found a bed and sacked out. After a while Laila joined me. I still wanted her, but my body wouldn't cooperate, so we just lay there contentedly.

I got up to take a piss and stumbled towards the john. I opened the door and walked into a tremendous, mirror-covered bathroom still seeing everything through a red haze. It suddenly dawned on me that I wasn't alone. Miss Judith, the leopard-woman, was staring at me. "Excuse me," I mumbled. I wanted to get out of there but I couldn't seem to move from the spot and just stood there swaying. Judith, who was combing her hair, didn't look the least bit surprised to see me there. "Are you coming or going, honey," she said. My heart and my cock jumped up at the same moment. "Coming, if that's OK with you," I managed to say. She made it obvious that it was fine with her, this vampire-woman I'd been eyeing all evening. I got excited just looking at her, with her green fingernails, green lips and green eyes. There she was, not two feet away, standing with me in a john and just asking to be had. My favorite fantasy come true! I fought to clear my head and make the most of the situation.

"I . . . uh . . . I saw you dance," I said, just to make conversation.

"Yes, that's what I'm here for. I'm a dancer," she replied.

"Are you alone?" I asked. Yes, she was.

I don't remember who made the first move, but suddenly we were up against the wall, she with her back to it and me glued to her body, both of us wriggling and writhing and breathing hard. Then I was inside her skirt and she was inside my pants and we fell onto a straw mat on the tiled floor. I could see countless hairs and drops of water set off against the fibers and the tiles. Her face glowed with a witch's ecstasy and she shoved and wiggled underneath me, moving my cock up and down with one hand and running the green fingernails of the other up and down my back. I could feel the hot blood pounding in my ears. I pulled up her leopard-skin dress, pulled down her damp panties and rammed my hard tool into her. We rose and fell on the hard floor and I humped her hard until we came, together, with a shout. She was marvellous, vulgar, a real good lay, and I had never felt more in the mood for fucking. I would have liked to collapse and sleep on top of her, so I could wake up and fuck her again.

We stood up. She pulled her panties off over her high-heeled shoes and, with practiced efficiency, used them to wipe the come from between her legs, finally stowing them in her purse. "It was delightful," she said. I said, "Better next time!" The whole session had taken about five minutes and by now my head felt clear again. Together we left the john and I didn't give a hot shit who was staring at us as we came out. We strolled over to the bar and had a drink, but then she started making plans for us to go back to town together. When some creep asked her to dance, I disappeared and went upstairs to look for Joseph.

I walked into one bedroom where two guys were carrying on with three or four broads. I couldn't make out what was what in the pile of flesh on the bed, but I think one of the guys was the ambassador. I finally found Joseph in the garden and we said good-bye to some of the people. I kissed Laila and made a date with her. I shook Maurice's hand and he invited me to come and hear his record collection some time. Then we got into Joseph's Cadillac and tore off to Montparnasse for a snack at La Coupole.

122

What I haven't done in crappers! Once I was having a quiet beer in a well-known bar. I was dead sober and didn't feel like doing anything but sitting still and enjoying a drink. The place was full of people—it was Saturday afternoon and all the boys were drinking up their paychecks. I got up to take a piss. While I was standing in the john, an old guy came crashing in, bouncing off the walls, stewed to the gills. He stood next to me, muttering and slobbering. I knew the old prick vaguely, a cat with a lot of loot and a lot of lip, an ex-major or something. I couldn't stomach him. He looked at me and said, "It's good to have a piss, isn't it?" I didn't reply, turned away, zipped my fly and started to leave. He grabbed my arm and shoved his nasty face up under mine: "What are you, anyway, one of those goddamn beatniks?" Then he rattled out a stream of obscenities in a voice thick with liquor. I let him have it square on top of his head. He went down, right into the trough. There was no one else in the place. I pulled him up. His body, like a dead man's, was soaked with piss. Opening the door to one of the stalls with my elbow, I pushed him inside and jammed his head into the bowl. I closed the door on him just as someone pushed open the door to the crapper. I went back to my seat and joined in the conversation with my pals as if nothing had happened, but keeping an eye on the john.

About half an hour passed and I saw a waiter go into

the john, emerge almost at once, hotfoot it over to the owner of the bar and whisper something in his ear. The boss hurried into the crapper, accompanied by the waiter and some curious bystanders. A hubbub arose and people crowded around the door, peering inside. After a minute or two, two men came out with the major hanging between them. Vomit and piss ran in a nauseous mess down his suit and he kept babbling, "It was a goddamn beatnik, it was a dirty beatnik!" People started to laugh, me loudest of all, and when he was dragged past my table I made a crack about soldiers who can't hold their liquor. He was too far gone to recognize me. Every time I run into him in the same bar, stinking drunk as usual, he gives me a long, wondering look and mutters into his beer.

123

I'm still on my way to faraway places, sitting in the crapper on the tourist-crowded train, an international shit session, with the landscape rolling by beneath my asshole.

124

The things I've lost in johns! My passport (it fell out of my back pocket when I pulled up my pants, and disappeared down the drain of a toilet in Paris), two silver bracelets, money, a toothbrush, combs, a pair of shorts, rings (an engagement ring among them) and even a revolver (I had hidden it, wrapped in plastic, in the tank of a girl friend's toilet; I always checked to see that it was still there. One day it wasn't! And I didn't dare to ask about it.)

125

In Paris a friend of mine, Coronet Jack, hanged himself at a Christmas party. Sandy, his girl, found him in the bathroom, dangling from a noose tied to a pipe. He'd hanged himself because the Negro chick he was trying to make wouldn't have him. He'd been shooting a lot of heroin lately and hitting rock bottom regularly. He hung there naked except for a jacket, his swollen, purplish tongue hanging out of his mouth. The heating pipe he'd strung himself up on dripped scalding water onto his contorted face.

What a way to go, swinging above the toilet bowl! A perfect celebration of the birth of Christ!

126

In Antwerp I opened the window of the john to look for a guy peddling beer and sandwiches along the station platform. A newspaper vendor walked by, dressed in a blue uniform with gold braid on his cap. I caught sight of a headline: *"Beginning of Terror in Holland: Intellectual Beatnik Tries to Seize Power."* I bought a paper, closed the window and lit a smoke.

"Revolution in the Netherlands! Uprising of the Angry Generation!" There, staring at me, was a photo of myself, with the caption: "The Animal." I turned to the inside page, as instructed, and found that the whole page was devoted to a Warning to the People. It described the perverse intellectual friendship between myself and Armando, the Phenomenon, hinting that we might come into power and turn the placid Dutch art world upside down. The print screamed, "Sabotage! Treason!" Under the heading, *"What is the Minister Going to Do?"* it said, "Can one be silent in such a situation? Can one continue to smile while these germs of infection, these carriers of disease, these so-called 'intellectual beats,' penetrate alarmingly deep into certain circles? Have we forgotten that there have been other such movements which were treated as jokes but which turned out to be dangerously serious? These beatniks have little sense of humor and are in deadly earnest about everything they do. They are biding their time. Would the Minister of Arts and Culture, if he knew that their neo-Fascist utterances are not only read with smiling approval but also devoured in the comfortable rooms of Dutch museum directors, still continue to do everything possible to promote these people abroad?"

Where in hell had the newspaper gotten these wild ideas? According to the article, we had secret plots to turn Holland into a communistic state and censor the theater, literature and art. An action committee was being organized to raise funds, membership dues and taxes and to force record shops to feature only jazz, rock 'n' roll and "These Are Your Leaders Speaking" propaganda. All theater, dance and art was to come under the supervision of our Union Barbariste. All the works of those not affiliated—the anarchists and the partisans—were to be burned in public and the artists heavily fined. Museums and art galleries were to be painted red. Opponents of the movement would perform forced labor, redecorating the entire parliament building

234

with nude photographs and bullet shells. And so on and so on.

Was this then good-bye to my private Rolls, M.G., Jaguar, racing boat, yacht, Harley-Davidson, and cream-puff-and-eclair bakery? Ah! Farewell to my thirty-square-yard bed, my requisitioned women, my fashion-setting *"Ligne des Barbaristes"* clothing, the celebration of "The Adoration of Cremer" in every church in the land! I was not even to have the pleasure of seeing my enemies—the critics, the gallery owners and the cops—plodding and sweating on the chain gang, mowing in my palace gardens, stretching my canvases, mixing my paints, grooming my horses or tearing down rows of houses, brick by brick, and then rebuilding them a few blocks away. *The Daily Cremer* would not be run off in the Government Printing Office. The film, *The Life and Works of Jan Cremer* (in twelve parts), would not be shown daily in every theater. The opera *Don Juan Cremer* would not be performed in the National Cremer-torium. The daily TV broadcast—*How the Leaders Spent Their Day*—and the radio programs—*Jan Cremer Dines, Jan Cremer Sings, Jan Cremer at Seven O'Clock* and so on —were not to be. Gone, too, the continuous football and boxing matches and the auto races in Cremer Stadium, the grenade throwing on Armando Boulevard and the booby-trapping of police stations! No Cremer Striptease Society, no Mutually Organized Night Society, no weekly Armando Shooting Festival on Main Street and in City Hall! My thou-sands of idolators would be unable to enjoy the weekly Cremer Photo Contest. I could not, after all, send tossed-off girl friends to work draining the canals with rags, stoking the central heating system at party headquarters, pricking holes in rubbers, satisfying the sexual whims of hound dogs, cleaning out the snake pit at the zoo and watering and binding up the flowers in all the parks. Alas, cruel fate! How Hard Life Can Be!

127

I had a large house in the inner city—two vast floors with windows overlooking a busy square, the church and a night-club for artists. The City Hall and the Literary Museum were a stone's throw away. The roof was flat and spacious, so on the Queen's Birthday and other festive occasions, such as state visits by friendly powers, I allowed press photog-raphers to take their shots from this ideal spot, at two and a half guilders a head. In the summer I sunbathed on the roof with my girl friends, but this was soon prohibited by the police because workers in surrounding office buildings were disturbed by it. With binoculars! Below me was the kitchen of a Chinese restaurant and the air vent went up through my studio to the roof. The smells from the vent always sent me into fits of hunger. Ill-fed visitors liked to stand near the vent, claiming they derived nourishment from the fumes.

I threw weekly parties, reunions and meetings for my fan club. The people living in the neighboring houses went around with a petition aimed at driving me from my abode. They collected hundreds of signatures, but it didn't do any good. They did, however, manage to get me on the cops' shitlist, "to be checked regularly for suspected illegal activities." Now and then a couple of dicks with briefcases would drop by. Leering, they would pull out snapshots of people coming in and out of the house, friends, girl friends and casual visitors. "Very good!" I'd exclaim, examining the shots, "Who's your photographer?" Day and night people arrived: people with half-empty bottles of whiskey, fur coats and transistor radios; people who just wanted a flop for the night; poetesses with odes dedicated to me; junkies, pimps, whores, striptease artists, sailors with smuggled goods, playboys, playgirls, girls who had escaped from correction homes, gypsy musicians, boxers in training, artists who came to watch me paint and girls who just came to watch me.

I was becoming a Personality and everyone wanted to get into the act. People read about me in the papers, saw me on TV, heard me on the radio and stopped me on the street for my autograph. They called me by my first name, asked me why I painted such crazy things, slapped my back, said "well done!" and wished me luck. Whenever I walked into a bar I was asked to get drunk at their expense. I heard my name whispered every time I entered a shop or strolled past a terrace. To the population at large I was "The animal," the barbarian who had stated in an interview, "I'm not an artist. I'm a laborer, a common laborer." Such remarks caught on big. Years after I invented *Peinture Barbarisme* in 1957, there followed *Peinture Atavisme, Réalisme, Banalisme,* etc. My own image as the Barbarian became extremely fashionable and a sharp newspaperman put into the mouth of some harmless artist such phrases of mine as, "I'm a barbarian! (Boo!) I paint like a barbarian (Boo!) for these barbarian (Boo!) times! I fight the paint, I hit and kick the canvas! (Booooo!)"

On my first manifesto, there were pictures of me, looking arrogant and aggressive, with a luxuriant head of hair, and a cigarette dangling from one corner of my mouth. After at every two-bit artist had similar publicity pictures taken himself. They were all quoted as having proclaimed—with a peppering of Cremer slang, of course—"I'm a simple borer. I don't care about art. Rembrandt? Who's he? I'm the greatest painter in the world today. I hate sentiment. People don't interest me."

I wore a white suit. Every artist wore a white suit. I dug Elvis Presley. Every artist dug Elvis Presley. I produced massive, dripping canvases, painted with red oxide, tar, pitch, gypsum and silver. I constructed works of two, three and five panels. So Young Holland began to create three-panelled works in silver and five-panelled works in gypsum and to experiment with red oxide and pitch.

Imitation is a sure sign of success. No sooner will I have written the last word of this book (which will, without a doubt, be a bestseller), than a dozen painters will lay down their brushes, pick up their pens and begin to describe their adventures. One good piece of advice from Jan Cremer: write as much as you like, but don't write my story, write your own!

If I decide tomorrow to paint a picture during a football game, standing on the field in a canary-yellow suit and a purple cap, next week every football field will be crowded with painters, all sporting canary-yellow suits and purple caps.

The first of my manifestos was written for me by a young bearded poet. I was attending a reading at the local arts council, where all sorts of literary types were trotting out their latest efforts. A girl, whose breasts were struggling like a couple of pups to burst out of her dress, read some touching couplets about dead birds and kids who do dirty things. Then this guy came on in green pants and a purple sweater. He had long hair and was barefoot (in the middle of winter!). His poetry was good. I was fascinated by his wife, a girl with long, loose-hanging black hair, wearing a long, purplish dress, obviously without a bra, and black silk stockings that clung to her well-shaped calves. We got together after his reading, had some drinks and put together our first bill of propaganda. We handed it around at every gallery that ran my show. There were bloody battles between the pro- and the anti-*Barbaristes* and the police had to block the streets and empty the galleries. The night three of my shows opened, wild with success, I tossed beer bottles through the windows of the Artists' Society, rubbed spaghetti into the hair of an academy director's wife, drank five bottles of wine, seventeen of beer, four brandies and eight

shots of rum (I love rum) and wound up on the floor c
the john throwing up my guts.

I had arrived! The papers were full of me. My scrapbook
bulged at the seams. My exhibitions—in all the major citie
of Europe—were enormous successes. But I ended up witl
out a cent because my manager gypped me out of th
works. He was a crook in a Brooks Brothers suit, a greas
little queer who had been "trained" by an amorous galler
owner in the ways of the art world. The bastard had arrive
at my studio one morning, stinking of cologne, and an
nounced in a high-pitched American accent that he'd bee
sent by the director of a certain museum. He was energeti
I'll say that much for him! He organized exhibitions c
Peinture Barbarisme all over the Continent, moving like
whirlwind. Then he moved out, taking with him every
thing I produced in 1959 and the proceeds of all the ex
hibitions.

128

The road to success is long and hard. At the beginning,
simply liked to paint. I'd start in at eight A.M. and wor
until five. At eleven I'd break for coffee and cream puffs a
a girl friend's place, have a sandwich at lunchtime an
spend the rest of the time painting. At five I'd stop fc
dinner, then go to the flicks or to a bar. It was
pleasant life and I liked the regularity of it. I was turnin
out about two paintings a week and was completely absorbe
in my work.

But after the public "discovered" me, I found that m
place was always full of "old buddies" who'd "always know
I had it in me" (funny that they never mentioned it before)
They hung me up and kept me from working, but I couldn
help being impressed with all this sudden popularity. M
work became secondary. I started to drink a lot. One morr
ing, I discovered to my horror that, wielding a knife, I'
chased my girl friend onto the roof. The fire departmen
had to be called to bring her down because she had a morbi
fear of heights. I found myself constantly attending cock
tail parties and openings, visiting colleagues, playing foo
ball with the artists' eleven, being polite to old ladie
and nodding with a smile to old gentlemen, admiring th
work of my friends, and going to museums to see how th
old masters did it. (This was after the TV interview durin
which I said, "Rembrandt? Who's that? I don't know any
thing about sports!" My comment resounded like a thunde
clap in thousands of neat, little living rooms where the

238

opped chewing peanuts long enough to send me dozens of
ngry letters and about half as many sympathetic ones. A
ouple of sweet old ladies sent me books on Rembrandt. I
old them for a hundred guilders.) I felt that, like other
rtists, I should be polite to museum directors, going to any
ngths to avoid conflict with these guys and laughing at
eir worst jokes—like one of Prince Bernhard's retinue. But
never managed it.

129

venings I used to drink at the Posthorn, the local artists'
angout. The walls of the place were covered with the works
f its habitués, and many of mine began to appear there.
nce I had to remove a gouache. Someone had discovered
at it was a painting of a prick.
A gallery owner asked me to send him two canvases for
group show. I sent my two latest, which I also considered
y best. They were monochromatic impressions in white
—snowscapes, or ice craters. I allowed the workings of relief
speak for themselves. The canvases were never hung.
hen I asked the owner why, he exploded, "You don't
ally think I would hang such nonsense in my gallery!
here is nothing there, they're plain white! Ridiculous!" Six
onths later he exhibited paintings by the monochromist
erre Manzoni.
My work was refused twice by the Higher Arts Council,
vice by Pulchri Studio and twice by The Circle. I roughed
one critic (and was fined for it) because he wrote some
sty words about me. Not about my work, about me—
cause I had come between him, a good man and father of
x, and his mistress.
When my paintings were exhibited I had to change the
les: *Orgasm* became *Organism*, and so on. Even a genius
s to make concessions!

130

. . that evening we ran riot again. I was knocking around
th Barry, Lex and some American chick. We had a big
ene at Le Chat when the bill arrived, because we didn't
ve any bread. Barry had been around to a few dives to
e if he could push a little weed, but nobody was buying.
hen I ran into Anita, who was with some guy, I borrowed
little loot from her. We blew it all on sweets and ouzo
a Greek joint. Then we were broke again.
It was the time of the Algerian riots and Paris was

crawling with cops. Flags at the Palais de Justice flew a half-mast and the entrance was shrouded with black crepe Every day at least a dozen cops kicked the bucket and the entire force was out for blood. A few days earlier I ha seen them gun down an Algerian against a kiosk when h tried to get away from them. The atmosphere in the cit was one of shocked dismay. Packed patrol cars move through the narrow streets, machine-gun barrels jutting ou of the open windows on either side. That evening, durin the time we were there, the Rue de la Huchette wa blocked off four times, with patrol cars stationed at eac end of the street so you couldn't pass. Then there was raid. Everybody was searched and papers were inspecte God help you if you'd left your papers at home or hap pened to be carrying a weapon! And God help you if you skin was dark! With rifle butts they knocked the unfortu nates into cars, and resistance met with death or worse. Th cops were paying back in kind for their colleagues who ha been decapitated and castrated.

I told Barry to get rid of his stuff before they found on him. He met a few American friends of his, Negroe outside Storyville and decided to try there, while Lex an the girl and I waited in front of a bar across the street. was dying for a drink. Every time someone opened the doo a delicious alcoholic breeze wafted out into the street. dopey little character passed by and gazed with interest a the American chick. He turned around and walked past u again, obviously hungry for skirt. When he thought w weren't looking, he beckoned to her. I nudged her in hi direction. After all, my throat was dry! The creep asked he if she'd like to join him for a drink. She looked at me an I nodded. The two of them went in, but Lex and I staye outside, waiting for Barry. After a while I said, "Why don you go inside, sit down with the broad and see if the gu buys you a drink. And if she can pick up some cash, that all right too. When Barry gets back we'll join you." So Le went into the bar.

A minute later Barry arrived. He'd sold thirty franc worth. We found the three of them inside, sopping up booze The chick was a nice piece of tail, but boring as hell an stupid the way American broads can be. She kept comin on with me, bugging me. I was already fed up with th constant shortage of dough and the French creep rubbe me the wrong way. All the same, Barry and I tried to shoo the breeze with him, but he only had eyes for the chick He bought drinks for her and for Lex, but we had to pa for our own. The guy was well dressed and looked like h

240

had plenty of dough, the type that pinches pussy in the dark: while his head was turned to talk to Lex, his hand was creeping slowly up under the chick's skirt. When he pulled out his wallet to pay for a round, I saw that it was stuffed with lovely blue and yellow notes. Barry and I exchanged glances. An idiot like that was sitting there with all that cash, while we had to wag our tails for scraps, like a bunch of hungry dogs. The Frenchman excused himself for a trip to the john and we called a quick conference.

The girl told us he'd offered her a hundred and fifty francs to spend the night with him. We decided that she should agree and entice him into the pitch-black alley, next to the bar, that ran from the Rue de la Huchette towards the Seine. Barry and I would pay up and leave ahead of them, then wait across the street. When the three of them came out, Lex would say good-night and take off down the alley. Then he'd call to the chick as though he'd forgotten something, and she'd follow him into the alley. After a while—we hoped—the guy would go into the alley to see what was up, and then we'd jump him.

The creep returned from the crapper. After a few friendly remarks, Barry and I took care of our bill and left. Outside, we tossed a coin to see who would do the deed. I was it. I would knock the guy down and Barry would grab his wallet. After about fifteen minutes Lex came out of the pub and made straight for the alley. The Frenchman and the broad sauntered out behind him.

We were tense and excited. Lex called to the girl. She turned and walked quickly into the alley. The prick waited a couple of minutes and then made off after her. Everything was working right on schedule. The street was empty except for a crowd of teenagers hanging around outside a cellar dive down the block. As casually as we could, we crossed the street and walked into the alley. It was as murky as a coalpit but we could make out three silhouettes set off by the streetlights near the river. We crept along, flat against the wall, until we reached them. The Frenchman's back was turned towards me. I raised my fist. Just then he must have sensed something. He whirled around, so that my fist glanced off his face. There was blood on his face and on my hand, which hurt like hell. Then Barry sprang at him, but the bastard, with surprising strength, flung him off. I hit out at him again, with all my might, and he fell. He began kicking out in every direction, whining and screaming, "Help! Help!" Lex and the chick had taken off at the first blow.

Barry tried to grab the flailing legs and I kept hitting the

241

little asshole in the face. But he wouldn't give up. He grabbed me by the lapels and pulled me down. I began to get nervous. It was like being chased in a nightmare and not being able to run. By this time—the whole thing had taken only a few seconds—a clump of people had gathered at the entrance to the alley. Some of them started coming towards us. Shit, I thought, it's all over! The goddamn idiot was yelling his guts out. I was exhausted from the struggle but I finally managed a violent kick in his face. He let go of me then, but kept on yelling. It was a hell of a sound.

Supported by Barry, I stumbled out of the alley. Luckily, there was no one in sight on the Quai Saint Michel and we crawled under a parked car. I was so worn out and disgusted that I would have given myself up then and there, but as soon as the coast was clear, Barry got me moving again and we ran towards the bridge. We could hear the stupid Frenchman still screaming bloody murder.

We walked across half of Paris before we dared to go home. We were shivering from the cold because we'd had to take off our jackets, which were white—and thus easily identifiable—and spattered with blood besides. When I finally fell into my pad, I fell right asleep. Five times that night I was startled awake by nightmares, bathed in sweat. When I got up the following afternoon, the room was bathed with sunshine. My knuckles were shapeless lumps of raw flesh and on the inside of my wrist I found black crusts of blood.

OPERATION BULLET WOUND

131

It was a fine, cloudless day and I was lying near the water with some friends: the ballet dancer, the gypsy violinist, the bartender and my two bodyguards. On a dare, I swam out to a boat that was advertising suntan oil. When I reached the spot where I thought it was, I found only its wake. The boat was already about two hundred yards away. I swam further out to sea, lolling lazily in the waves and letting the sun sear my body. The crowded beach looked like a busy anthill. With great difficulty, I spotted my chums and waved to them. They waved back. I continued swimming out, saying to myself, "ten more strokes and then back," and then deciding to try another ten.

All of a sudden, I saw a yellowish, jellylike mass on the dark water, not two feet from my face. A jellyfish! I immediately dived down and swam underwater as far as I could. The thought of that repulsive creature sent me shooting along under the surface until I almost exploded from lack of air. I came to the top. It was like a cave of horrors: slimy threads trickled across my face, pricking and stinging. I was surrounded by a mass of jelly. A purplish shimmer reflected off the water as far as I could see and thousands of the monsters bobbed along in the water, quiet and deadly like the plague. I was in the middle of a school of jellyfish! Their tentacles brushed my body, sending through it currents of revulsion, shocks of pain and itching. They were in my hair, my neck, my face and my eyes; I saw as through a gauze mask. I screamed like a lunatic, crying with pain and thrashing my arms and legs around. But no one noticed.

I was trapped in a mass of slime. I tried to get underwater again, but the jelly remained glued to my body and the currents of pain kept shooting through me. The jellyfish had attached themselves to me like bloodsuckers. I waved and screamed again, desperately trying to attract attention. I kept going under . . . coming up . . . going under . . . coming up . . . swallowing water . . . drowning! Every time I surfaced I found myself in the middle of the horror. And then the glutinous ooze became so thick in my mouth and nose that I couldn't breathe. I struggled for air and felt the tentacles snaking around my legs and circling my body.

Suddenly I was crawling on the sand. Without realizing it, I had somehow been moving towards the beach all the time. Exhausted and heaving, I collapsed. Half-conscious, I felt someone scraping the monsters from my body with sticks and knives. Somebody went for help. I was glowing as if I had suffered an attack of malaria. Then everything started to spin and I fainted. I was taken, on a stretcher in the back of a police jeep, to a hospital. The doctors were amazed. They told me that even a dozen stings had been known to finish off a man.

I had fought a battle with that old bastard Death, and I had won. *"Alles was mich nicht tötet, macht mich stärker."*

On the beach sprawl the vacationers, tired, dusty and worn out. The Indonesians are clustered in small groups, crouching in the sand and strumming guitars, obviously planning to be "discovered" and get rich quick. Body-builders, fresh from correspondence courses with Charles Atlas, show their muscles, kick balls around with their bare feet, do handsprings and stop to run combs through their hair every five minutes. Some of them even get their feet wet in the surf. Women—fat and skinny, tall and short, blond and brunette, pale and suntanned—bask in the sun, their hands motionless beside them, the straps of their bathing-suit tops undone. Oil glistens on their bodies. On the bathhouse terrace, sullen waiters fetch Cokes for old ladies in expensive sundresses. Drenched in Solotan ("tan in an hour without the sun") and peering arrogantly through their Polaroid sunglasses, smart-looking broads trip by in high heels. Irritating little chicks, accompanied by irritating little guys, pile out of irritating little sports cars and head for the Beach de Luxe, a screened-off strip of sand where the ocean is supposed to be cleaner and brighter. Lazy kids sit in the water in their jeans, to bleach and shrink them. Every few minutes a dreamy little girl passes, carrying some treasure of the seaside, a shell, some pebbles or a piece of driftwood. Females slink by, on the prowl for a man. They've all got pointed rubber tits, deep tans and all the bare flesh the law will allow.

Germans show up with shovels, spades and axes, marching along the sand to the sound of music from their Grundig and Blaupunkt transistor radios. They've come to the beach to dig holes. When someone else gets too close to one of their holes, there's an awful commotion. Occasionally a heavyset German, his pants rolled up so that his varicose veins show, a Tyrolean hat perched on his bullethead, can be seen standing and staring out at the ocean through binoculars, just as he stood on the same spot twenty years earlier. Fat German mothers, in flowered dresses, with little boys clinging to their fat hands, point with pride at the deserted gray bunkers in the dunes, saying, "Look! Your Papa built that!" Pale, hollow-chested beach bums with long oily hair discuss the gas consumption of their motorbikes or play mumblety-peg with jackknives Radio newscasts, with sports results, resound everywhere. Even the cops walk around in shorts and sneakers. They chase stubborn little boys out of the water with their sticks and whistle at bathers who stray too far out. Or try artificial respiration on the ones they didn't notice in time.

Dirty old men, flagellants, fetishists, Peeping Toms and exhibitionists populate the beach. They watch, unobtrusively, the young lovers making out on the sand. They peep through cracks in the walls of dressing rooms where young girls are changing They jerk off in the toilets and make passes at women. There's one weird group that call themselves "detectives," a particularly nasty species of the mentally disturbed. They follow girls strolling along the beach, interrogate couples hidden behind dunes and ask intimate questions. Apparently it makes them come. Usually, they carry cards that identify them as Deputy Sheriffs. They're small, fanatical men who seek the limelight at riots, quarrels and necking parties. They act like they belong to the FBI.

I've been stopped from time to time, usually early in the morning, by one of these creeps. The little runt usually begins by asking the girl I'm with whether she's of age and whether her parents know where she is. I'd love to give him a quick poke on the chin, the insinuating son of a bitch, but there's always a chance that he really is a Deputy Sheriff. Then you've really had it, because the police are always on the side of these dung flies. One girl I know was raped by one of these "Deputy Sheriffs" when she went out one morning for a stroll along the beach. There seems to be a whole army of these psychopaths populating our beaches, woods and parks.

About four o'clock in the morning, near the marketplace, you can get freshly baked fish. Everyone gathers there at that hour, those who've been out on the town with money in their pockets as well as those who've been sleeping on the beach with only a few cents in their jeans. They all pick over the bones, smacking their lips. At the crack of dawn, I go tearing along the beach on my Norton 500 with a girl friend, splashing across the waves that roll in from the misty sea. We can drive along like that for miles and stop somewhere where I can take nude shots of her for my album. Then we fuck right on the beach, the sand scratching her ass and getting into her cunt. Planes from the air-force base circle over us at low altitudes and we wave to them.

Where do all these waves come from? And this empty toothpaste tube lettered in Chinese, this narrow leather belt, these empty beer cans, liquor bottles, sardine tins, wooden cases and condoms?

During the war, on this same beach, a bunch of German soldiers gave me candy and a pack of cigarettes for my mother. Later, the older boys grabbed them from me, because it was wrong to accept things from the lousy Krauts.

132

It had been a sweltering day and the evening had a kind of afterglow. Barry had run into some rich guys who wanted to make a night of it, so we'd been touring the boulevards and making the rounds of the clubs with them and their chicks in a big American convertible. One guy, a fat queer, was after me. He was a good-looking cat with lots of cash to play with. It was getting late but nobody felt like quitting, so Barry rounded up a few more guys to help pay for the booze. They were hicks from the North and Barry promised them an unforgettable evening of strip teasers and strip poker if they coughed up plenty. And they did. Henry, the gay boy, bought two bottles of champagne ("Especially for you," he told me). Armed with gin, rum, Coke and beer that we'd taken from the Pelican Club, we climbed into cars—ten of us in the convertible and the others in horse-drawn buggies and taxis —and tore off toward my studio in the inner city. After all, it was their bread, so we could at least provide the place.

We got rid of the crashers and opened the bottles. The hicks were having a ball. Their chicks kept ooohing and aaaahing and gaping at all the wild goings-on, but after a while they too were shedding their clothes and dancing like gypsies. They did everything that was expected of them and the evening started swinging. We spread out over two floors and most of the merrymakers moved upstairs. Barry and I stayed behind, digging Charlie Parker on my tape recorder (At least Barry was! Parker leaves me cold.) and, when we had the chance, going through our guests' jackets and purses, to finance a vacation. In another room my fiancée was doing God knows what with a student who fancied himself a lady's man. We let him cherish his illusion in honor of the subsidy he'd just received from the Ministry of Arts and Culture. Only Henry was in our way.

Tom, one of the regulars, a short, stocky neurotic, suddenly staggered in. Barry had his hand in a purse at this point. Tom launched into a long, complicated story. Drinking, smoking and feeling great, we let him rattle on. Then Tom pulled a pistol out of his pocket and started waving it around with a silly, gangster-type sneer on his mug. One of the girls gasped. Barry reassured her, "Don't be silly, honey, it's not loaded!" Tom put the thing back in his pocket and disappeared.

Meanwhile, fresh booze had arrived, and fresh faces. We were careful to screen the new arrivals, because we'd once let a dick in by mistake with a group of guests. The party reached its umpteenth climax and Barry, Rick and I were high out of our minds. I fell into a deep easy chair. I allowed chubby Henry to fetch drinks and cigarettes for me and dozed off, only half-hearing the talking, the shuffling and the music. Then something woke me with a start. It was Tom fighting with a broad. She was screaming at him, "Prick! Pig-fucker!" and finally shattered an empty bottle on his head. Our guests were upset. But Tom just laughed, immediately forgot the incident and started dancing by himself. Soon everyone else relaxed and started dancing too, and I dozed off again. The next thing I heard was the crash of shattered glass and a great thud as the breakfront toppled to the floor. I was on my feet in a second. In the middle of the confusion I spotted Tom, the pistol in his raised arm, shooting at the ceiling. I could see plaster spattering down in chunks, but the shots could hardly be heard above the music. Tom was shrieking with laughter and everyone was shouting "Olé!" and "Hooray!" after each shot.

Henry, who had been sitting on the arm of my chair all the time, suddenly jumped up and began to bounce around like a rubber ball. He grabbed his backside with both hands and screamed, "My ass! My ass! He's ruined my sex life!" Barry turned up the tape recorder. I grabbed Henry. The seat of his expensive gray pants was burnt and a red trickle ran down the legs. His fingers clutched at the broken flesh and his face was screwed up in a knot of pain. Rick, talking fast, maneuvered most of the crowd back upstairs. The hicks and their chicks were grabbing their coats, not wanting, you understand, to get involved in anything out of the way.

Meanwhile, Henry's shoes were filling with blood. He kept pleading, in a shrill, frightened little voice, "Please take me to a doctor," and we kept saying, "Yes Henry, of course Henry, right away Henry." But we realized that this wouldn't be at all wise. We knew that a bullet wound is easily recognizable as such and we couldn't afford any trouble just before our vacation. We decided, in short, to operate.

When everybody was safely outside (Tom had taken a powder in the meantime), one guy stood guard at the door, leaving three of us to attend to Henry. Groaning and scared shitless, he started to drag himself towards the door, leaning on Barry and Rick. I cut him short with a wallop on the nut but, instead of passing out, he twisted free of the other two in such a way that they fell against each other. He turned his stupid puss and looked at me with terror in his eyes. He started to yell for the police. So the three of us went at him, to shut him up and to knock him out for the "operation." But we didn't get anywhere, because of his immense weight. He kept screaming like a pig in a slaughterhouse, which made me very nervous. I pulled a hammer out of a drawer and bopped him on the noggin. With a grunt, he collapsed between us onto the floor. In a feverish hurry, I plugged in a small electric hot plate, took a switchblade from my jacket pocket and laid it across the heating element. Rick and Barry, meanwhile, had pulled Henry's pants down and were cleansing his wound with gin. He was still moaning once in a while and we were scared to death he'd come to. People kept knocking on the door and the guy standing guard had a bitch of a time keeping them out. We had to work quickly.

By now we were cold sober. We wanted to mess up the wound a little so that it couldn't be identified as a bullet wound. We tossed a mat over the couch to sop up the gore and rolled Henry onto it, ass up. Barry and Rick held down his legs and I lifted the knife from the hot plate. It was red hot.

By this time the wound had turned a dark color. Barry kept wiping the blood away with a reddening towel. The wound—a deep gash several inches long, surrounded by blue-black flesh—would show for a second, but then fill up with blood again immediately. I forced the hot knife into the cut, just under the skin. We smelled a sickening stench of burning human flesh, an odor I had smelled before in Algeria. I suddenly realized what I was about to do. I felt like throwing up. We looked at each other, making faces at the blood and stench, and then we started to laugh. My hesitation vanished. I started carving away with abandon. The bloody gash grew into a large red sun, with spreading rays. To the rhythm of the music, which was still coming on loud and clear from the tape recorder, I scratched, hacked and sawed my way through the quivering flesh. I was getting a kick out of it! Then the knife, which had cooled, suddenly stuck in the wound and I jerked it out with a quick yank. Henry woke up screaming.

For a minute I was stunned by the discovery that a human head, eyes and brain were attached to the mountainous pink ass. Henry's sad-sack face loomed up at me, infuriating me. I think I would have plunged the blade straight into his mug if Rick hadn't caught my arm. The three of us began to beat the shit out of Henry, who didn't know what the hell was going on. We punched him and kicked him, all the while screaming "dirty fag!" and "cocksucker!" Horrified, Henry broke loose and scrambled toward the window, apparently intending to jump out, bare ass and all, but he tripped over his pulled-down pants. We caught him again and continued our beating, smashing him all over. My knuckles were raw from the blows and, angered by the pain, I connected with a haymaker and knocked him to the floor. Barry kicked the inert body a few times for good measure.

Attracted by the racket, a few people had come down from upstairs and were standing in the doorway, trying to see what was going on. One of them started towards me, but I jerked around, white with rage, and shouted, "If you bastards don't get back upstairs I'll knock your fucking heads off!" They disappeared. Barry, in the meantime, had grabbed a shirt out of my dresser, torn off the sleeves and wound the remainder around Henry's bleeding buttocks. The improvised bandage turned bright red within a minute. We got Henry into his pants, stuffed more rags into them and wiped the sweat from our foreheads.

Daylight was starting to stream through the windows and birds were chirping. I lit a cigarette, but the sour taste made me throw it away. It was ringed with red from my bloody fingers. The music started again and we could hear the loud voices and shuffling feet of the merrymakers. We helped Henry into his white raincoat. Though he looked pretty shaky, he managed to stand by himself.

"Look, boy," I said, "you have to understand—we only want to help you. You know that firearms means trouble. And none of us wants to get into trouble, especially *you*, right? So, to save us all a lot of nonsense and bother, we managed to . . . uh . . . disguise the wound a little. Now they won't be able to tell *what* hit you. I'm sorry if we got a little rough, but you were loaded to the gills and you weren't helping any! After all, it wasn't very nice of you to panic like you did!"

Henry, choking and crying, screamed at us, "I'll get you bastards for this, every one of you!" Barry socked him again, but he still didn't want to play ball. I proceeded to kick him in the nuts. That only made him feel more like a martyr. So we gave him an ultimatum: "OK, you little cocksucker, if that's the way you want it! But just remember this! If any one of us gets into trouble because of you, we'll find you, wherever you are, rip out your balls with a wrench and cut off your cock with a hacksaw. It's up to you!"

He turned pale and almost passed out just thinking about this fate. He looked imploringly into our stony faces and, realizing that we meant business, broke into sobs again. "Don't hurt me . . . I won't get you into trouble . . . I promise! Believe me, I won't. Just let me go, please let me go. . . ."

He had the look of a beaten man. Rick wanted him to sign a declaration to keep us in the clear, but I told him it wasn't necessary. We slipped into our jackets, threw some newspaper over the bloodstains on the floor and the couch, and cleared away the bloody mat and rags. Rick ran down to roll up the top of the convertible and start the engine. Barry and I managed to haul fat Henry down the stairs. He was smart enough not to give us any more trouble and, on the way to the hospital, calmly accepted our final instructions.

He was to say that, during a party at my place, he'd fallen about thirteen feet from the roof onto a heap of broken bottles in the garden of a restaurant in back. He was so drunk that he'd lain there, bleeding, for half an hour before we found him. Henry nodded his agreement, looking almost grateful. We felt a sense of relief, of exultation, like soldiers after a successful patrol. Our heads cleared by the fresh air and the speed we were driving at, we started singing. All except Henry, of course, who had no particular reason for singing. He wasn't sure just what damage we'd done to his precious posterior and only knew that it hurt like hell. In the light of early morning I could see just how grubby we all looked, with our yellow eyes and bloody clothes. The spots stood out a clear, dark red on Barry's white jeans and light-gray polo shirt, but they'd turned into black splotches on my blue jeans. My knuckles were bleeding. Naturally, Henry looked the worst of the lot. To reassure him, I said, "You know, I'll need a doctor, too. My hands are in worse shape than your ass!"

It was broad daylight when we reached the hospital, but

all the lights were still burning. I told the porter that it was an emergency and he led us into a waiting room. Smells of ether and disease filled the air. Henry sprawled out on a bench. The doctor entered, a young guy in a spotless white coat, his hair plastered down. He sniffed disapprovingly at the obvious odor of booze. "What's the emergency here?"

"Our friend here fell down from a roof and cut his ass on a pile of broken bottles——"

"Would you kindly let the gentleman tell his own story?" interrupted the doctor.

"Of course," I said. "But he'll only tell you exactly what I was going to!"

I shot a menacing look at Henry, said "See you!" to the medic and turned to go. "Your name, please! I must have your name!" he yelled after me, but I was already halfway out the door. "Smith!" I shouted over my shoulder, and then I was off.

As it turned out, Henry only stayed in the hospital for two days. And they believed his story. We saw him one Sunday afternoon a few weeks later, strolling along arm in arm with a boyfriend. We waved and called to him from our car but he made like he didn't know us.

133

The nightclub didn't open until three in the morning, just in time to catch the nighthawks, sailors, bartenders, waiters, pimps, whores, truck drivers and newsboys—some having an early breakfast, some a late supper. We dropped in at about five to wind up a busy night. We had been to the flicks, an old-fashioned Western with lots of whooping and shooting. Then we'd gotten into a brawl at a bar when a bunch of Americans called Rick (who's Surinamese) a "goddamn nigger." They ended up bleeding in the gutter. We thought it would be smart to cut out for a few hours, so we took off for Amsterdam. Rick had picked up a new Chevvy somewhere and we tore along at 120 mph, stopping now and then for a beer.

When we got back to town, everything was closed, so we drove to Rick's place. Fatima was still there. We had some coffee and then made the rounds, picking up rent money from the whores. Barry wasn't feeling well so we left him with Fatima and went on to the nightclub. It was jammed, as usual. Next to me sat a huge man I hadn't seen before, a big, beefy guy in a corduroy suit. He was just sitting there, staring into space, not eating or drinking. Our poker

ame broke up when Rick left, so, out of boredom, I offered
o buy the guy a drink. He asked, very politely, if he could
ave soup instead. I told him to order anything he liked—
nder ten guilders. He asked the waiter to bring him a
owl of chicken soup, two hamburgers, a hot dog and three
ream puffs and gobbled them up in a matter of minutes. It
nust have been his first meal all week. He told me that
ie'd run out on his wife and been kicked out of the
Salvation Army. He was in trouble, out of work and had
no place to sleep. "And what line of business are you in,
if I may ask?" He spoke softly, very polite and formal,
probably in deference to my obviously expensive suit.

"I'm a pimp," I replied.

He was shocked. Though he might have suspected as much,
he hadn't been expecting such a blunt admission. I decided
to have some fun.

"Oh, well," I said breezily, "if ya like cash, the easiest
ay ta make it's ta push a few dames on their backs. Fucking's
ucking! Only the sun works fa nothin'!"

Under his worshipful gaze I kept ordering more drinks
and paid the waiter with a hundred-guilder note each time,
pocketing the change without counting it. "Sure, I've had
my hard times like everybody else, but never again! Nah, it's
the easy life fa me all the way. I've only got five girls workin'
fa me now, but I'll be openin' a bar before too long, wid
rooms upstairs—if ya know what I mean!" I slapped his
back heartily.

"Well, of course, I've been to . . . uh . . . such places.
But I've never seen you around before."

"No, you ain't! I just done tree years."

His eyes widened. "What for?"

"I don't like ta talk about it."

"Oh, but I wouldn't tell anyone!"

"It ain't dat! Everyone knows about it—it's been in all
the papers, front-page headlines: *'Black Nolly Found Dead
wid Smashed Skull!'*"

The man gasped. "And . . . did you . . . did you do it?"

"I *told* ya, buster, I don't wanna talk about it! Lay off,
will ya!" And then, bitterly, "Dese dirty bastards ratted on
me, my so-called 'friends.' But I'll get 'em for it! All of 'em!"

"I could help you!" he said, shaking.

"Lemme feel yer muscle." He bunched up his biceps for
my approval. With his muscles, he could have knocked me
into the middle of next week. "Hmmmmm . . . not bad . . .
not bad! Tell me, could ya keep yer trap shut? Are ya
good in a fight? Can ya stand the sight of blood? Could ya
kick somebody ta death if ya had ta?"

His face turned white. "Well, I've never done *that* before. No, I'm not sure . . ."

I shrugged. "It's up ta you, pal. If potatoes an' beans in grease is all ya want——"

"It's just that I wouldn't want to get involved with the police."

"Hahaha! The fuzz. The Commissioner's one of my best customers. Ya don't run any risks in dat direction."

My imagination was running wild. I told the guy how I'd kicked in the skulls of enemies, terrorized bars and raped women. I said I made at least five hundred guilders a day out of my various enterprises.

He accepted my offer of a sack for the night and we left together. He carried a lumpy jute bag over his shoulder. Walking along the deserted street, we passed a policeman. My hand flew to my inside pocket and I whispered behind my hand, "I hafta watch dese lousy coppers. Dey know my mug from the *Police Gazette* and if one of 'em happens ta be a little wise and trigger-happy, he'll gun me down as soon as look at me."

When we got to the square in front of my place, I said, "I'm just stayin' here till things blow over. With some odd-ball akstruct painter!" I pointed out the life-size posters in the windows of the studio. "Cremer, his name is. When I moved in, he moved out. Just as well for 'im—I'd make a meatball out of 'im for a guilder, the punk!"

As I fitted my key into the lock, my companion laid a restraining hand on my arm. "Listen," he said, "I don't feel so sleepy any more. I don't think I'll come in after all." He started to draw away, but I stopped him.

"Cut it out! Don't be an asshole! Ya could use some sleep and prog!" I glared at him.

"No . . . no . . . no! I'd rather not go to bed right now, if it's all right with you!" He quickly retreated across the square. I went upstairs. From the window I could see him standing, lonely and undecided. I opened the window and shouted as loud as I could, "Hey! Ya rollin' in or ain't ya?"

He backed away, shaking his head vigorously. Laughing to myself, I undressed. He was still there. Suddenly I had a great idea! I took out a bayonet, clenched it between my teeth and ran, stark naked, into the square. He was still staring at my window and didn't see me coming. When he heard my war whoop and saw me running bare assed towards him, the bayonet glinting in my teeth, he jumped a foot off the ground. I screamed, "Bahahahoeeoeoebraaaah!" He ran down the empty street like a bat out of hell. Back

253

upstairs, I looked out and saw him stop a man who was cycling across the square. He pointed at my window excitedly. The man patted him on the back and they continued on their way together.

A few weeks later he came into a bar where I was having drinks with a girl friend, a Spanish dancer. He came right over to me, hand outstretched. "Please forgive the way I acted last time we met. I must have been tight!"

I dismissed the affair with a wave of my hand. "Ferget it! You ain't the first person I scared out of 'is wits."

When the girl got up and went to the john, he leaned over and whispered, "Is she one of yours?"

"Dat's right. If ya dig the bird, I could give ya my special rate for friends! One hundred bucks for a sixty-nine."

I had told Barry about the guy and he was ready to play his role when we ran into him early one Sunday morning in a coffeehouse. We'd been in a brawl the night before and my knuckles were covered with gauze—for a change. He noticed this and asked, suspiciously, "Another job?"

Barry looked at him menacingly and turned to me. "Who's dis sack rat?" he demanded.

"I'm all right," my friend assured him. "I know all about it! I mean, your pal here knows me!"

"Yeah, he's OK," I said.

"All right, den, ya could stay, but don't get no ideas . . . understand?" Barry turned back to me and we held a muttered conversation, letting certain phrases be overheard, like "lead pipe," "death-blow" and "knife wound." The guy listened with eyes and mouth gaping. Barry continued in a stage whisper, "We can cross *dat* one off the list!"

"Check!" I said, rubbing my bandaged knuckles. "Too bad fa him he had such a big mouth. Did ya see the way he squirmed when I held dat hot pipe in fronta his nuts? Dere's one guy ain't gonna be blowin' his dough on the broads no more!" We screamed with laughter. Then, more seriously, "But ya shouldn'ta set dat car on fire!" "I thought sure he'd a jumped outta it—if he'd a been alive! Hahaha! I'd like to see the look on his chick's face when she opens up dat can of ashes!" Suddenly we pretended to remember our companion, who was laughing painfully. "Wait a minute," Barry growled. "You ain't been . . . uh . . . listenin' by any chance?"

"Oh, no! I didn't hear a thing!"

I quietly asked Barry how much he'd taken in the night before. When he answered, "Tree G's," the guy couldn't contain himself any longer. "Three thousand guilders?" he blurted.

"What did ya think, dat we work fa nothin'? What's tree G's for a little action? Chicken feed!"

We ordered another round of drinks and I paid for them with a hundred-guilder note. His eyes opened greedily. "Do you have any work for me now?"

"Nothin' doin', pal," I said. "Ya missed the boat the first time around."

"You'd better move to another table for a minute," Barry told him. "We have some business ta talk over." Obediently, he got up and sat down a few tables away. We continued the game, whispering to each other.

After a while I called to him, "Ya could come back now." He picked up his beer and joined us again. Just as he was sitting down, I cut short our "talk" with, "So all we need is the powder!" The big ox leaned over eagerly. "Dynamite, huh? You're planning another job already? Yeah, I know you guys!"

"Dynamite? What dynamite?" we said together. "We was talkin' about tooth powder!"

I looked around. The place was empty except for a few people in the far corner. I pulled a gleaming pistol from my inner pocket and aimed it straight at his head. "My! What big ears ya got, Grandma! Mind I shoot one of 'em off?"

134

In the summer the beach was my backyard. I spent whole days there and even slept there. I lay sprawled in the sun from early in the misty morning until late in the evening, when the sun had long since drowned in the sea. I had my meals in the snackbars on the boardwalk. In the afternoon, when the sun was at its zenith, I'd stroll over to the record shop and come on with the chicks for a while. I'd sit for hours in the cool shade of the place, dreaming to the music of China, Russia, Spain and other places I'd been to.

135

One piping hot day I got to the beach early in the morning, hung over from two days of drinking and gambling at every bar in town. I spread out on the yellowish sand and dozed off, but nightmares kept waking me. I'd get up, my mouth full of sand, run into the water for a quick five hundred strokes, then sprawl out again to let the sun dry me off. By noon, you could hardly see the sand for the people. A man in black sunglasses was lying on the same spot where I'd seen him all week, stretched motionless in the sun. His vacation was obviously doing him a world of good. He'd started the week as pale as a ghost, the ribs showing through his pasty flesh. Now his sunburnt belly stood up as round as a ball, red and peeling. I thought for a moment of waking him, for he'd obviously fallen asleep and was in for a painful burn. But it wasn't really any of my business. Probably a civil servant, I decided, and very good at doing nothing!

My gaze fell on a working-class family nearby: a man, his wife, a small boy of about five and a baby who could hardly walk. The father's chest was white where an undershirt would have been, contrasting with the brown flesh of his arms—probably a road-worker. His cow of a wife, corseted into a bathing suit that was at least two sizes too small, kept peeling bananas, one after another. She popped a bit of each into the baby's mouth and the rest between her own greedy chops, chucking the peels at passersby and quickly turning her head after each bull's-eye, grinning with glee. She paid no attention to her husband, who was turning somersaults and cartwheels, leering at girls in bikinis and puffing out his brawny chest. The little boy occupied himself by blowing sand across the well-oiled bodies and into the lemonades of the people sitting around him.

"Dickie!" the father roared. "Go find us a couple of beach chairs!" And then, more quietly, "But watch out the attendant doesn't see you!"

The baby was crawling about on all fours, pulling the noses and ears of sunbathers and crowing with pleasure. Then he disappeared. His mammoth mother went looking for him, searching in a frenzy among the beach chairs. After she'd found him, she changed his diaper, shaking the turds out of the dirty one and rubbing them into the sand with her foot.

After a while little Dickie returned, glowing with triumph, dragging two beach chairs behind him. His parents sat down in them. "If the attendant comes around," the father warned his wife, "out of the chair and onto the sand, understand?"

Dickie amused himself by spearing jellyfish with a stick and flinging them at people in beach chairs, preferably bikini-clad girls. Dad took him into the water and then they wrestled on the beach. "See if you can pin me!" shouted the bearlike father, and his son, with a child's faith, attempted to get the better of him. Then the father started emonstrating judo for his son, throwing him playfully over is shoulders. He put his foot on the floored child's chest. he boy wriggled, screaming with delight, while his father nouted, "Now say 'uncle'!"

I dozed off, the sun burning my eyelids. I awoke with a art. The baby was holding my hand and trying to stuff it nto his mouth. I gave him a little shove towards his mother, hich made him slip and fall on his head. He began to awl something awful. The next time he came crawling over was ready with a lit cigarette. A slight touch to his pink esh and he took off with a howl, in the direction of the man the black sunglasses.

Dickie and Dad were playing cards now, while Mom noozed with a newspaper over her face, her flesh oozing ut of her bathing suit. The man shouted, "Well, can you pen or can't you, goddammit?" The boy must have been :ry advanced for his age, playing poker already.

Meanwhile the other kid was making a meal of Mr. Sun-lasses, pulling his ears, rubbing sand into his hair and cking his toe. When I saw the brat bite solidly into the uy's nose, I expected him to wake up and wallop the kid. ut no, he didn't bat an eyelid! Dad looked up from his ards and nodded lovingly at the little bastard. When the aby started jumping up and down on the man's belly, the ther poked his wife and said, "Take a look at that!" They ad a good laugh over it, but then the father, winking to is wife, yelled at the baby, "Don't do that, son! Uncle-unkle will be angry-bangry!" I was amazed at the patience f the sun-bather, who seemed determined, at any cost, to eturn to work with a suntan.

I dozed again. I woke to hear the woman saying, "Doesn't aat man look strange!" Opening one eye, I saw the baby a his mother's arms, the man's sunglasses dangling from his nubby paw. The man was still stretched out, but now I oticed that he was staring straight up into the sky, not ven blinking. "You know, Bram," continued the old cow, t looks to me like this guy's had it!" Cursing, Bram threw own his cards, got up, went over to the sunbather and icked him in the side. No reaction. "You're right! He's ead!"

Dead! I thought back to the beginning of the week, when first ran into the guy, a pale little runt with a green wel slung over his shoulders. He had asked me politely, Excuse me, but is anyone occupying this spot?" And now e was red and bloated. His face, I suddenly realized, had blackish cast. I didn't want to get involved, so I just stayed put. I would keep quiet until the police arrived, the disappear into the crowd.

"Keep your claws off him, Dickie!" the woman yelle She was back in her chair. Dickie was poking the belly wi sticks and hopping merrily around it. "You too, Bram," sh commanded, "or they'll think you did it!"

"He stinks," the man said soberly. "What a stinking mess He sat down again, too.

I sniffed. Yes, the smell was unmistakable. I had notic it all day, but hadn't been able to place it, a sweetis irritating odor like DDT.

"Can I play with him?" asked Dickie. "No!" his fath roared, "are you crazy?" Then, to his wife, "Do you thi I ought to tell the cops?" "No . . . why bother? The pla must be full of dead bodies. Take a look at that one!"

She was pointing at me! To prove I was among the livin I pretended to awake suddenly and jerked my head aroun After they'd forgotten about me and things quieted dov again, I kept watching them from behing my shades. T civil servant was still lying there, seemingly asleep, only t sickly sweet smell indicating that something was not qui right.

Then Dickie asked, "Dad, can I have his hand?"

"Hand? Whose hand?" his father snapped.

The boy pointed to the dead man. "His, Dad, pleas Pete at school has a hand from a dummy. He has a ba with it! I want one too!"

"No, no, no," answered Dad. "Impossible!"

"Please, Dad, for my birthday! Then I wouldn't care if got an air rifle!"

I caught bits of his parents' hushed conversation: "fif guilders for an air rifle" . . . "only for a lark" . . "won't matter to him . . . so the worms eat one ha instead of two, so what? . . ."

I thought I must be dreaming.

"All right, Dickie. Get some beach chairs and shove the around the man, carefully!" The kid was jumping up a down, yelling, "Hooray! Hooray! Hooray!"

"Shut up!" snarled Dad. He helped his son arrange t chairs around the body and then, with a great show of no chalance, drew a rusty pocketknife from his clothes an whistling merrily, sauntered behind the chairs. My stoma turned over.

A minute later I heard him whisper, ". . . damn thi won't come off! Go find a brick, son, for under the wris Dickie ran off and returned with the required surgical i strument. A little later Dad emerged and exchanged

aningful look with his wife. "It's fixed!" Then he moved
beach chairs away. There was Dickie, bursting with
e, holding a bleeding human hand by one finger.
"Dickie!" his mother shrieked, "Go wash it off, right now!
herwise you'll get a disease!"

136

a Canadian prison, St. Vincent de Paul, a prisoner was
ot dead. He and another prisoner had pushed a guard into
cell, demanded a transfer to another prison and given the
arden fifteen minutes to make up his mind. Meanwhile,
ey began to carve up the guard's leg with knives. The other
ards decided to take matters into their own hands, shot
e prisoner dead and wounded the other. The guard died
the hospital. As a small boy I used to go to the railroad
tion to wait for my grandma. She was killed during a
mbardment of Budapest. The Soviet Union today launched
unmanned spacecraft in the direction of the moon. It
ould reach the moon in three and a half days. Was
akespeare queer? A problem which has perplexed scholars
r centuries is tackled by a noted biographer. President
lal of Yemen has accused the counterrevolutionaries of
oding the country with pornographic pictures, trying to
ison the revolutionary spirit of the people. Heavy punish-
ents and fines have been decreed for possession of such
ctures. America's Greatest Sex Experiment: an account of
e mass test of omnigamy that took place at Oneida, New
ork, during the second half of the nineteenth century.
very adult male had call on every adult female in this
precedented experiment in communal conjugal relations.
"I'm going to Venezuela with Frank," said Agnes.
"Oh, yeah?" I said.
"That's right! I'm going to Venezuela with Frank."
"No you're not!"
"I'm going to Venezuela with Frank!"
"Goddammit, you're not going!"
"Oh, yes, I am, whether you like it or not!"
"All right, then! Go!"
"No I won't!"
Their stomachs contracting with hunger and their throats
rched, the man and woman walked arm in arm amid
e ruins of the bombed city. They held on to each other
ghtly, afraid of stumbling into the gutter, where the dead
odies lay. "Here," the man said, and with a piece of broken
ass he cut into his jugular vein and offered his blood to

the woman to drink. Then she offered him her body. Th
died ravaged.

I've been in love with Jayne Mansfield for years. Why
Ray Charles blind? Thirteen is unlucky and so is a bla
cat crossing your path. She had been to the Riviera
bus. Her eyes were bloodshot and her nose was peeli
The Jivaros of Ecuador cut off your head and shrink it
the size of a knickknack for the mantelpiece. In London
learned the hand-jive. Pastors who screw virgins in t
confessional—united in the sight of God! Sergeant Knoch
fresser gave me a fresh supply of bullets to shoot gulls
the roof. After all is said and done, I've been looking for m
self for eight years.

137

One room of my studio was painted red, the ocher-red
the *Venus of Willendorf,* the color of prostitution. T
walls, floor, ceiling, door, bed, sheets, night table, cha
lamp, alarm clock, blankets, curtains, telephone, radio
were red. That way the virgins' blood blended with
decor. Besides, I found it restful. But one time the l
started to stink. Some chick must have gotten her month
all over it. I couldn't find the stain in all that red, and
days the place had the sour smell of eels.

I rented the room to friends who wanted a wild place
screw their chicks. It cost me a thousand guilders to
stall a toilet, sink and shower. A month later I was bro
so I ripped them out and sold the lot for sixty-five guilde
I kept my Harley in the studio. It was nice to sleep s
rounded by the smell of gasoline. One of my girl friends
ballerina, used to dance for me on the table, dressed co
pletely in black—bra, lace panties, garter belt, silk stocki
and spike-heeled shoes. She inspired me with Stravinsk
Firebird, The Four Seasons and the Charleston. I've h
fourteen dancers in all, so I'm something of an expert
ballet. They all cooked for me—always vegetable stew,
cause they had to watch their calories. And I got free pas
to their performances.

I had a complete set of stereo components. I could t
in police and ships' broadcasts. There were loudspeakers
every room. I played the stereo so loud that people in
street stopped to listen. In those days I went wild over
Blakey, Donald Byrd, Bobby Timmons, Chico Hamilt
Miles Davis, Dave Brubeck and Chet Baker. Now it's Jo
Coltrane, Thelonius Monk, Ornette Coleman, Charlie Ming
Eric Dolphy, Cannonball Adderley and Ray Charles.

There was a short but sweet affair with a countess from a
[...]y old and distinguished family. She was married. She
[...]nd me fascinating because I smoked pot. She wanted to
[...]ow if I was hooked. In the nightclubs, I paid with her
[...]t, tipping the waiters generously. They loved me.
[...]I became an ace at poker. I was a match for anyone.
[...]ofessional gamblers and rich boys came to my place in
[...]e middle of the night to play for stakes of thousands of
[...]ilders on my special gaming table. I hocked my stereo
[...]enever I lost. The police tried to raid the place, but we
[...]naged to keep them out. You had to enter through a
[...]p door that weighed a hundred pounds, so unwelcome
[...]ests could be avoided just by standing on it. My front
[...]or was painted red so I could find it even in the worst
[...]por. One time Marilyn caused a traffic jam when she
[...]nt out to pick up a bottle of milk at the grocery. She
[...]s wearing red embroidered panties and a scarf.

HERE I AM
OUT OF THE FRAY

138

We took off for Spain on my Silver Monster. We w
tearing along the road to Barcelona at three in the aft
noon, siesta time, still a hundred miles from the city.

"If we're lucky," Barry shouted over the roar, "we'll ma
the seven o'clock boat. Otherwise we'll have to hang arou
Barcelona for a week."

There was no sign of "blue Spanish skies," only da
surly clouds. The roads were spotted with muddy pools.
we sped along, yellow clouds of mud flew about our e
and we were soon soaked through. Near Gerona we enter
a landscape that was like a surrealist painting, includ
a very depressing reddish skyscraper—the state prison,
huge, cold-looking place, bathed in an eerie sunlight th
barely pushed its way though the clouds. The glistening roa
the red buildings, everything was washed with this sa
dull light. There wasn't a soul in sight, except for a f
farmers in covered carts and, every hundred yards or
the Guardia Civil, in flat caps and long green capes, carbi
and machine guns hanging across their chests.

It began to pour and streams of hail battered our fac
Barry yanked my arm. "I've got to piss!" "Goddammit, agai
No time now," I yelled back at him. We were alrea
soaked and I didn't feel like stopping in the rain. So
hurtled on through Gerona and pulled to a quick halt a
bar beside the main road.

Inside, we had some coffee and something stronger. "I

cking rain! If it keeps up like this, we won't hit Barcelona
til late tonight. You can't make time with rain running
over your goggles. When it gets dark we'd better camp
mewhere."

Then, as suddenly as it had begun, the rain stopped and
e were off. In the middle of nowhere, after we'd left
erona far behind, the Silver Monster sputtered to a halt.
hopped off and checked the bike over. The rain started to
me down again, in buckets.

"Shit! The battery isn't recharging. The dirty, rotten
stard!" Barry jumped out of the sidecar. There wasn't a
ilding in sight and we were standing at the bottom of a
ep hill. I gave the bike a few good kicks and jiggled a couple
wires, but nothing happened. So we started to push.
om time to time a car whizzed by, but not one of the
icks stopped to help us. My shoes were full of water
d I kept slipping. Finally an M.G., carrying two English-
en with glasses and crazy moustaches, pulled up beside us.
ueers!

One of them asked, "Would you be so kind? Is this the
ay to Barcelona?"

"Yes."

He closed his window, stepped on the gas and waved,
ughing: *Have a good trip!*

"Fuck off, you cocksuckers!" we yelled.

Dog-tired, we reached the top of the hill and saw, about
mile beyond the foot of the hill, a building of some sort.
e climbed on the Silver Monster, pushed off and started
asting down, slowly at first but finally at a good clip. It
as an inn. There were lots of Bugattis and Ossas parked
der a straw canopy, so we slipped my bike in beside
em. The locals came out to inspect us and the Silver
onster. They tapped the motor, ran their hands over all
e handles and buttons and pointed at the speedometer.
ne hundred and fifty mph? *Es verdad?*" they asked, their
es wide with amazement. "*Sí, sí,*" we assured them.
e asked if they could direct us to a mechanic, but they didn't
ow of any. So we went inside. The farm workers treated
like visiting royalty, not letting us pay for anything. A
te chick—she must have been about sixteen—brought our
ub and even sat down with us while we ate, all smiles
d pointy tits. Barry said, "Why don't we stick around here
r a day or two? We've already missed the boat anyway."
I told him he was out of his mind. He'd never get any-
here with the chick. In small Spanish towns like this one,
e girls are like sacred cows and Spanish cats can be very
sty where their women are involved. "Finish your meal,"

263

I told him, "and we'll get going. I want to sleep in Bar
lona tonight, in a good bed with a good broad."

Some of the workers were playing cards and others w
dictating letters to a little old man. Suddenly there was
roar of engines. Through the window I saw two Guardi
both bearlike men, dismount from their heavy BMWs. Th
were both wearing helmets and packed two pistols apie
They looked over my bike and then came inside. The fa
workers rose nervously from their seats and greeted th
profusely. The Guardias' eyes skirted the room and fell
us. When they came nearer, I asked, very politely, if eit
of them happened to know anything about engines. We w
on our way to Barcelona and had had a breakdown, I
plained, and needed some advice. One of the guys w
out to have a look at the machine. He came back and told
that the wiring was out of order. He then rattled somethi
off to his colleague, who excused himself, jumped on
bike and drove off. The Guardia told us he'd gone to fe
a mechanic from the next village. We offered him a dri
while we waited and he asked us to take his pack of cigarett
apparently considering it a great honor.

Most of the other men, after their exaggerated greetin
to the Guardias, had retired to a back room. Only a few w
left—those who hadn't been able to make a graceful exit
cause of their proximity to the Guardias—and they seem
to be shitting in their pants. With downcast eyes and mu
vigorous shaking of their heads, they refused the Guardi
offer of cigarettes. He shrugged his shoulders, irritated
their servility, and ordered wine for the three of us. T
girl at once brought three decanters of white wine, sweet a
delicious. We toasted everybody's health: hers, the Guardia
Barry's, mine and Franco's (why not!). The Guard
was enjoying himself and so were we. After quite a wh
(it had grown dark in the meantime), the other Guar
returned with the mechanic, who tested our engine with
few primitive instruments and managed to find the fau
wire. I felt like kicking myself for not having found
trouble on my own. Still, our time had not exactly be
wasted. We paid the mechanic. He charged more than
expected, but we figured this included a little something
the Guardias, which was all right with us. With enthusias
good-byes all around, we took off.

We stopped once for gas. I asked the attendant
"plomo," but he looked at me, puzzled, and scratched
head. I found out later that it means "gas" only in Portug
in Spain it means "lead." Every time it started to rain,
looked for a haystack. We found plenty of them, but o

after it had stopped raining. The mechanic's fee had left us nearly broke, so there was no question of stopping at an inn. We had to make it to Barcelona in one jump, whatever the weather. "Once we're there," Barry said, "we can decide what to do next. We could find us a couple of American chicks—there ought to be plenty of them around. And we could pick up a little cash and get going again. To Ibiza. Or, if we have enough loot, to Tangier."

"Take it easy," I told him. "You've got us in Africa and we haven't even made it to Barcelona yet!" By now it had gotten cold and it was pitch-dark on the road. There were no lights anywhere, and half the trucks we passed were without lights too. Only in the towns we roared through were there a few feeble gas lamps. The country was hilly and the narrow road, full of S curves, ran alongside deep ravines. I wondered how many massive American cars had cracked up along this route. Heavily loaded trucks crept slowly and painfully up the steep grades. If we happened to wind up behind one on an S curve, I'd blink my lights to show that I wanted to pass. But the truck wouldn't budge an inch, so I'd be forced to slow down to about ten mph, either by shifting into first gear, which was broken, or by double-clutching quickly, which usually stalled the engine. Every time we stalled, usually with one truck in front of us and one in back, we had the uncomfortable suspicion that they might roll right over us, not wanting to run the risk of braking suddenly. So we had to hop off and roll the bike back down the hill, get it into gear again and try once more. After an hour on hills, we'd come to a ravine. Speeding along at 120, I'd occasionally hear a shriek from Barry, whose sidecar had skirted the edge of the ravine. Far below, little lights from houses were visible, indicating the distance of the drop. After a while, the Silver Monster was acting like its old self again. Spanish gas seemed to agree with it. Before long the road was dotted more and more frequently with neon signs, and then we were in Barcelona. We'd covered the last seventy miles in one hour flat, curves, hills and all!

There was heavy traffic in the city, and it wasn't easy to adjust ourselves to it after the long, empty stretches we'd just speeded through. When we came to a fountain on a wide boulevard, we stopped, parked the Silver Monster and stretched out on the benches to catch our breath. The fountain was illuminated with pink and blue lights and several well-dressed passersby paused at it. Apparently we had chosen a rich neighborhood. The weather had improved and we felt much better. I got up, washed at the fountain and, twisted into the sidecar, managed to change into my best suit.

Barry waded right into the fountain, wearing only his shorts. That created something of a stir. In no time at all a policeman, white-helmeted and gripping a stick, approached. "Hey!" I called to Barry, "You'd better get out of the bath. We have a visitor!"

The cop made a big fuss and I attempted to calm him down in my broken Spanish, telling him that we'd come all the way from Paris without stopping, that we'd been very anxious to get here because our *señoritas* were waiting for us and, of course, we couldn't meet them covered with mud and sweat. Spaniards always seem to soften at the mention of *señoritas*. This one was no exception. He smiled and sent us on our way towards the Ramblas.

At midnight, pushing through the large crowds that jostled and hummed in the Ramblas, the full, delicious realization that I was in a southern land came over me. It was a warm, lazy evening and palms lined the avenue. Smiling people moved casually through the street, in no particular hurry. Barry said we should park the Silver Monster in front of the police station. Spaniards have tremendous respect for uniforms and nobody would dare touch it there. Sure enough, there were two sentries there, their Sten guns slung over their shoulders. *Todo por la patria!* With our last pesetas we bought a couple of beers in the Plaza Real, hoping to run into someone we knew. We dropped into every bar and jazz joint, saw no one we knew, gave up and drove to the port. A customs man told us that the next boat to Ibiza wouldn't be leaving until the following evening. Just our luck!

"Let's sack out," I said to Barry. "Tomorrow we can try to dig up some cash for the boat fare, maybe from the consulate." We parked the bike on a pier across from a bright and busy sidewalk café. An orchestra was playing under Chinese lanterns while slim waiters rushed around with full trays. We waited for the place to close down so we could get a good night's rest. But it must have been an all-night joint. People at the tables kept watching us with interest. If we'd had the loot we'd have gone across and drunk until dawn. After a while the place quieted down and most of the people left. It was warm—a fine night for camping out. I curled up in the sidecar and Barry lay on top of the bike with his ass on the saddle, his back on the tank and his head on a cushion over the light. We spread a canvas tarpaulin over us and got comfortable. Or at least I did. Barry was OK until he moved his head; then the pillow slipped off and he had to balance himself carefully while he retrieved it; otherwise he'd have fallen off too. Some of the drinkers at the café must have thought they were having the DT's:

staring dully at a motorcycle apparently parked for the night under a tarpaulin, they'd suddenly see a hand creep out from under the canvas, scratch around on the ground, pick something up and disappear again! Our sleep was continually disturbed by curious night owls who, attracted by the flashy silver spokes, came over to take a closer look. I could feel their hands on the canvas. I'd toss the cover back abruptly and shriek like a banshee, sending them, white-faced, scuttling off into the darkness. Then there was a Spanish creep serenading his chick on a nearby bench, with a very limited repertoire of songs. After a couple of hours we were sick and tired of the lot of them. So Barry got out of "bed," sat down next to the amorous couple and followed their every move with a great show of enthusiasm. They left and we finally got down to some serious sleeping.

I awoke very early, chilled to the bone. The docks were already lively. Steam whistles were sending their mournful calls across the water and ships were bobbing about like corks. The sounds of the city were beginning, too. I heard Barry mumble, "Hey, take a look at that swinging broad!" She was swinging all right, right past us, with everything she had: tits, ass and long black hair. The southern atmosphere and the night in the open air had gotten me horny, so I sat up straight in the sidecar to inspect her more closely. "Hot shit!" exclaimed Barry. "That's the first time you ever woke up that fast!"

"Barry, my boy, you should know Jan Cremer is always interested in tail first thing in the morning! It's a great day and we should pick up some pleasant company. As my dear old Dad would have said, 'You don't know Spain if you haven't fucked a *señorita!*' And we can get some cash from the Dutch Consulate. They can't refuse."

We washed in the water off the pier. A dead rat, its belly bloated, drifted by. A clock struck eight. Barcelona had come to life. Down by the statue of Christopher Columbus, the street was buzzing with hundreds of cars, crowded trolleys and loaded trucks. One of the cars, a black Peugeot, pulled away from the rest and stopped not far from us. A man wearing a rumpled summer suit, white shoes and sunglasses hopped out and came toward us, while three others peered at us from the windows. I nudged Barry, "The Spanish underworld must have heard about us!" The guy pulled an ID card from his inside pocket. "Police," he said. "Passports, please."

Muttering nervously, we passed him our papers. "Merely routine," he assured us. Then he retired to his car and the three men examined them, checking them against a black

267

book. These little episodes always leave me sweating, so I was really relieved when he returned, smiling, and handed us back our passports, saying, "It seems that all is in order." We took the opportunity to ask if he could direct us to the Dutch Consulate. He checked with his office over the two-way radio in the car, then gave us directions, even taking the time to draw a little map for us. We changed our shirts and set out for the place, the third floor of a big office building on a large avenue near the Plaza Cataluna. We got there in no time and took the elevator up. A few Dutchmen were hanging around the counter, peasants from the North with huge cigars stuffed in their mouths, inquiring in comic dialects about hotel reservations, money and so on. I elbowed my way to the front, but was immediately bawled out by some snooty bitch of about forty with a shrill voice, "Sit down on that bench and wait your turn!" Controlling my temper, I took my place on the bench, whispering to Barry, "Just let me handle this. And watch yourself with that scummy bitch or we'll never get anywhere."

After a long wait we were interviewed by a young man, the prototype of healthy Dutch officials: red cheeks, red hair and no eyebrows. His attitude seemed to be: *Whatever it is you want, the answer is no!* Calmly, I asked to see the Consul on a matter of some urgency. He blinked. "The Consul! But, my dear fellow, the Consul hasn't time . . . you'll have to tell *me* what it is you want." So I explained the situation to him. "You see, our money has been lost—or stolen! And since we have to get to Ibiza, it's essential that the Consul advance us a little money. Not much, you understand, say twelve guilders or so. I could repay it tomorrow, as soon as I've met my friends in Ibiza."

Loudly, for the benefit of the onlookers, the redheaded creep exploded, "What do you think we are? The Travelers' Aid Society? The Welfare Department? You can't just barge in here off the streets and expect us to finance your vacation. Nor is there the slightest possibility of your seeing the Consul. Go to the police if you haven't any money, and ask them to put us over the border as undesirable aliens. But you won't get a penny out of us here, I can assure you!"

The blood rushed to my head and I saw red. I wanted nothing more than to grab the little prick by the throat and throttle him. But again I controlled myself and, quietly, insisted on seeing the Consul. He shrugged his shoulders, left us, and went behind a partition. I could hear him whispering, something about "dirty hoodlums," "dangerous characters" and "gypsies." After a long wait, another official came over to us. He turned out to be the publicity director, easily the

268

hippest cat in the place. He had heard of me. He was more sympathetic, but he, too, assured us that the Consul could do nothing for us. Then he reached into his pocket and pulled out five hundred pesetas, saying we could pay him back when we were able. Laughing inwardly at the astonished pusses on the others, we took off. Every time I went back to the consulate to make a payment on the loan, I got the same treatment from the redheaded prick. Much later, when I went back just for information about registering my bike, it was siesta time. Red was alone. He played the busy-busy role, not even looking up from his work, answering my questions arrogantly while he continued to write. When he finally stood up and came to the counter, I grabbed him by the throat, screwed up his tie and spit into his pink face. I hissed at him, "If I ever run into you in Holland, I'll beat the living shit out of you, you cocksucker!" I yanked him halfway over the counter and then flung him onto his desk. He skidded right across it, pulling down his papers and inkwells with him. I turned and left, satisfied at last. Just about every Dutch official I've come across abroad was unsympathetic, if not downright nasty. The worst are in Spain. The women at the consulate call themselves Carmen or Rosita (their names are Gert or Annie) and they all look like death warmed over. The Dutch Vice-Consul in Ibiza is a Spanish exporter who can't speak a word of Dutch, has never been in Holland and doesn't give a shit about any Dutchman. His only connection with Holland is the portrait of the Dutch royal family that hangs on the wall behind his desk.

When we went to buy our tickets for the crossing, there was a tremendous crush and we were told that the Ibiza boat was fully booked. We could either stay another week in Barcelona, which we couldn't afford, or go to Palma first and try to get a boat to Ibiza from there. So we booked on the seven o'clock steamer to Palma. We didn't have enough money to have the Silver Monster shipped with us, so we parked it in a garage near the docks and went off for a meal. At one of the cafés along the Ramblas we spotted Buck, a Negro piano player from New York that I'd met in Paris. We joined him and hit a few other places before he had to take off to meet a chick. Sitting at a sidewalk table, we had a first-class view of the whores parading up and down the street, some of them beauties. A few came over and sat down but, when they realized we were broke, didn't stick around. One girl in particular caught my eye, a beautiful piece. We waved and she came over. "Fuckie fuckie?" she asked pleasantly.

"More than gladly," I answered, "but we've got no pesetas. *Nada!*" She gave me a long look and then said it

269

didn't matter, we should come along with her. We paid the check and followed her out, explaining once again that we really didn't have a cent, that we were on a trip around the world and would be leaving on the seven o'clock boat. But she merely shook her lovely head and repeated that it didn't matter. She looked great: clean, well dressed, with gorgeous long legs and tits you could get lost in. You could see them trying to burst out of her low-cut dress, dark-brown nipples set against well-tanned skin. She smelled good and the features under her heavy make-up were beautiful. Her name was Corrita.

I asked if she had a friend for Barry and she said yes, she lived with another girl. On the way to her place, we stopped off to do some shopping, because she insisted that we have dinner with her. It seemed almost too good to be true and, suspicious bastard that I am, I began to wonder if it was, especially when we got to her place. She lived off an alley, in what was apparently some kind of whorehouse. We passed dark shadows on the stairs and the air was heavy with perfume. Two guys alone in a strange city and, within a few hours, offers of dinner and afters with a gorgeous hooker . . . and she knew we didn't have any money.

Her room was very nice—a big, soft bed covered with cushions, fur rugs on the floor and prints and knickknacks all over the walls. Corrita opened her purse and handed me a pack of Chesterfields, then left to get her roommate. Barry and I collapsed onto the bed. "Shit, man, this is the life!" he said. "Too bad we've got tickets for tonight's boat." We put on the radio and relaxed, listening to the noises of the house —voices, footsteps on the stairs, laughter. There was a knock on the door and a girl walked in, wearing only panties and sandals. She said something softly in Spanish, took something from the washstand and went out again, smiling. Then Corrita came back with her roommate. She too was good-looking, just a bit chubby, but with a pretty face and a good body. We were introduced all around and Barry disappeared with her, arranging first to meet me in about an hour. It was five already and we still had to pick up our gear from the Silver Monster.

Corrita, without a trace of coyness, poured drinks for both of us and lay down beside me. We lay there, listening to the muffled noises from the street. I kissed her, getting hornier by the minute. Soon she was lying nude beside me, more beautiful than ever. Her breasts were firm, with dark-brown, pointed nipples, and her hips were broad. Curly black hair grew in a lush triangle of promise around her pussy. She was sucking my tongue now, with slithering intensity. I tore off

270

my shirt and she pulled down my jeans, wiggling under me like a snake. When I grabbed her buttocks in both hands and pushed myself deep into her, she screamed, clawing at me like a tigress, panting and rubbing up against me. I felt, without pain, her nails digging into my flesh. I was riding the waves of a wild sea, falling into deep crevasses, riding a runaway mare, being sucked into a big, red, churning tornado. Afterwards, with Corrita stroking my back and cooing into my ears, I fell asleep.

I awoke to find Barry shaking me. He was looking very dapper, his hair wet with sweat but neatly combed. "Wake up! What are you going to do—stay here or go to Palma? Man, I got a great lay from that chick. She's a real doll! But we've got to get going if we want to catch that boat! Corrita says that if you want to stay here, she'll take care of you. So make up your mind. It's after six already. I'm taking off."

Well, now! Corrita was a hell of a chick, all right, but on the other hand, I didn't want to be anybody's pimp, and that's what it would amount to if I stayed, flat broke as I was. And I didn't want to get stuck in a strange city where I didn't know a soul. So I got up and started getting ready to go. Corrita tried every trick in the book to get me to stay. She finally started to cry, but I told her that I had no choice, that I'd be back soon and that then we could stay together. We didn't even have time to eat what she cooked for us. She cried some more. I promised to write and, if possible, to arrange for her to come and join me. She brightened a little at that and gave me a few hundred pesetas for travelling money. We said good-bye. I really felt sorry for her. She was only about twenty-two and already tied irrevocably to her profession. It was a shame, but life is full of sacrifices and quick decisions, and I'd made mine. We ran down the Ramblas towards the docks. It was past 6:30.

We stopped off to get our gear from the bike. We stuffed everything we could into our kit bags and left the rest in the sidecar—pots, pans, a stove, tools and winter clothes. Later on, when we came into a little money, we could come back for the Silver Monster and our other things, or have them shipped over to us. We hopped a cab to the pier. Our steamer, the *Ciudad de Alicante*, was getting ready to leave and the last passengers, clutching their bags, were hurrying up the gangplank. We were travelling deck class so, once aboard, we made for the upper deck and parked our gear on a couple of chairs that we found tied up with rope under a reddish yellow awning. Then we sauntered back towards the gangplank to watch the last people boarding, on the slim chance that we might run into some old acquaintance. Five minutes before sailing time, three whistles sounded and the crew set to work untying the gangplank. Just then I noticed, in the pack of people milling about on the pier, a familiar face. It was Corrita. I hid behind a fat guy. Corrita was running up and down the pier, nervously searching the faces of the passengers. Afraid she might spot me and want to come along, I kept out of sight. The last people to come aboard had been the Guardia Civil. The passenger list was handed over to the harbor police and the gangplank hauled aboard. The steamer started drifting away from the dock. People on shore were waving handkerchiefs and some Germans on board started throwing serpentines and confetti. I came to the rail and was immediately spotted by Corrita. She stopped short and began to wave at me, wildly, with both arms. She was making signs, pointing to her purse, but I couldn't make head or tail of what she was trying to say. The ship was now free of the dock and turned to start off full speed ahead. Barry, who'd gone off to the can, returned, and I pointed Corrita out to him. She kept getting smaller and smaller and her gestures more and more puzzling. The others had left the pier and she was the last one waving at the departing steamer. I felt obliged to keep waving back. Then a big, black car swung over beside her and a guy got out. He grabbed Corrita by the arm, hit her, opened the car door and pushed her inside. She was holding her arms over her head, for protection. The car door slammed shut and the sedan drove off the pier. It all happened in a few seconds.

"Did you see that?" I asked Barry, amazed. "Did you see what happened just now?"

"Yes, of course," he answered, but he didn't understand it any better than I did. We talked about it for a long time afterwards, trying to figure out just what Corrita had been trying to tell us and just who the character in the car might have been. Maybe it was her pimp. Or the police, on one of their "routine investigations." I never found out and I never saw Corrita again.

Downstairs, in the saloon, we treated ourselves to a few beers and a good meal. We ran into a couple of German gay boys, a movie star and his companion, who joined us and bought us drinks. Barry spotted a couple of English chicks and took off after them, while I stayed behind to enjoy the free brandy and steak the Germans were lavishing on me. When they had gone off to bed, I started scouting around for Barry. I couldn't find him, though, so I decided to catch a snooze on the upper deck. That was a mistake! People were snoring, coughing, groaning and even fucking up there. Some

izened old dame next to me smelled so bad that I couldn't
stand it. I took my blankets to a lower deck. There I ran
into Barry. He was trying to make it with one of the chicks
and wanted me to take care of the other one, her sister.

"Why don't you take on the pair of them yourself?" I
suggested. "I couldn't make it at this point unless I had a nice,
soft bed under my ass. Besides, I'd freeze my balls off fucking on deck!" I once fucked an Arab girl on the deck of
the Algeciras-Tangier ferry. We waited until all of the crew
had left the forward deck. Then I put some rags and ropes
on the floor behind the big chain winders and fucked her,
three times. She was some hot kitten. She just couldn't get
enough. I was sitting there, exhausted, staring at the dark
African sky, and she was busy playing the temptress, using
all sorts of tricks that were new to me. But I was too tired
and the motion of the ship was putting me to sleep. Finally
she pulled her panties back on and slipped away. Next
morning, at dawn, I was kicked awake by the crew. I was one
hell of a mess! We'd been lying in a pool of oil, the sticky,
black kind they use on chains. Everybody found the sight
of me highly amusing and the smell of me highly repulsive.
I wasn't allowed back in the saloon, and little wonder! Not
only was I spattered all over with dried-up come and smelly
oil, but the bitch had bled all over me as well. I never got the
stains out of my suit.

Barry kept insisting we could make the two of them. But
we'd have to catch them while their mood was right. I'd seen
the chicks and could tell they were the kind you had to chat
with for two hours before they'd put out with the goodies.
So I left Barry sulking and found a warm, well-sheltered spot
for myself behind a big air funnel. I lay down, hoping to get
some sleep. On the other side of the funnel a boy and girl
were carrying on to beat hell, arguing from time to time in
what sounded like Swedish and hitting the deck in a regular
rhythm with plenty of panting and giggling. I thought of
Corrita for the thousandth time and got so horny I couldn't
be still. I got up, leaving my blankets behind, and made for
the railing. On the way I stumbled over an old man, whose
legs were protruding from beneath his blanket. In horror I
watched one leg shake for a second and then begin to roll
away from his body. The old guy woke up, cursing in Spanish. He reached over and picked up the leg, a wooden leg all
fitted out with a shoe and a sock. He clasped it to his breast
and went back to sleep. I felt like crying.

139

We finally arrived in Ibiza by way of Palma and looked up a couple of girls we knew, but they were as broke as we were. We found temporary shelter with a Dutch bullshit artist and snatched small change from his cigar box to keep body and soul together on *bocadillos* and absinthe. All the girls we met were either provided for or else looking for shelter themselves, so we didn't have much luck in that direction. Sometimes we slept in caves along the beach and swam and lay in the sun all day.

We were waiting for the action to begin, any action. We had come to Ibiza to get together enough cash for a trip through Spain, Portugal and, if we were lucky, North Africa. We found, in the upper part of town, a very chic art gallery that exhibited Tapies, Millares and Saura. I had brought some of my lithos with me to Ibiza and I took them to the gallery. I came out with five thousand pesetas, a contract and the key to a house near the port.

A month later my first show was held. It was a tremendous success. Out of twenty-four canvases, eighteen were sold on opening day and four later on. I was rich again. We decided to stay.

We had rented an eight-room house, bought new clothes and opened charge accounts at the best bars and restaurants. I must have been the richest hipster on the island. Never in the history of the Ibiza artists' colony was an exhibition quite so successful as mine. Jan Cremer came, saw and conquered. The gallery had advanced me another ten thousand pesetas, and I had to produce some paintings. But the weather was always hot and the beach was very tempting. And at night the bars and the broads kept me busy. Every day the owner of the gallery dropped by to see how my work was coming. I sent Barry out to reassure him and tell him that I never showed my work to anyone before the official showing. One week before the opening, I decided I'd better get to work.

Energized by shots of benzedrine and cocaine, inspired by hash and marijuana, I worked without stopping, day and night, for a solid week. I never left the studio or slept. Barry helped keep me going. He cooked, stretched canvases, mixed paints, made frames, cleaned the place and turned visitors away. I hacked, gouged and splashed my way through the canvases like a madman, and on the last day I just slopped the paint on with my fingers. On opening day, sitting in the taxi that was transporting my work to the gallery, I applied he finishing touches. I had to give the driver a few hundred pesetas to cover the damage to his cab. I worked at the gallery until an hour before opening time, then put away my brushes, went home and got cleaned up. When I got back to the gallery, it was overflowing with enthusiastic art lovers and most of the paintings were already spoken for. The show brought in eight thousand guilders. I lost fifteen pounds, came down with some kind of fever, slept through three solid days, and couldn't see right for weeks.

I stayed in Ibiza for two years altogether, interrupted only by short jaunts to Tangier, Marrakesh, Madrid, Barcelona, Paris and Amsterdam. The second year was as lean as the first was fat. That first year Barry, Dick (an asshole buddy that everybody thought was my brother) and I were the toast of the island. We set the fashion, parading through the streets barefoot, in faded jeans and cowboy hats. The ladies loved us. Our pad was the most popular on the island. Instead of a dish of candy on the table, we had a big jar of pot and cigarette papers. Cats fell by our place at all hours and walked out ten feet high. I had an affair with a famous American model who wanted to take me back to New York with her, another with a Spanish *condesa* who wanted to take me to Brazil, and one with a French-Italian beauty who took me to Paris. From there she wanted me to fly with her to Los Angeles.

I made a lot of good friends. On a small island, people are thrown together more than on the Continent. You get to know everybody. I began to like people I had loathed. It was all so cool, so relaxed, that I could feel the aggression flow out of me like semen. I laughed and sunbathed, fucked and smoked. Everyone on the island called me *"Medalla"* because of the Russian medal that hung around my neck, inscribed with a submarine, a cannon and the words, "For Bravery." One time, in Leningrad, I'd grabbed a pistol from a mutinous sailor, a kid of sixteen who was out to kill his superior officer. Not that I gave a shit whether or not he shot the officer! It was simply that I was standing too close for comfort. I got the medal from the Russian Embassy years after I'd completely forgotten the incident.

I was king of the island. Years later I came across a big picture story about myself in an American newspaper, with a fat headline, *"James Dean in Art."* Two American chicks I'd met on Ibiza had written it.

One lazy Sunday afternoon I had an accident near the dangerous crossroads at St. Eulalia. The American model was with me. The scooter we were on slipped into a forty-foot-deep ravine off the side of the road. The scooter landed

on top of me and knocked me senseless. In the sizzlin
heat, and with three toes broken, my glamour girl set off fo
help. It was siesta time, so she couldn't get anyone to com
back with her until three hours later. That evening I wa
back at the Domino Club, my arms and legs all bandage
up. A few days later I was down with tetanus. There wer
huge boils all over my body. Every three hours I got a sho
of penicillin from the druggist, a little sadist who rammed th
needle into my tender backside like a spear. It was a painfu
period: I wasn't allowed to drink, could barely walk, and
had to sleep on my stomach. Any movement sent pain shoot
ing through me. I awoke from my short naps drenched i
sweat. Sex, of course, was out of the question, and it wa
pure torture to have to listen to Barry carrying on with hi
Swedish chicks in the next room.

We were the terror of every boyfriend and husband on th
island. Walking along the dock, we'd pass groups of guy
with their girls and make suggestive cracks to the receptiv
chicks while their escorts looked on with hate in their eyes

I was always inviting people in for meals. Barry, a maste
chef, puttered away for hours behind the charcoal stove.

At the beginning of winter the weather became cooler and
it started to rain often. We took down the shutters and use
them whenever we ran out of fuel for the fireplace.
bought an air rifle with a very heavy caliber. I could hav
put holes through oil tanks with it, or shattered streetlight
or shot at German yachts. I could hit a target three hundre
yards away. We shot at fishes in the harbor when they cam
up for air, shot the porcelain caps off telegraph poles, shot
hole through the Spanish flag on the ferry to Salamanca, sho
through six doors with one bullet, shot waterpots off th
heads of native women and shot cigarettes from people'
hands. I even shot the cap off a Guardia Civil. The guy
blew his whistle like crazy and a few minutes later six othe
cops, guns in hand, started inspecting everyone in the area
We suspended our rifle practice for a couple of weeks an
kept out of sight of the Guardia.

We used to sit in the Domino until late at night, listenin
to Ray Charles, Charlie Mingus, Eric Dolphy, the Monk an
Peggy Lee. All the records on the island wound up ther
sooner or later.

I was after the daughters of the island's governor. Th
eldest, who spoke French, seemed unapproachable, but yo
never can tell with those *señoritas*. They were all lush pieces
with the dark beauty of Rita Moreno or Gina Lollo
brigida. They greeted me in the street with come-to-bed eye
and brushed against me as they passed. It seemed that every

276

Spanish belle on the island was hot to trot. But I never got the chance. One girl was beaten with a stick by her father because she'd gone swimming with me. Any guy who had put away a Spanish girl was thrown off the island, after a bit of roughing-up at the police station. They weren't so anxious to get rid of me, though, because I had lots of money and a big reputation. But I was strongly advised to diminish my interest in the Spanish women. Men had been shot for less.

The island colony was small. The bishop, a dirty old queer, was obviously boss of the place. The population grovelled before him. He must have been over a hundred years old, and looked and smelled like a corpse. In the streets the villagers knelt at his feet as he went pattering along, leaving the stench of death in his wake. He preached from his pulpit that the faithful were not to mix with foreigners, who were scum out of hell. And, with few exceptions, they meekly subscribed to his doctrine. As Ibiza became more and more overrun with tourists and artists from the Continent, his sermons grew more and more fanatical. He all but advocated lynching. The Spaniards, fired by his madness, raped the foreign girls, molested the women and crashed into tourist bars to start drunken brawls. But if you hit a Spaniard, you'd be thrown off the island, even if he'd been molesting your wife or had hit you first.

140

A friend of the police commissioner had a wife who was a sturdy, sensual piece with bleached hair and dresses open almost to the navel. She was after me. Of all possible dangerous alliances on the island, this was the most suicidal. Her husband was an old, bald tyrant in heavy glasses. The lower classes all but kissed the ground he walked on. Waiters, if they noticed her giving me the eye in a bar, took me aside and warned me that if I ever came on with this woman I could count on being murdered. So I avoided her. If I got to the small beach where I usually swam and found her lying there, I'd quickly go somewhere else. If I passed a terrace where she was sitting with her husband and other officials, I'd force myself to look the other way. It felt like the entire Spanish population was lying in wait for me, looking for my first false move. The woman always managed to wink at me or, if we passed each other on the street, she'd brush against my body. She was about thirty, and had incredible breasts and a tiny waist, a cross between Sophia Loren and Hildegarde Neff. I got a shock through my balls just watching her ass as she walked away. When she saw me, she'd lick her full lips and unobtrusively rub her tits. If I met her in a narrow street, my heart would stop. I couldn't keep myself from staring at her. She'd gaze into my eyes, provocatively and expectantly, and finally I'd just run.

I discussed my problem with my friends and they too warned me that if I succumbed to the woman's advances, I'd pay with my blood. Her husband would have me slaughtered like a pig. In Spain, they told me, dozens of foreigners had been killed or hanged because they'd dishonored Spanish women. No trials, just good, old-fashioned, home-style justice. A few years ago, a Spanish sailor had commited just such a murder right on Ibiza. Members of his family had written to him at sea, informing him of his wife's infidelity. He'd come home and shot his wife and her lover, one after the other. He was arrested and locked up. But, when his ship was ready to sail a few days later, he was taken aboard by a police escort and allowed to sail with it, waved on by cheering villagers. He had avenged his honor.

It was uncanny, but all my Spanish friends and every Spanish waiter in town knew that the woman was after me. I had never even spoken to her, not so much as a word. My one mistake, shortly after I'd arrived on the island, was calling *"Ola!"* at her when she passed me in the street. I asked the American owner of a jazz joint who she was. He turned pale when I pointed her out to him.

141

About five o'clock one morning I was lying alone on the rocks, after a long swim in the sea. The sun was already beginning to show itself. The water was calm and the rocks were majestic—ocher, gold and red like a painting by Tapies. Everything was absolutely still. Only the occasional lapping of waves against the rocks broke the silence. I closed my eyes, in perfect contentment. Tears sometimes come to my eyes from the thrill of this landscape, probably the most beautiful in the world. Suddenly I heard a very slight sound next to me. I opened my eyes, startled. The Spanish woman was standing beside me. My heart jumped into my throat and I started shaking all over. She greeted me in a very friendly way and began to loosen her belt. Under her thin dress I could follow her beautiful legs. She pulled the dress over her head and stood before me in a skin-tight bathing suit. What a body! Everything was stacked in just the right places—firm, heavy breasts, a slender waist, wide hips, round buttocks and well-shaped legs. I took a deep breath and swallowed. She kicked off her shoes and started to run a comb through her long, blond hair. Then she offered her hand to me and, laughing, pulled me up. We walked together onto the springboard jutting out over the sea, dived and then swam for a while in perfect silence. Words were unnecessary. I knew what she wanted and she knew I wanted it too. She swam, a few strokes ahead of me, towards the rocks a few hundred yards out to sea. I was scared to death that someone would see us. I cursed under my breath and prayed that one of my friends would show up—at least I would have a witness that I hadn't raped the woman. I turned and swam back to my rock, dried myself and lay down in the sun. A few minutes later she was standing beside me again. From where I lay I could see the little black curls creeping out of the wet bathing suit that clung to her brown crotch. I would have given ten thousand guilders to fuck her, or just to touch her. But I wasn't about to pay with my life. So I controlled myself. She put her dress back on.

Meanwhile the beach was getting crowded with tourists. Pointing to a palm-fringed beach a little way down the rocky coast, she whispered to me, "Come to the beach over there this afternoon, at three o'clock!" She left. I dived right into the water and then, my head cleared, walked back to the village. I told Barry about my predicament and he said I'd have to make up my own mind. He thought it would be very dangerous to play around with the broad, but, on the other hand, maybe I could get away with it.

When three o'clock came I was sitting in the cool shade of the Domino, in a drunken stupor. I felt like a hairy horse's prick, but a live one.

142

Towards the end of the year, Barry decided to go to the States with his American girl friend, Barbara. She went on ahead to Madrid, and from there would be flying to Florida. Barry planned to join her there later. I stayed on Ibiza while he went off to Tangier for a few days, on business. We were to meet on the Plaza Real in Barcelona.

The Spanish Secret Service was very interested in my movements just then, suspecting me of involvement in a narcotics syndicate. Some cats had been tossed off Ibiza and were later caught by the cops in Barcelona. Nude, screaming and high as birds, they had stoned the crucifix in a church. They had landed in a nut house after taking overdoses and attempting suicide. Soon after that, detectives arrived on Ibiza. The American and British embassies also sent representatives, agents who worked with Interpol and the FBI. They tailed me and asked about me in every bar on the island. The waiters all warned me to watch my step. I was stopped and searched on the street three times in one day, but they never found anything. I decided to cool the scene for a spell. I had a suit custom-made, bought a gold ring for myself and some trinkets for the girls back home, and took off. Behind me, on the airport bus and on the plane, sat two secret agents. They followed me all over Barcelona.

143

Walking across the Plaza Real, I felt like the Saint of Charteris, Mr. Simon Templar. I looked tanned and healthy, my hair was lightened from the salt air (when I got to Amsterdam, everyone whispered, "Jan Cremer has bleached his hair!"), and I was wearing my new cobalt-blue suit. Barry showed up, just back from Morocco. We drank *horchata* and hit the night spots along the Plaza Real. The following day Barry and I took off for Paris. He hitchhiked and I went by train, having decided that travelling together might be risky. We were to meet at a certain hotel in Paris. He didn't show. I waited three days, getting more and more worried, afraid that something had happened to him. Late the third evening, returning to the hotel, I found him sitting in the lobby.

We ran into Peter Kuiters, walking along the Boulevard St. Germain. He should have been in New York, studying at a conservatory. At the Select we met Arthur, who was just back from Heidelberg, where he'd been working for the American army. All of us were headed for Amsterdam, so we had a little celebration. Peter was going to quit his job at Le Chat qui Pêche, where he was playing jazz with Hank Mobley and Art Taylor, and he took us along. Thelonius Monk had heard him in New York and given him introductions to the Paris jazz joints. But by now he was fed up—things had gone wrong from the very first night, when he'd overslept and showed up two hours late.

It wasn't long before we were out of bread and getting desperate again. I was waiting for a Dutch girl friend, who would have lent me enough to tide me over, but she never turned up. I couldn't even pay my hotel bill. So one night I packed my suitcase and tossed it out the window, into the waiting arms of Barry and Peter. Then I sauntered out through the lobby. Barry and I got a ride in a meat truck and arrived late at night in Rotterdam. The truck driver, pissed off when he found out that we had no money on us, wouldn't let us out of his sight until we paid the fare. So we called two friends, who showed up in the middle of the night with some loot. Barry went on to Amsterdam but I decided to stay put for a while. I needed the rest.

144

The yellow island, speckled with sun and sand. There are six thousand soldiers up in the old fort with the ancient, horse-drawn cannon. It gets so hot that waves of heat are visible. All the action is down near the water's edge. Bearded artists strum their guitars. The clerk from Cincinnati masquerades as a painter. The literary prodigy from Amsterdam rolls up his trousers, takes off his watch and wades into the water. Little bourgeois on vacations with pay, trying to get out of their ruts. Women from Paris, New York, Cologne and London—photographic models, mannequins and actresses. The Dutch girls have the worst reputation: every other day they trade in their lovers for new ones with bigger houses and bigger bathrooms. Women sit, with dogs or babies in one hand and their daily ration of absinthe in the other, eaves-dropping, hearing things they've never heard before and wouldn't dare repeat, about weed, hash, palfium, benzedrine, horse, belladonna, sniff, hip, joint, pot, tea, shit. Oh, how they *adore* John Coltrane! "Yeah, man, we dig'm, he's the greatest!" Boys in paint-spattered trousers read *Howl* and draw portraits with felt-tipped pens. Ibiza bursts with beat-niks from all over the world, who've heard they can live on credit there, and former SS-men and war criminals, protected by the Spanish police.

My house is on the water. Twenty-five yards below my window, the ocean pounds on the rocks. I have a lot of company. A Dutch actor drops in to shoot the shit and stays eight weeks. He never takes his socks off and he can't swim. Sometimes I retire to my farm, a few miles out in the country, to relax and paint. My cowardly neighbors string wires across the road, hoping that I'll drive into them on my motorcycle and cut my head off. I complain to the police, who regret that they can do nothing until an actual murder has occurred. Fortunately, because Claudia is pregnant, I have to drive very slowly and carefully at all times. I sleep with a hunting rifle under my bed and go around with a loaded pistol tucked into my belt. Electricity is unknown out in the country, so I play my transistor radio. The Spanish brats run from me in terror, not understanding where the music is coming from. Their fathers make a wide circle around me when I walk with the radio, but they snap to attention whenever Franco's voice booms out from it.

The permanent core of the island's residents is made up of war invalids, Korean War veterans, war widows, war criminals, deported mental cases, artists, Americans, Dutchmen (who claim they discovered it) and Germans (who claim *they* discovered it). The younger generation speaks English and the older generation and the Spaniards speak German, both souvenirs of World War II.

145

The night is purple-red. Black circles whirl into bright yellow spirals before my eyes. The atmosphere is hot. Thousands and thousands of fireflies light the sky. I enter a house, a building with a glass roof and purple walls blackened by oil smoke. The odor of blood meets me on the staircase. On the landing, a girl is leaning against a door, a cigarette in her hand. She steps provocatively in front of me, wearing only red panties and a bra. Her breasts are spilling out. She looks at me, laughing, says something in a language that I don't understand, and turns her shimmering body from side to side in front of me. I am still on the stairs, my eyes on a level with her mound of Venus. Short, black hairs shimmer between the embroidered roses and I catch a whiff of pent-up semen. She takes my hand and leads me up another flight of stairs. She snuffs out her cigarette on my arm.

The stench of gasoline is everywhere. At the top of the stairs is a baby-blue door. A purple trickle seeps through the crack at the bottom. We enter a large, bare attic. In the center of the room two boys are standing over an old man, hacking him up with samurai swords.

The boys look vaguely familiar, but I don't know where I've seen them before. The gray-haired old man is croaking like a frog, trying to pull away. One of the boys pulls a rusty hatchet from under his belt and cuts off the old man's head. It rolls along the floor, leaving a trail of blood. The body, still kneeling, shudders. Blood spurts from the neck and then the body suddenly crumples, like so much cellophane. "A-one, a-two, a-three," and they toss the corpse across the room. It lands in a corner, setting up a cloud of dust. The boys smile proudly. The girl shoves a stick into the gray head and, laughing, holds up the trophy.

I turn and dash down the stairs, ducking for fear that they'll throw the dripping head after me. I stumble down the last flight and finally get outside again. Day is breaking. Aghast, I notice a large spot of blood on my white raincoat. I try to take it off with spit, rubbing and dabbing at the spot like a maniac. It becomes lighter but, instead of going away, it keeps spreading into a fuzzy pink circle. I see lights in the café downstairs, so I go in through the wool-and-leather curtain covering the door, my hand in my pocket trying to hide the blood spot with my arm. I order a drink and sit down at an empty table right near the entrance. The bartender, a huge guy, looks me over suspiciously. I try to keep calm, telling myself that it's only because he's never seen me before. Or has he? The place looks slightly familiar, as if I'd been here before—in a dream, or in a drunken stupor. I try to look inconspicuous, but everyone stares at me. Suddenly I realize, with a shock, that all the customers are gray and wrinkled, like the old man upstairs. I get up to leave.

But it's too late. Sirens scream and car doors slam. I hear the clamor of voices and the pounding of heavy boots on the stairs above and then someone kicks in a door. The other customers, oblivious to all the commotion, continue to chatter. A group of old men around the stove have taken off their shoes and propped their feet up on it. There's a strong smell of singed wool and sweaty feet. I glance around the room. Nobody is watching me. The bartender, with his back to me, is drying glasses. I lift up a tip of the curtain and look outside, but I don't see any police cars. It must have gotten cold out, for the passersby walk by quickly, heads tucked deep into turned-up collars. Nobody lifts his head or looks around.

Now I can feel the bartender's gaze boring a hole in the back of my neck. How stupid of me not to have fled, to have chosen a café right at the scene of the crime! With shaking hands I try to roll a cigarette, finally managing on the fourth attempt. I light up, inhale deeply and puff the smoke out in the direction of the bartender. Through the cloud I can see that he is still staring at me. He looks unreal, standing there motionless like a statue, a glass in one hand and a blue-and-white checkered towel in the other.

I stare indifferently at the grease spots on the leather of the curtain, where countless hands have grabbed it. From upstairs I hear heavy footsteps descending, car doors slamming, then silence. My heart is pounding harder and harder and I can feel the butterflies in my stomach. I hope I don't get sick. I've forgotten my pills.

All of a sudden the curtain sweeps in and a cold gust of wind strikes my legs. Two men enter, wearing cheap trench coats and pulled-down hats. Detectives! They always turn up eventually, crawling in through the cracks just when you're beginning to breathe easy. I can feel my heart beating in my throat. Just sit here quietly, I tell myself, stare straight ahead. I fix my gaze on one of the blackened patches on the curtain, which is again hanging motionless. I stir the spoon around and around in my cup of coffee, but my hand is shaking. I try with all my powers of concentration to keep it still, but I can't stop it. And then it's too late. My shaking hand has given me away. The dicks nudge each other and watch me. I'm lost.

The old people, who had stopped their chattering when the detectives came in, now start screaming. As if a secret signal had been given, pandemonium breaks loose. The old men start cursing at me, inciting the detectives to action. The bartender breaks a bottle against the sink and grips the jagged neck menacingly in his fist. My choice is clear. I can get up right now and make a break for the back door, in which case the old guys will probably lynch me—if the bartender doesn't get me first—or the dicks will shoot me in the back. Or I can get up slowly and walk towards them, surrendering. I finish my coffee (so they won't think I'm nervous), rise and approach the two dicks, hands in the air. They don't say a word, but motion me through the curtain. From the street, they push me into the house and up the stairs. I've got to steel myself for the worst. This kind of interrogation, like the Japanese third degree during the war, is the worst thing that can happen to you. You're helpless, lost, right where they want you. Pretending that I've never climbed these stairs before, I hesitate at the landing, waiting to be directed. When we get to the top, one of the detectives kicks me in the back. The other one chuckles and throws me against the baby-blue door.

The wooden floor inside is, as before, covered with a layer of dust, except for one spot in the middle. A circular area has been scrubbed clean and in the center of it, neatly arranged, lies the headless corpse. Next to it stands a water pitcher, and on top of that rests the head. The eyes are shut and the hair is neatly combed.

In the corner are the two boys, cowering, manacled, their heads bowed. When they don't respond to the questioning, the detectives rain blows on their faces. Then the only sound is the sniffling and dripping of their bloody noses. I keep quiet and try to look disinterested when one of the dicks grabs the body by the neck and the ass and holds it up in front of me like a carcass at a slaughter-house. When the body gets too heavy for him, he throws it to the floor and kicks it back into position. He looks at me, starts to speak, then stops and walks to the other side of the room, where there is a Japanese screen covered with pictures of birds. I see a robin and a canary. I don't know anything else about birds. He shouts something in a secret language and his colleague strikes me on the back of my neck with the flat of his hand. The other detective disappears behind the screen and reemerges with the girl who had first brought me here.

She is completely naked and blood runs from her crotch, down her wet legs. She is handcuffed and has bloody lash marks all over her perfect body. Planting her beside me, the detectives begin to get rough. Cursing, they beat me and burn me with cigars. But I don't feel anything because I don't want to feel anything—like Jesus Christ.

Then they start on the girl. They get hoarse and they have to keep stopping for long drinks of water. When they turn away the girl touches my leg as a sign of recognition. I pinch her arm in response. They ask her filthy, irrelevant questions. When she answers in her strange language the moronic bastards, thinking that she's putting them on, start to beat her. She spits in their faces.

They put a large, iron butcher's hook through the legs of the headless body, throw a rope across the beams and haul the corpse up to the ceiling, where it swings upside down. It has long since bled dry, so only a few drops of watery, pink liquid fall to the floor, forming a tiny pool. One of the detectives watches me closely while the other picks up the neatly combed head and grips it in his crotch. I clench my teeth with terror. The eyes have opened and the head is nodding to me calmly, encouragingly. The girl clutches me, clings to me wildly and starts to scream . . .

Amsterdam, December 1962

(TO BE CONTINUED)

SIGNET Novels You'll Enjoy Reading

A GREEN TREE IN GEDDE *by Alan Sharp*
An outspoken novel, abounding in exuberant language.
The talented young Scots author calls his first novel
"a celebration of the individual trying to realize his
true nature." "A superb example of the contemporary
picaresque."—*Harper's*   (#T2908—75¢)

SATURDAY NIGHT AND SUNDAY MORNING *by Alan Sillitoe*
An earthy roisterous novel about a young English
worker on a spree. A bestseller in England.
                                           (#P2776—60¢)

DARLING *by Frederic Raphael*
The story of a beautiful girl who becomes an interna-
tionally known actress and loses herself in an amoral
and restless world. A motion picture starring Laurence
Harvey, Dirk Bogarde and Julie Christie.
                                           (#D2766—50¢)

TOMORROW'S HIDDEN SEASON *by George Byram*
The highly-acclaimed novel of a young Mexican's
struggle toward manhood in the horse country of Colo-
rado—and of the sensual woman who helps him.
                                           (#T2657—75¢)

THE FLY *by Richard Chopping*
A deeply satirical view of corrupt humanity, seen
through the microscopic vision of the common house
fly. "Fascinating and fresh."—*The New York Times*.
                                           (#T2835—75¢)

THE GROUP *by Mary McCarthy*
A brilliant bestseller, this is the daring story of eight
Vassar graduates trying to cope with life and love
during the turbulent depression of the Thirties.
                                           (#Q2501—95¢)

THE COUNTRY GIRLS *by Edna O'Brien*
An impudent novel about two Irish girls who deliberately set out to be wicked in Dublin. (#P2680—60¢)

A SHARE OF THE WORLD *by Andrea Newman*
A daring novel about the sexual entanglements of
three college girls trying to cope with the new freedom
of their generation.   (#P2692—60¢)

Short Stories, Plays, and Poems
in SIGNET Editions

LOVE POEMS *by Elizabeth Sargent*
The earthy and lyrical outpourings of a contemporary poet about love. (#T2889—75¢)

THE CHILDREN'S HOUR *by Lillian Hellman*
The taut drama of a schoolgirl's spiteful accusation and its tragic results for two young teachers.
(#D2129—50¢)

THE NIGHT OF THE IGUANA *by Tennessee Williams*
The emotion-charged drama about two women who compete for the affections of a defrocked minister. Now a movie starring Richard Burton, Ava Gardner, Deborah Kerr, and Sue Lyon. (#D2481—50¢)

CAT ON A HOT TIN ROOF *by Tennessee Williams*
A drama of the seething passions that beset a Southern family during a shattering moment of revelation.
(#P2855—60¢)

SWEET BIRD OF YOUTH *by Tennessee Williams*
The drama of an aging actress and her protégé and lover. (#P2856—60¢)

MEMOIRS OF HECATE COUNTY *by Edmund Wilson*
Six stories present the manners and morals of U.S. suburban life in unsparingly satirical prose by one of America's foremost critics. (Not for sale in New York State.) (#T2004—75¢)

I LOVE YOU, I HATE YOU, DROP DEAD! *by Artie Shaw*
Three short novels united by the common theme of marriage-on-the-rocks: "Grounds for Divorce," "Whodunit," and "Old Friend." (#P2804—60¢)

THE BEST READING AT REASONABLE PRICES

---

signet (signet BOOKS) paperbacks

SIGNET BOOKS *Leading bestsellers, ranging from fine novels, plays, and short stories to the best entertainment in the fields of mysteries, westerns, popular biography and autobiography, as well as timely non-fiction and humor. Among Signet's outstanding authors are winners of the Nobel and Pulitzer Prizes, the National Book Award, the Ainsfield-Wolfe award, and many other honors.*

SIGNET SCIENCE LIBRARY *Basic introductions to the various fields of science—astronomy, physics, biology, anthropology, mathematics, and others—for the general reader who wants to keep up with today's scientific miracles. Among the authors are Willy Ley, Irving Adler, Isaac Asimov, and Rachel Carson.*

SIGNET REFERENCE *A dazzling array of dictionaries, thesauri, self-taught languages, and other practical handbooks for the home library.*

SIGNET CLASSICS *The most praised new imprint in paperbound publishing, presenting masterworks by writers of the calibre of Mark Twain, Sinclair Lewis, Dickens, Hardy, Hawthorne, Thoreau, Conrad, Tolstoy, Chekhov, Voltaire, George Orwell, and many, many others, beautifully printed and bound, with handsome covers. Each volume includes commentary by a noted scholar or critic, and a selected bibliography.*